The Postwar Naval Revolution

Norman Friedman

The Postwar Naval Revolution

Norman Friedman

CONWAY
MARITIME PRESS

FRONTISPIECE

If 1945 was a year of triumph for the carrier, the postwar
decade was a time of uncertainty, as the carrier had to
show that it could adapt to a new generation of naval
aircraft. HMS *Eagle*, steaming through the Channel in
October 1957, displays two main elements of successful
adaptation: the angled deck and the mirror landing sight
(part of which element is to starboard, aft). At this time
she still had hydraulic catapults. Aircraft on deck include
Sea Hawk jet fighters, and US-supplied propeller-driven
Skyraider airborne early warning aircraft, essential to
deal with jet attackers. [*CPL*]

First published in Great Britain in 1986 by Conway
Maritime Press Limited, 24 Bride Lane, Fleet
Street, London EC4Y 8DR

ISBN 0 85177 414 8

Designed by Baseline Creative, Bath

Typesetting and page make-up by Swanston
Graphics Limited, Derby

Printed and bound in Great Britain by The Bath
Press, Bath

CONTENTS

INTRODUCTION

The navies of 1985 differ strikingly from those of, say, 1935, in their missions and also in their structure. Much of the change occurred during the decade following World War II, and this revolution in naval affairs is the subject of this book. The changes in navies reflected changes both in naval missions and in technology, the former in turn deriving from fundamental changes in world politics after 1945.

This account concentrates on the US and Royal Navies. As the largest navies of the West, they led and, to a considerable extent, defined the revolution. Changes in the structure of the other Western navies largely date from 1955 and later, and generally incorporate the technology and concepts developed in Britain and in the USA during the preceding decade. The Soviet Navy did not really begin its radical transformation until after 1955, when Khrushchev introduced his Revolution in Military Affairs.

Fortunately, alone of the major Western powers, Britain and the United States have declassified many of their internal documents for this period. They describe the rationale for postwar ship and weapon development, and for postwar fleet structure, and what the major Western navies tried, and sometimes failed, to do. The story of what was actually built is well known by now, but it cannot be fully understood without the background of planning. For example, the British retention of a large – and largely obsolescent – reserve fleet is understandable in terms of planning for modernization and for mobilization, planning which in turn clearly reflects the nature, and the limitations, of the British industrial base.

Constraints of space have limited this account to major surface combatants, submarines, minecraft, and coastal craft. Amphibious forces experienced their most dramatic development later, with the widespread introduction of helicopters (already in place on an experimental basis in the early 'fifties). Hopefully, they will form the subject of a later book.

The accounts of actual warship development emphasize the British experience, both because I have already published extensive accounts of US warship designs of this period and because so little of the British design work has previously appeared in print.

Some account of the structure of the Admiralty (and therefore of the British warship design process) in the postwar period may therefore be helpful. The Board of Admiralty consisted of a military branch (Five Sea Lords, the Vice and Assistant Chiefs of the Naval Staff), and a civilian branch (First Lord, Civil Lord, Parliamentary and Financial Secretary, and Permanent Secretary), corresponding (respectively) approximately to the US Chief of Naval Operations and his deputies, and to the Secretary of the Navy (First Lord) and his Assistant Secretaries. However, the Permanent Secretary was a permanent civil servant, who did not change office with the other civilians when the Government changed. Nor did the division of responsibility among the naval members of the Board correspond to that in the US Navy. Each Lord was concerned with the work of the Board as a whole, but he was also responsible for a particular set of departments within the Royal Navy. The First Sea Lord might correspond to the US CNO; he was also Chief of Naval Staff. The Second Sea Lord was also Chief of Naval Personnel. The Third Sea Lord was Controller, responsible for warship production. The Fourth Sea Lord was also Chief of Supplies and Transport. The Fifth Sea Lord was responsible for naval aviation and was Deputy Chief of Naval Staff (Air).

In theory, then, the Controller was responsible for initiating and then approving particular warship projects. However, many ideas originated, not in the Board, but in the Staff. Actual staff requirements for warships were drawn up under the Director of Tactical and Staff Duties Division (DTSD); other important figures within the staff were the Director of Plans (D of P), Director of Navigation and Direction (DND, responsible for fighter control), Director of Gunnery Division (DGD), Director of Torpedo, Mine and Anti-Submarine Warfare (DTASW), and Director of Naval Air Warfare (DAW). Senior operational commanders also often influenced design development. Prime examples were the Flag Officer, Submarines at Portsmouth and the Captain commanding HMS *Hornet* (Coastal Forces).

The ship designs themselves were the province of the Director of Naval Construction (DNC); weapons were developed by the Director of Naval Ordnance (DNO), and machinery by the Engineer-in-Chief. Each of these individuals presided over a large Department. Note, however, that both aircraft and missiles were developed outside the Navy (albeit with considerable naval input) by the Ministry of Supply, on a tri-service basis.

This was part of a larger pattern of integration among the three Services, extending back in time to the Defence Resources Committee which had devised the overall plans for British rearmament. Postwar rearmament planning always required some decision as to the proper balance among the Services, in their demands for national resources which were also required for civilian consumption, and for the exports which supported the entire British economy. The postwar Defence Production Resources Committee (DPRC) and Defense Research Committee (DRC) periodically reviewed overall programs on a tri-service basis. They also had to be consulted for permission to export equipment, as in the case of the Vickers private-venture 4-inch gun described in Chapter 3. Similarly, the Chiefs of Staff Committee was responsible for several of the major postwar strategic shifts, which in turn were reflected in overall fleet planning (see Chapter 1).

Again, in theory, the matériel departments and the Naval Staff came together in the Ship Design Policy Committee (SDPC), which had evolved from the wartime Future Building Committee. Like the parallel US SCB (Ship Characteristics Board), the SDPC was sometimes described as a means of formalizing agreements already reached more privately, in this case between the DNC and the First Sea Lord.

Once initial staff requirements had been stated, a design evolved as the staff modified its ideas and as the DNC department explored their feasibility. The path was not always smooth; the staff could propose, but the DNC need not listen. Once a suitable sketch design had been completed, DNC submitted it for Board approval. Generally, a sketch and a legend (characteristics and weight breakdown) were provided. In some cases several draft legends were developed and circulated before one was formally submitted or accepted. Several sketch designs might well be developed within the DNC organization well before formal staff requirements were developed. This was certainly the case with several frigate designs.

Compared to US practice, British practice was far less formal, resting far more on a variety of inter-departmental 'working parties' and on decisions made outside the theoretical staff-constructor-board structure. Moreover, the departments (such as DNC) did not have the independence of the Sea Lords which, in US parlance, would correspond to the independence of (say) the Bureau of Ships (of the day) of the US

CNO. Due to its historical antecedents, the Board of Admiralty was far more concerned with warship design and production than was the US Office of the Chief of Naval Operations (Opnav).

Notes on Sources

Material for this book has come largely from official documents, now declassified. The US war plans are described in some detail in the official *History of the Joint Chiefs of Staff* for 1945-52, and much material has been taken from the postwar records of the US General Board, now transferred from the Navy's Operational Archives to the US National Archives. These records include a General Board study of Navy Contributions to US National Security over the Next Ten Years (1948), including a survey of current weapons developments; a General Board study of the future of the Reserve Fleet (1948/49), including requirements for war; and a General Board study of the FY51-60 Shipbuilding and Conversion Program. I have also used the official sources cited in my books on US warship design.

British material was taken largely from records now held by the National Maritime Museum (NMM), Greenwich, and from records now held by the Public Record Office (PRO), Kew. 'Ship covers' in the NMM are the DNC records of particular designs. They became particularly complete after much of the warship design staff moved from London to Bath in 1939, and they currently include files describing the postwar cruisers (but not yet the cruiser/destroyer), and several of the postwar destroyers, frigates, and submarines. Covers for the Type 42 frigate (the East Coast Gunboat, not the current missile destroyer) and the fast ASW escort exist but have not yet been declassified. The NMM also holds sets of the personal papers of the DNC for 1946-50, which include considerable material on the Type 14 frigate and on harbor defense against midget submarines and other 'small battle units'.

The PRO series of greatest interest are ADM 1 (general files), ADM 116 ('cases,' or collated files), 167 (Admiralty Board minutes and memoranda), and 205 (First Sea Lord's papers). ADM 116 contains SDPC papers for the period through 1952, including early sketch designs for the cruiser/destroyer and for the third-rate frigate. ADM 205 contains the Admiralty files on the Radical Review of 1953-54, including the 1954 Director of Plans proposal that presaged much of the post-review Navy. Ministry of Defence files (DEFE) include papers on the post-Korea rearmament program, and Prime Minister's personal files (PREM) included the third-rate frigate legend reproduced in Chapter 6. The PRO also holds the official publication, 'Particulars of HM Ships,' for the period 1939-1951. The Naval Historical Library (MoD) holds copies for 1952-55.

Although virtually all material dating from 1955 and earlier should have been declassified under the thirty year rule, in practice material is not released until it has been reviewed. The review process is, naturally, relatively cumbersome, and as a consequence information on this period is still somewhat incomplete. For example, the Admiralty Board Minutes and Memoranda, which should include the legends of several designs submitted in 1953-54, have not yet been released for the period 1951-55. PRO catalogues show every evidence that caches of material turn up unexpectedly from time to time: for example, the PRO received a series of legends dating from 1905 through about 1940 as late as 1983. Therefore, this account cannot be considered definitive.

I have largely avoided published sources on this period as they tend to be inaccurate. There are two important exceptions: David K Brown's *A Century of Naval Construction* (Conway Maritime Press, 1983) and Willem Hachmann's *Seek and Strike* (HM Stationery Office, 1984), For gas turbines I have used CE Preston's *Power of the Fleet: The History of British Marine Gas Turbines* (Eton, 1982).

Acknowledgements

David J Lyon of the National Maritime Museum was extremely helpful, particularly (but not only) with the relevant ship's covers. Eric J Grove shared his insights, gained in the preparation of his own forthcoming book on the postwar Royal Navy. JD Brown, of the Naval Historical Branch, granted me access to several issues of 'Particulars of HM Ships', and also shared his own views of postwar British naval policy-making. For French material I am indebted to Captain Phillippe Roger of the French Embassy, Washington, and Ing-Gen Jacques Waser of The French Ministry of Defense. I appreciate the assistance of Dr Dean Allard (of the US Navy Operational Archives), AD Baker III, John Campbell, Martha Crowley (of the US Navy Operational Archives), Chuck Haberlein, Louis Lovisolo (of Grumman Historical Center), Lon Nordeen (of McDonnell-Douglas), Alan Raven, HJ 'Schoenie' Schoenberg (Grumman Historical Center), Captain Peter Swartz (USN), Michael Vlahos, and Chris Wright, not to mention the staff of the PRO.

I hope this book justifies the encouragement, support, and patience of my wife, Rhea.

1
MONEY, POLITICS AND STRATEGY

As it developed after 1945, Western naval strategy derived from a new political situation (the Soviet threat) as it interacted with new technology within, often, severe financial constraints. The latter, in turn, caused the inter-service (generally Navy – Air Force) rivalry which shaped postwar national strategies. For the first time the two great Western maritime powers, Britain and the United States, joined in a peacetime alliance against the greatest of all land powers, the Soviet Union. On the national level, the most important element of the new technology was the atomic bomb, which threatened to make existing forms of warfare obsolete.

Postwar military strategy, and the postwar place of navies within military establishments, was largely shaped by the existence of nuclear weapons.

The postwar navies themselves were largely shaped by the combination of fast submarine, jet airplane, and guided missile. Because each was extremely difficult to intercept near its target, each encouraged a shift from escort strategies to concepts such as 'attack at source' and (in the case of anti-submarine warfare), area attack (based on 'flaming datum' and then on undersea surveillance systems). In contrast to World War II practice, then, some argued that sea control could be gained only by attacking enemy submarines and bombers at their bases, or in transit towards their attack areas. In more modern terms, sea control and power projection were associated, rather than opposed, naval missions. More generally, the rapid pace of technology reduced the very large fleets built up in wartime to obsolescence. At the least they would require expensive modernization.

For all its supposed omnipotence, the actual efficacy of the atomic bomb depended on two factors: the extent to which it could damage or destroy the Soviet Union; and the extent to which threats by the Soviet Union might deter its use. The evolution of these two factors in turn defines the eras of the postwar period.

In the first postwar era, lasting roughly from 1945 to 1955, the net destructive effect of nuclear weapons was limited. Until about 1952, they were, moreover, quite scarce. Their explosive power was

proportional to the amount of nuclear fuel they contained, and, as the story of the Manhattan Project showed, that fuel was difficult to manufacture. For example, the US Air Force bitterly opposed early US Navy plans for a nuclear submarine because the submarine reactor would compete with nuclear weapons manufacture for scarce weapons-grade uranium.

In a period of nuclear scarcity, bombs could be used only against the most important strategic targets. The Air Force, for example, planned to follow up an initial nuclear shock attack with a World War II-style conventional (high explosive) bombing offensive.

Moreover, analysis of the effects of the two bombs in Japan suggested that it would take far more than a single weapon to destroy a large Western or Soviet manufacturing or political center. After all, the Japanese cities had always been considered quite flimsy, hence quite vulnerable to heat and blast. It seemed likely that any substantial increase in explosive power per bomb would have to be bought with a proportionate increase in scarce bomb material

Postwar Western naval thinking was driven, above all, by the threat of a massive Soviet submarine force, backed up by large numbers of modern jet bombers. Four decades later, despite an ambitious Soviet surface ship construction program, that is still the primary Soviet naval threat. Ironically, it was later discovered that the bulk of Stalin's new submarines, the Whiskeys, were ill-suited for long-range operations into the North Atlantic. A much smaller number of long-range submarines, such as this Zulu, constituted the main anti-shipping threat. Subsequent Soviet diesel-electric submarines, the Foxtrots and the Tangoes, were derived from the Zulu rather than from the Whiskey. This Zulu was photographed in April 1979. [MoD]

and thus at a cost in numbers of weapons. Thus, it might be argued that although nuclear weapons might change the details of warfare, they were unlikely to change the overall form of a war.

Bomb design became more efficient and US bomb material production expanded, so that after about 1952, nuclear weapons were sufficiently plentiful that they could be used tactically, as a direct counter to massed Soviet tank and troop formations on land, or as depth bombs, targeted against individual submarines rather than against submarine bases.

By this time the Soviets had a limited number of nuclear weapons of their own, but hardly enough to end a war on their own terms. Prospective Western use of tactical nuclear weapons was, therefore, entirely conceivable. For example, when the first virtually all-missile warship, the *Leahy* class missile frigate (now classified as a missile cruiser), was being designed, there was some concern about the loss of shore bombardment capability. The answer at the time (1956) was to use a nuclear version of its Terrier anti-aircraft missile.

The first postwar period ended with the appearance of the hydrogen bomb. Unlike a nuclear (uranium or plutonium) weapon, an H-bomb is fuelled largely by an abundant material, deuterium. The first H-bomb was about a thousand times as powerful as the 1945 bombs, its explosive power being measured in megatons rather than in kilotons. Its advent therefore radically changed perceptions. It seemed clear, for example, that a single hydrogen bomb could wipe out even the largest city, and therefore that the most alarmist predictions of the first nuclear strategists had been fulfilled. Although the United States first tested an H-bomb in 1952, such weapons were not really available in quantity for some time. At first they were so massive that they could be carried only by large bombers such as the B-36 or B-52. However, the Polaris missile was designed on the basis of a prediction that a small enough warhead could be devised by 1963.

Hydrogen bombs were so powerful that for the first time it was possible to imagine actually destroying a country as large as the United States

or the Soviet Union. That ended the expectation of protracted warfare. For example, a 1954 British study projected the shrinkage of the period it would take to destroy the Soviet Union, from six weeks down to six days of an air offensive about a decade later. It argued that wartime naval support would be required to sustain the six week offensive, but that the six-day attack could be mounted using only resources available at the outbreak of war.

In 1955-65, moreover, the United States had a decisive strategic nuclear advantage. Its large strategic attack forces could almost certainly penetrate primitive Soviet defences. The Soviets were limited to an impressive bomber force and to a very few cumbersome and unreliable missiles, which would take so long to set up that they would probably be destroyed on the ground. US continental air defenses would almost certainly be capable of defeating the limited Soviet bomber force. As a consequence, the United States could expect to destroy the Soviet Union at little or no direct cost. The Soviets could have occupied or destroyed Western Europe, but the threat of one-sided thermonuclear war would have deterred them from such an adventure. Indeed, US strategists argued that US nuclear forces were intended, not so much to preclude Soviet attack on the United States but rather to deter the Soviets from attacking Western Europe. This strategy reached its most extreme expression in President Eisenhower's threat of 'massive retaliation'.

As Soviet strategic offensive forces evolved, they eroded the power of the US strategic attack force. US nuclear forces could still deter the Soviets from attacking North America, but they lost their power to counterbalance the existing (and threatening) Soviet non-nuclear superiority on the ground. This equation was well understood in the 'fifties; it explains, for example, the very large sums (including naval resources) spent on North American air defense, and the early efforts to deal with a postulated Soviet missile submarine threat. Only in the 'sixties did a new American Administration (led by President Kennedy) conclude that it would be virtually impossible to defend against the growing Soviet ballistic missile force, and therefore that US nuclear power could no longer extend to prevent a Soviet offensive in Western Europe. That in turn led the United States towards an increased emphasis on conventional defense and flexible response in Europe.

Although the relative strategic balance and its policy consequences seem clear in retrospect, US intelligence estimates of the late 'fifties and early 'sixties, often tended to overrate Soviet strategic capability. Certainly President Kennedy seems to have been unaware of the extent of American strategic dominance at the time of the Cuban missile crisis. The lesson seems to be that effective deterrence (or at least the self-deterrence of the West) rests, not so much on the estimated outcome of war but on the mere existence of even small numbers of weapons. Nikita Khruschev's

After 1945, Stalin revived his prewar policy of building up a large surface fleet. Fourteen *Sverdlov* class cruisers were the most impressive fruits of this program. Their appearance in turn convinced the Admiralty to invest more heavily in anti-(surface) raider systems, such as the Buccaneer carrier bomber. It now seems much less likely that Stalin had anything so specific as surface raiding in mind when he ordered the class. His fleet seems more to have been a throwback to pre-1945 ideas, a conclusion which might have been more apparent if he had lived long enough to complete more of it. *Admiral Suvorov* is shown in the Philippine Sea. One of her twin 3.9in gunhouses has been tilted over by its stabilization mechanism. [*USN*]

taste for bluffing helped considerably, of course.

The British position foreshadowed that of the United States. She was much closer to the Soviet Union, hence subject to attack by weapons at an earlier stage of technology. For example, the Soviet medium-range bomber force (the Tu-16 Badgers) posed a serious threat to Britain at a time when the Soviet Union had few (and ineffective) intercontinental bombers (Bisons and Bears). The Soviets also had substantial numbers of medium- and intermediate-range missiles, which could reach Britain and which could not be intercepted by Fighter Command, well before the Soviets had enough intercontinental missiles to bypass the North American Air Defense Command.

*   *   *

Despite the urgency of the postwar Soviet threat, no Western nation could afford wholesale replacement of its existing weapons. The pressure to demobilize was irresistible. Moreover, the Western European and British economies were exhausted. Even though the United States ended the war in excellent fiscal health, there was no question of massive new military expenditures. The great postwar priority was, rather, to revive the exhausted Western economies. This was not a simple choice of civilian luxury over military necessity. Rather, it was a calculated long-term policy matched to what was perceived as a long-term (rather than a short-term) military *and political* threat.

Having conquered Eastern Europe, Stalin seemed bent on bringing all of Western Europe under his control. Both of the great maritime powers, Britain and the United States, considered such control intolerable, as it would have tipped the balance of world power much too heavily towards the Soviets. This central goal of denying the Soviets Western Europe and Japan was the modern equivalent of the traditional British policy of maintaining a balance of power in Western Europe and resisting any attempt by a European power to gain control over the entire Continent.

This did not mean surrendering interest in the rest of the world (what would now be called the Third World). For Britain, that was traditional for the British Empire encompassed much of the Third World. The Royal Navy had always policed the Empire before World War II, and no doubt would continue to do so postwar. For the United States, continuous involvement in the Third World, quite apart from denying the Soviets control of Western Europe or of Japan, was a much more uncomfortable idea. It remains so today and advocates of a 'continental strategy' (which would emphasize European security) strongly oppose the maritime strategy which provides forces for Third World intervention as well as for general (European) war. This is the sense in which Americans found Korea and Vietnam so uncomfortable. Europe was clearly an area of vital American interest, but where did that interest stop? How important was (is) it to prevent the Soviets from organizing the Third World against the West?

This question is extremely important from a naval point of view, because the forces needed to win (or to deter) a global war may well have little in common with the forces required to deal with Third World problems. How are the two to be balanced?

The architects of postwar US policy, such as George Kennan, argued that the character of the Soviet Union promised a long-term struggle, quite

The other great driver of postwar Western fleet development was the weight of recently-completed ships whose designs no longer matched the new naval technology and the new naval missions. HMS *Swiftsure* is shown leaving Gibraltar in September 1950. Despite her substantial light and medium anti-aircraft battery, she was considered ineffective because her 4in guns were controlled by the obsolete HACS director. On the other hand, the Royal Navy considered her 6in anti-ship fire control equal or superior to anything in the world. Such a cruiser could deal with a Soviet cruiser, but only if she were protected from Soviet aircraft. On the other hand, she was eminently suited to the other major British naval role, policing the Empire. [*CPL*]

possibly *without* erupting into armed conflict. Kennan hoped that, if the Soviets could be denied victory, then over the long-term they might evolve into some less threatening posture. Meanwhile, it would be essential to deny them the possibility of either military *or* political victory. To deny Stalin or his successors the balance of world power, they had to be denied the two great industrial potentials of Western Europe and Japan.

Both concerns were equally important. The Soviet Union presented both a conventional military and a political (subversive) threat. It appeared that, by virtue of his tight control of Soviet society, Stalin could maintain whatever standing forces he wanted. The West could not. It could not, for example, afford to spend without limit on the combination of standing forces and the development and production of the new weapons which wartime technical developments seemed to require. This was not a new problem. More or less tacit US and British doctrine had always been to maintain limited standing forces, depending on mobilization to create the much larger ones required to win wars. It was always assumed that any potential adversary would need time (ie, would provide strategic warning) to develop the scale of forces needed to win. However, it appeared that Stalin had solved this problem. His political power was so absolute that his regime could (it was thought) maintain, in peacetime, sufficient standing forces to overrun Western Europe. He could, therefore, strike almost without warning. The military problem, then, was how to maintain some means of stopping a massive Soviet land offensive in Europe.

Stalin was generally credited with 175 active first-class divisions, and a proportionate tactical air force. In 1941, he had had the world's largest submarine fleet. Postwar, he soon built up a substantial navy, well adapted (it seemed) to the sort of shipping war which the Germans had waged, with large numbers of (obsolescent) submarines and land-based naval bombers, as well as large numbers of motor torpedo boats. The Red Army had captured some of the latest German submarine designs, and it seemed likely that they would soon be put into mass production. Although the Soviet Navy had had few wartime successes, it seemed likely that a combination of captured German equipment and collaborating German instructors would soon greatly improve matters. Ultimately, then, the Soviet Navy would be able to threaten the West with the sort of submarine offensive which the Germans had planned in 1945 (using fast snorkel craft) and with the sort of air attacks experienced in the Mediterranean runs to Malta and in the convoy runs to Murmansk. In the early 'fifties it became clear that Stalin had also decided to invest heavily in surface ships, such as the *Sverdlov* class cruisers. The British in particular had reason to remember the combined effect of powerful surface craft (such as the *Tirpitz*) with submarines and aircraft near

the European land mass. Finally, as in World War II, enemy light craft might attack NATO shipping in coastal areas such as the North Sea and the Channel.

Stalin could supplement his purely military threat with the political threat of subversion by local communist parties, which were particularly powerful in France and Italy. Unless the conventional military threat was contained, citizens in Western Europe might well become convinced that a communist victory was inevitable, and so might give Stalin his victory without a fight. Similarly, unless the Western European economies were rebuilt, they were unlikely to achieve much in the way of political stability. Yet such reconstruction would be expensive, and its cost might well preclude the maintenance of the large standing forces required to stop a Soviet land offensive. Thus the importance of economic reconstruction (through the Marshall Plan), followed, in its later stages, by military reconstruction (through mechanisms such as the Mutual Defense Assistance Plan, MDAP).

Success in this struggle would require that the Western powers deter Stalin and his successors from attacking while restoring and then maintaining healthy civilian economies. Perhaps more fundamentally, it was unacceptable for the West to militarize to the extent of destroying its political freedoms, the preservation of which was the point of the entire exercise. These goals in turn demanded a permanent cap on military expenditure. In the United States in 1949, President Truman had to abort a rearmament program (intended to counter such Soviet initiatives as the seizure of Czechoslovakia and the Berlin Blockade) in order to maintain US economic health. Later, President Eisenhower made major cuts for much the same reason, albeit in a much larger budget. In each case, the result was increased reliance on the one relatively inexpensive new weapon, the atomic bomb.

Because the deterrent threat of the atomic bomb was clearly limited in application, this economics-dictated strategy was risky at best. The outbreak of the Korean War demonstrated that it had very definite limits, and throughout the post-Korea period strategists argued that the Soviets might be attracted to 'salami tactics'. They would go just far enough to gain useful objectives, without ever going far enough to justify Western use of nuclear weapons. Moreover, once the Soviets had enough atomic weapons of their own, the Western deterrent would lose much of its value, and the West would be forced back upon more traditional (and more costly) forms of defense.

However, Western economic health was clearly essential in any long-term confrontation. Ironically, it would have been relatively easy to justify the sacrifices of crash rearmament in a period clearly leading up to a major war. For example, both Britain and the United States greatly increased defense spending after the outbreak of war in Korea, which many considered a prelude to World War III in Europe. The US defense budget increased threefold. However, neither could sustain a high spending level for long, and both were forced to make heavy cuts after Korea. The spending increases had permitted changes in strategy away from a nuclear emphasis but the cuts pushed both governments back towards it.

Britain was the most extreme historical case of economic impact on defense policy. After World War I, she adopted a 'ten year rule' (an assumption that war would not come for at least ten years) to cut defense spending so as to rebuild a damaged economy. The rule was, moreover, renewed annually. Britain sought to maintain her relative level of military power at reduced (affordable) cost by relying on arms control treaties. The 'ten year rule' was abandoned only when Japan directly (and unmistakably) threatened British imperial power in Asia. Even so, the British Treasury argued that releasing funds for military expansion. From 1932 until about 1937 it consistently maintained that it was as important to maintain the health of the economy, the 'fourth arm of defense', as to build up the three fighting forces, since the build-up could not be sustained in the face of economic collapse. Only in 1937, with war clearly imminent, would the Treasury agree to massive deficit spending. The big prewar loans bought the weapons which ensured British survival in 1940. However, the Treasury's estimates of costs had been correct. World War II cost Britain about a quarter of her national wealth. As a result, economic reconstruction was the primary postwar British priority.

For example, postwar carrier construction (the completion of ships laid down in wartime) was delayed for about five years to allow yards to build merchant ships to replace war losses. British internal naval documents refer again and again to shortages of electrical draftsmen – who were required by the exporting industries. British defense development lagged behind that of the United States partly because, given the shortage of foreign exchange, Britain could not afford to buy American weapons. The Royal Navy even had to scrap its lend-lease aircraft because in 1946 it did not have the dollars to buy spare parts.

Even so, Britain had postwar military responsibilities she could not lightly abandon: the historical one of Empire security and the new one of occupation, both in Europe and in Japan. Both drew on a more expensive British Army. In the past, the Indian Army had provided much of the manpower needed to maintain both the Empire in Asia and the British position in the Middle East. With Indian independence, this resource was no longer available, and the British Army had to expand to fill the gap. The postwar Labour Government had to maintain the British draft, and its Army consumed funds which might otherwise have gone to modernize the Royal Navy.

Nor was there any question that an impoverished Britain might surrender her great power status. The price had risen very considerably. She had to have both the atomic bomb and the means of delivering it. Although the United States had agreed during World War II to share nuclear information, this agreement was abrogated (largely by an isolationist Congress) soon after the war. That in turn raised the prospective price, not merely in money but also in scarce scientific manpower, of a British bomb. Even so, there seems never to have been any question that such a weapon must be built.

Similarly, Britain continued to develop the full spectrum of modern weapons, even though her industrial (and, perhaps, more important, scientific) base was limited. To some extent she could limit the burden by convincing the two most advanced Commonwealth countries, Australia and Canada, to undertake particular development projects (such as the Australian Jindvik jet target drone and, later the Ikara anti-submarine weapon,

The British postwar government deliberately chose to forego the earliest forms of the new technology, such as the first jets, in order to pay for the development of more advanced equipment, on the assumption that war before 1957 was unlikely. HMS *Ocean*, in Malta in December 1951, shows Sea Fury fighters characteristic of the last stages of World War II, plus Firefly fighters adapted to ASW. The ultimate Firefly ASW aircraft, the AS7, proved so unsuccessful that the Royal Navy had to replace it with US-supplied Avengers, while waiting for its planned successor (the 'ultimate' ASW airplane), the Fairey Gannet. [*CPL*]

and the Canadian hydrofoils and variable-depth sonars). To some extent, too, the choice was based on economics: the British government had to buy its weapons (and their development) within the sterling area to avoid draining its hard-currency reserves. However, the price, through the postwar period, was high costs and protracted development periods.

As a postwar global power, then, Britain had to try to maintain forces comparable to those of the United States on a much smaller economic base. in 1948, for example, the US GNP was $257.6 billion. Britain's was about $35 billion. Yet the British defense budget represented a much higher proportion of GNP: 10.3 rather than 3.8 per cent, or about $3.6 billion compared to the US figure of $9.75 billion. At this time US intelligence estimated the Soviet GNP at $95 billion ($25 billion for defense), and the next largest Western GNP, that of France, at $16.8 billion (9 per cent for defense). In 1955, at the end of the period covered by this study, the US GNP was $398 billion (equivalent to $348.5 billion in 1948 terms), of which $35.6 billion (8.9 per cent) represented defense outlays. The full defense budget, including obligations for future outlays, was somewhat larger, and defense outlays were as high as $44 billion in 1953.

Economics gradually forced Britain into alliance with the United States. In 1945, the Admiralty could still contemplate maintaining a massive global fleet. It assumed that the United States would never be an enemy, and that US assistance would be forthcoming. However, as in 1940, Britain might have to fight alone for a time. As the depth of the postwar economic problem became more obvious, this assumption became less and less tenable. In 1948, therefore, the planned future fleet was recast on much more modest lines, on the basis of a new assumption that US forces would be engaged from the beginning of the war, and therefore that the United States would be responsible for much of the security of global sea lanes. For the first time the Royal Navy had to admit that it could never, in future, expect by itself to guarantee the security of sea lanes, and that cooperation with the United States would have to be assumed. Thus Britain no longer really had the option of an independent military policy; the price of such independence had risen beyond her means.

British postwar thinking reflected these realities. Contemporary US officials might believe that Stalin had managed to maintain an enormous standing army with corresponding tactical air forces, and thus the capability to overrun Western Europe and much of the Middle East. The British, with more direct experience of the effect of World War II on their economy, tended to be more skeptical. In 1947 their official position was that the Soviet Union must be so badly damaged as to be unable to fight during the next five years, ie, until about 1952. Over the following five years she would gradually acquire the industrial base needed to attack. 1957, then, would be the 'year of maximum danger'.

The British may have assumed that 1952 would be the probable date of the first Soviet atomic explosion. Certainly many US experts thought as much in 1948. When the Soviets actually exploded a bomb in 1949, the US government proclaimed 1954 – five years after the explosion – the 'year of maximum danger', which suggests parallels to British reasoning that the Soviets would be able to move five years after 1952. The US calculation was based on the estimated time for the Soviets to manufacture 200 atomic bombs (ie, the number needed to destroy 100 American targets).

This argument was used to justify the central postwar British policy decision. Money would be saved by running down existing forces, and also by cancelling many new weapons just entering production. These 'interim' systems would clearly be obsolete by the time war broke out, in about 1957. Better, then, to concentrate limited resources on rebuilding the British economy and on the research and development needed to develop the mature systems needed to fight the 1957 war. Thus the Admiralty's modernization and new construction plan, developed in 1948, was due for completion in 1957. It became known as the Nine Year Plan. Similarly, the specifications for the principal British postwar combat aircraft, such as the V-bombers and the Hunter, were all written in 1946-48; all envisaged nine- to ten-year development and production cycles.

This was hardly the prewar 'ten year rule'. It was not that war was impossible for ten years, but rather that war was quite likely in ten years, and therefore that modernization (to meet the new conditions of warfare) was to be keyed to that date.

In retrospect, the British were right. We now know that Stalin never had anything like 175 divisions in the early postwar period. Those he did have were under strength and lacked mobility. At the time, however, Stalin seems to have decided to bluff. He feared the strength of the Western powers and, like a good communist, expected them to attack him to finish him off, given the damage already done by the Germans. He therefore announced that he had been unable to risk demobilization. He risked (or appeared to risk) war over Berlin in 1948-49. War now seemed much more possible. The British government approved minimum rearmament measures in August, 1948, and in cooperation with the United States it began to draw up emergency war plans.

However, Britain did not really attempt to rearm until the outbreak of war in Korea. The result was disastrous. There was insufficient 'fat' in the economy to support both large-scale production and the rest of the development program, particularly given the demands of the civil (export) sector of the economy. Production could not meet the desired goals, and defense prices rose. The British were forced to re-evaluate their basic strategy.

One example will show just how tight the British industrial economy had become. In 1952, the Brazilian naval attaché sought to have a small fleet built in Britain: two light cruisers, one (probably two) escort carriers, six large destroyers, and ten coastal minelayers. British firms had already agreed to build six escorts for Venezuela (only three of which were actually built), at a cost in delays to the ongoing frigate program. The Admiralty had to refuse, because the Brazilian program would have precluded anything approaching completion of the naval rearmament program, already badly delayed. At this time 11,800 men were engaged in new naval construction, and another 6500 in warship repair. This compared with 70,600 engaged in merchant ship construction, and 69,100 in merchant ship repair. The naval construction figure was about half of what was required, and the Brazilian order would require an average of 4000 men for three to four years. Ironically, by late 1954 British shipbuilders were facing empty merchant order books and a sharply declining naval program; presumably they would have been more than happy to build the Brazilian ships.

The new global strategy of 1952 emphasized nuclear warfighting (ie, RAF V-bombers) as a substitute for substantial (expensive) land and sea forces.* It was assumed that the Western strategic air forces would largely destroy the Soviet Union within six weeks. The Royal Navy therefore had to maintain sufficient forces to assure British national survival during that period of intense warfare. Ironically, those within the British defense establishment knew that the Army and the Royal Navy constituted the main British offensive power. The 240-bomber RAF strategic force (supplementing about 800 US SAC bombers) was justified as a way of making 'British voices' heard in US strategic councils. US policy, after all, might well invite a Soviet pre-emptive or retaliatory strike on Britain. Recently declassified papers produced as part of the British Radical Review (1953-54) suggest that this force was more facade than reality, with only about a dozen weapons in 1954, and only about 100 programmed through 1957. This scarcity of weapons made it particularly important for the British to publicize their force, eg by an early H-bomb test (1957). The United States had followed much the same policy (many bombers, few bombs, carefully concealed stockpile figures) between 1945 and about 1948, but later built up production, so that there were about 300 in 1950. The United States (including the Navy) had about 2250 weapons in 1955.

A 'broken-backed' phase would follow the early nuclear attacks. The Royal Navy argued that its ships at sea, which would probably survive the initial attacks, would form the basis of the 'broken-backed' forces, and thus would probably decide the issue of the war. That in turn implied that ships would have to be able to operate for long periods with little or no base support, replenishing at sea. The United Kingdom would have to be resupplied in order to survive, so trade protection continued to be vital. The Royal Navy therefore continued to build up the escort forces it had previously justified on more conventional grounds.

Matters were further complicated when the US Air Force, representing the bulk of Western nuclear firepower, in the fall of 1953 shifted to a strategy of concentrating its attacks on Soviet airfields.** Cities and towns would probably not be struck, at least early in a war. The Royal Navy argued that this shifted the issue to British survival over the first six months (not weeks) of a war. The RAF strategic force would be less important, as Britain would need less of a say in US air policy. The Soviets would probably hit British airfields harder, and seaborne air power would represent a greater proportion of survivable British air power. Soviet tactical air power would become the primary British target.

Moreover, if the Soviets were unable to defeat Britain by direct air attack, they would attach greater importance to attacks on British trade. It would become more important (at least from a British point of view) for NATO to hold Scandinavia, with its vital ASW choke points, and its airfields so close to the British Isles. Similarly, offensive minelaying would become a more important NATO tactic, as nuclear attacks on Soviet ports would be, in effect, banned.

Although it differed radically from earlier ideas, the new strategy thus had little effect on actual British programs and hence on British spending. The following year, therefore, the Prime Minister, Winston Churchill ordered a 'radical review'. Each service began by offering piecemeal cuts; for example, the 5in gun cruiser/destroyer was cancelled in September, 1953. However, a new basic concept was needed. By May, 1954 the Royal Navy was suggesting what would now be called

* This shift, from what would now be called counter-value to counterforce, was probably a reaction to Soviet possession of a combination of intercontinental bombers and atomic bombs; it was the Air Force's equivalent of the naval 'attack at source' idea. Presumably, there was some expectation that both sides would avoid counter-value attacks, at least early in a war. In 1954, General Curtis LeMay, commanding the Strategic Air Command, argued in a lecture that, although in theory they were vulnerable to a Soviet air attack, his bombers would surely destroy the Soviet strategic air force before it could take off.
** Under this strategy British forces (particularly Army and RAF) in the Middle East and the Mediterranean were to be reduced to those sufficient for 'cold war'. In the event of major war they would have to be reinforced from the strategic reserve to be maintained in the United Kingdom. At this time the British were not willing to follow the United States in really drastic cuts to their conventional forces. In their internal debate, they quoted those within the US Joint Chiefs of Staff who still considered predictions of the prospective effects of the Atomic Air Offensive over-optimistic. It would, then, be important to continue to encourage the other NATO allies to continue their own non-nuclear rearmament, and the British Chiefs of Staff considered the British example important in this respect.

minimal deterrence rather than warfighting.

The Controller described it as an attempt to win the cold war, to resist a Soviet strategy of forcing the West to make the enormous and expensive preparations for a hot war they could not fight. These efforts in turn would destroy the Western economies. Soviet ideology, after all, envisaged victory entirely without war. It might, therefore, be prudent for the West to take some risks (which would matter only in the unlikely event of a hot war) in order to win the cold war.

The British parlance of this period reflected the spectrum of warfare particularly well. Until about 1952, the British wrote of 'global' and 'local' wars. Then they shifted to a distinction between 'hot' wars (World War III), 'warm' wars (Korea), and 'cold' wars (eg, the Kenyan Mau-Mau emergency or the Indonesian subversion of Malaysia in the 'sixties). The Royal Navy, it was said, had to be effective in wars of 'all temperatures'.

To fight the Soviets (hot war) Britain would need hydrogen bombs and their means of delivery, and a defense force of fighters, mine countermeasures ships, anti-submarine ships, and armored divisions in Europe. However, to deter the Soviets from attacking, she could rely on a 'threat force' consisting of a minimum number of deliverable hydrogen bombs.

Cold war would require a large Army and Air Force spread around the world, albeit not with the latest equipment. Similarly, Britain would need to maintain a global naval presence, provided by substantial ships which could 'impose the might of the British Empire on world opinion'. For maximum cold war impact, the Royal Navy would have to maintain active cruisers (not necessarily modernized), light carriers, and destroyers. Their running costs would be paid for by cancelling or laying up the numerous minesweepers and 'cheap and nasty' anti-submarine frigates (such as Type 14s) required to fight the large hot war previously envisaged. Moreover, if hot war could be excluded for the immediate future, there was little point in continuing the program of modernizing World War II-built hulls (eg, destroyers under conversion to ASW frigates) which had only limited remaining lifetimes, and which were intended for specialized hot war roles.

The British strategic bomber force would be maintained at a minimum size, until it was succeeded by missiles. Similarly, the defensive fighter force, useful only in a hot war, would be reduced to minimum size; it, too, would be succeeded by missiles. Cold war would require specialized close-support aircraft, since air opposition would be very limited. On land, Britain would maintain a few armored divisions in NATO, but most of her army would consist of independent brigades for minor wars.

The Royal Navy argued unsuccessfully that, given the increasing vulnerability of land bases, the British nuclear strike force should be based at sea, immune to counter attack. Instead, the British government of the time continued to rely on the RAF, which would operate land-based missiles (the US Thors and the British Blue Streak) as well as air-launched stand-off weapons (Blue Steel). The naval argument prevailed only after the failure of the Blue Streak program, and the US decision to cancel the follow-on air-launched weapon (Skybolt); the US government offered Polaris as an alternative.

At this time, only the British Army had really accepted such conclusions; the Controller argued that the Navy and the RAF were still too concerned with the defense of the United Kingdom against a major Soviet attack. However, the Chiefs of Staff did accept the new strategy. They went so far as to postulate a new 'year of maximum danger' about five or six years hence (1959-60). It presumably reflected an estimate of the date at which the Soviets would have sufficient numbers of hydrogen bombs or nuclear missiles.

The Royal Navy, for example, shifted from single-purpose (hot war) frigates to general purpose types which could provide a useful Third World presence, such as the Type 81 (*Tribal*) class. Similarly, advanced tactical aircraft (such as the thin-wing Hunter and the Vickers Type 545 Swift successor) and Army weapons (such as the 5in anti-aircraft gun), were cancelled.

The 1953-54 study was secret, but its general conclusions were repeated in the 1957 Defense White Paper, which sought further economies.* If hot war could be put off for some years, then there was little point in spending large sums to develop a new generation of manned bomber and fighter aircraft, which would be outdated (by missiles) by the time they saw combat. Moreover, the costs of developing those missiles would have to be borne by the same limited budget which would otherwise have paid for the future aircraft. Hence the swingeing 1957 cuts in new aircraft programs. At the same time, the large British reserve fleet, which had been maintained against the need for (hot war) mobilization, was finally discarded. It no longer seemed likely that there would be time to reactivate it for a major war, and its ships were far too outdated to be used in a minor one.

As in 1954, the choice was clearly to risk near-term hot war vulnerability in the interest of maintaining sufficient forces to fight limited wars in the Third World. Thus the British carrier force was retained as a major instrument of Third World intervention. However, its projected rocket-

---

* The connection was indirect. Neither the Royal Air Force nor the Army fully accepted the need for a new national strategy. By way of contrast, Lord Mountbatten was made First Sea Lord in 1955 partly to make the necessary cuts acceptable to the Navy. He formed a Way Ahead Committee which drew heavily on the Controller's 1954 paper, described above. In 1957, when new defense cuts were demanded of all the services, the Royal Navy already had cuts in hand. Cuts had to be imposed from above on the other two services, which suffered accordingly. That is why the Navy emerged after 1957 largely in the image forecast in 1954, whereas the other two services had to accept major shifts in configuration and mission.

powered deck-launched interceptor, the Saunders-Roe SR 177, was cancelled as the carriers would be unlikely to encounter the most sophisticated attacking aircraft. The only major new aircraft program to survive the 1957 cuts was a joint Navy–Air Force tactical aircraft, the supersonic P 1154 VSTOL.

Although the United States ended World War II on far better economic terms than did Britain, she, too, found it necessary to economize – and to build an appropriate series of strategies. By 1948, the US economy had experienced a recession. President Truman was determined not to make matters worse by excessive Government spending. He capped the defense budget just as procurement of a new types of equipment, such as jet aircraft, was increasing. Defense funds also had to cover purchases of strategic materials for stockpiling. The result was a combination of intense inter-service rivalry and a search for a less expensive defense policy. Ultimately, that meant drastic cuts in the expensive conventional forces, which were only beginning to be rebuilt following their post-1945 rundown.

The most visible naval cuts were reductions in operating forces in 1949 and 1950. The FY49 defense budget (as planned in 1948) included funds to operate 11 fleet carriers and a total of 260 combatants. In FY50 debates, with all three services badly squeezed, the Air Force proposed that the Navy active force be reduced to as few as four aircraft carriers, one task group. The Navy requested nine, and received eight. The overall budget freeze continued into FY51, a budget planned in 1948-49. Now the Army proposed to cut the force to four carriers; the Air Force wanted to eliminate fleet carriers altogether. The Navy asked for ten. Ultimately, the fleet carrier force was cut to six ships, with a seventh allowed temporarily in the Far East in view of ongoing conflicts (such as the Chinese Civil War) in the region. At the same time, the cruiser force was drastically reduced, from 19 in FY49 to 12 in FY51, with *Cleveland* class light cruisers the principal victims. This decline in the active Navy was reversed only by the Korean War.

Politically, however, the trend begun in 1948 continued. In 1949, the United States took a radical step, entering into its first peacetime alliance, NATO, having already begun economic aid to Western Europe, and having replaced Britain as the supporter of the Western-oriented Greek government, which was fighting communist guerillas.

To many in the US government, the atomic bomb was the natural (and economical) solution to the problem of a Soviet land threat. If the Atlantic Ocean was no longer a relevant physical barrier, perhaps the threat (or the use) of the bomb might so deter or delay a Soviet land attack on Europe as to allow the United States to mobilize. Thus, in 1948, the US Joint Chiefs of Staff hoped to obtain both a strategic nuclear striking force and the Universal Military Training required to develop

the basis for a mass reserve army which might be mobilized for combat in Europe. Presumably, the bomb would have slowed a Soviet advance sufficiently to allow the mass army to intervene, after a period of retreat and consolidation. However, as economic pressures intensified in 1949-50, the United States was pushed towards greater and greater reliance on the threat of nuclear attack, with less and less conventional military capability to back it up.

Even this strategy raised serious problems. The Air Force argued that nuclear attacks would suffice to stop a Soviet offensive. Without massive standing forces, the United States would be limited, at least at first, to a strategic air offensive mounted from bases in the United Kingdom, the Middle East (Cairo and perhaps Karachi), and the Far East (Okinawa). The naval contribution would be limited to securing the lines of supply to these air bases, and the army to guaranteeing their security.

The US Navy objected on two grounds. First, whatever the military efficacy of the plan, any willingness to abandon Western Europe without a fight would have profound political consequences in peacetime. If the Western Europeans found that they had little hope of protection in wartime, they might well just turn communist to preclude it. Second, the Navy argued that atomic attacks might well fail to stop a Soviet land offensive; even without resupply from destroyed Soviet stockpiles and factories, the massive Soviet army might succeed in seizing Western Europe, which would become (in current terms) the 'recovery base' of the postwar Soviet Union.

British policy required the purchase of small numbers of 'interim' jet aircraft, so that operational experience could be gained, and incorporated in the 'ultimate' aircraft. Here, a Sea Vampire, one of 18 delivered in 1948-49, is being moved onto the forward elevator of *Theseus* in the Channel, June 1952. The trolley at the edge of the elevator was used to move aircraft sideways and forward and aft along tracks on the hangar deck; note the connecting track on the elevator. Supermarine Seafires and four more Sea Vampires are ranged forward. The Vampire itself had nothing like enough range for naval work, but it was useful for training. The other interim type, the Sea Attacker, was also to have been ordered in very small numbers, but the Korean War showed that the 1957 estimate was wrong, and it had to be built in quantity. [*CPL*]

The US position was very different, not only because the United States was in good economic health, but also because her government was willing to concede that war was likely in the near term, given Stalin's aggressiveness. Korea came as an unpleasant surprise, but not as the sort of shock which afflicted the British defense economy. Thus the US 'interim' jet aircraft were produced in very considerable numbers. Grumman F9F-5 Panthers are fuelled aboard the carrier *Kearsage,* probably off Korea, 1953. The ship herself had been converted for jet operations under Project SCB 27A; note her enclosed bridge, and the absence of the usual *Essex*-class flightdeck gunhouses. The big radar visible behind the jet's wing is SX, a combined search radar and height finder. Above it is an SPS-6B air search set, and a YE homing beacon is visible just abaft the topmast pole. The white object at the very top is a secondary beacon; at this time the TACAN beacon had not yet been installed. The fork-like objects carry dipoles for her UHF ship-to-air radio. [*Grumman*]

Nor was it clear that protection of the air base areas would be so limited an operation. The security of the United Kingdom might well rest on the security of France and Norway, the natural base areas for intense air attacks on Britain. Operating bases in the Middle East would require massive tonnages of supplies through the Mediterranean and the Suez Canal, and that in turn might require the Allies to secure such potential Soviet base areas as Italy, Greece, and Turkey.

The Air Force countered that, using very long range bombers such as the B-36, it could attack the Soviet Union from the Continental United States.

However, B-36 range was limited, and it was never clear whether it had sufficient performanace to penetrate Soviet air defenses.* Through the 'fifties, the Air Force had to rely primarily on

* The B-36 was designed for a 5000nm combat radius carrying a 10,000 pound bomb load (ie, a 10,000nm range, the bomb being dropped halfway out). In fact, however, the B-36A was credited with a radius of 3370nm with the required bomb load. The later mixed-power (piston and jet) B-36D Featherweight III version was credited with a combat radius of 3760nm, carrying this load. The later B-36H(III) was credited with a combat radius of only 3165nm. These figures are taken from the official Air Force Standard Aircraft Characteristics charts for these aircraft, now declassified.

medium bombers based around the periphery of the Soviet Union. Only after the end of the first postwar decade did it have a truly intercontinental high performance bomber, the B-52.

The Navy had sought from the first to share control over US nuclear weapons, a status granted by President Truman as early as 1945. However, it tended to argue that they would not be decisive in themselves, and therefore that they should be used to achieve sea control by 'attacks at source', (eg, against submarine bases). Some senior naval officers, most notably Rear Admiral Daniel V Gallery (then heading the Guided Missiles Division of the Office of the Chief of Naval Operations) did argue that mobile naval forces were peculiarly well adapted to deliver strategic attacks. Both roles were to have been served by a new naval nuclear bomber, which in turn required a large new carrier, authorized in 1948 as the *United States*. Existing bombs, which weighed about 10,000 pounds, were beyond the capacity of existing carrier aircraft, although the new North American Savage (AJ-1) would soon be able to deliver them (at moderate ranges) from existing carriers.

The naval aviators therefore saw the *United States* and its heavy bomber as their future; the Air Force argued that both were superfluous. It seems more likely that the new service feared that it would lose its monopoly on nuclear attack, and hence its rationale as an independent service. In April 1949, the Air Force succeeded (through a Joint Chiefs vote and through having an extremely sympathetic Secretary of Defense in Louis S Johnson) in having the super-carrier cancelled, and funds diverted to heavy (nuclear) bomber construction. It appeared to have won the day, although the Navy carrier force was nowhere near dead. The Navy continued to develop a somewhat smaller (70,000- rather than 100,000-pound) version of its carrier-based nuclear bomber, which would be able to fly from existing (modernized) carriers. Johnson allowed the modernization program to continue, although he did support deep cuts in the active carrier force. Even as the supercarrier was cancelled, the Navy demonstrated an interim nuclear attack capability in the form of a carrier-launched version of the large P2V Neptune land-based patrol bomber.

The choice between all-nuclear and mixed strategies was not entirely clear-cut, as contemporary war plans show. A 1949 US planning exercise, published some years ago as Operation Dropshot, was typical. It envisaged a war fought in 1957, the 'year of maximum danger' at that time enshrined in British planning. Although such a war would probably involve nuclear weapons, it would resemble past wars, such as World War II, in its protracted duration and in its requirement for large land and naval forces.

Dropshot assumed an initial period of Soviet expansion into Western Europe and the Middle East, which would be halted at some natural

geographical line of resistance, the location of which would depend on standing Allied strength at the outbreak. This line might be, for example, the Pyrenees. In the next phase, the Allies would consolidate and gain strength through the mobilization of their industrial base. Finally, they would launch a decisive counter-offensive. It seemed unlikely that the limited number of nuclear weapons then available would materially alter the overall form of such a war. Studies showed that even nuclear strikes would not so damage the Soviet Union as to stop her army from overrunning large areas of Western Europe and the Middle East.

The outbreak of war in Korea the following year killed the nuclear-only idea. The nuclear calculus suggested that Stalin would have to wait until about 1954, when he would have enough bombs to deter the United States, before embarking on any military adventure. Instead, with only the most embryonic nuclear force, he had been quite willing to send his Korean proxies into battle against US and then allied troops.

Given the outbreak of actual warfare in Korea, the United States partially mobilized. With fiscal limits abandoned, it no longer had to choose between nuclear and conventional strategies. Carriers, moreover, immediately demonstrated their value. No US land-based aircraft were in place when the North Koreans attacked, and their initial advance overran most of the available air bases. Virtually all available airstrips were unsuited to modern jet aircraft which, flying from Japan, enjoyed only very short endurance in the combat area. The single carrier on station in the Far East, the *Valley Forge*, provided the bulk of available tactical aircraft, supplemented by the British light carrier *Triumph*. Only after the North Korean advance had been stopped, and after jet-capable air bases had been built, could land-based aircraft be used in any numbers.

The North Koreans attacked on 25 June 1950. On 11 July the Joint Chiefs of Staff decided to stop consideration of any further (FY52) reductions in carrier strength. By the fall the FY52 figure had grown to 12 active fleet carriers. The next day Secretary of Defense Johnson, the man who had killed the *United States*, offered the Navy a new carrier. It was ordered a year later. Slightly smaller than the *United States*, the *Forrestal* was given a very different rationale. The big carrier was now a general-purpose ship, to operate over the whole spectrum of war, from limited (Korea-style, non-nuclear) to central nuclear conflict. Ironically, too, nuclear weapons were soon so drastically reduced in weight (from the nominal 10,000 pounds of the 'forties to only 3600 pounds in the first US lightweight weapon, Mk 5, which entered service in 1952) that they could be carried by small attack aircraft which could operate even from un-modified World War II type carriers.

The more balanced military forces inspired by the Korean experience were extremely expensive. Thus the new Eisenhower administration, like

Truman's before it, feared the economic effect of unrestrained military growth. Substantial US ground and naval forces would be deployed to stop any initial Soviet advance, but the threat of 'massive retaliation' (ie, strategic nuclear attack) would be the primary deterrent to Soviet or proxy adventurism. This threat was more realistic than in 1949-50, because the United States had much greater strategic firepower, including the earliest hydrogen bombs. Strategic attack was now no longer the sole domain of the Air Force; Navy carrier aircraft and, from 1955 on, submarines were assigned to this mission.

The Navy argued that, although it might contribute relatively few aircraft to the overall US attack, those aircraft made a disproportionate contribution. Since they could approach from almost any direction, they greatly complicated the task of Soviet air defense, and so made it easier for the larger land-based bombers to penetrate. From the mid 'fifties, US carriers in the Mediterranean and in the Far East were part of the US strategic alert force, with atomic bombers on their catapults at 15-minute notice. Although the carriers were withdrawn from this role in 1963, they continued to be part of the US overall strategic force (SIOP force) until 1976.

The ships themselves had to remain within range of their nuclear targets, which restricted their movements. Carrier aircraft were still carried in the US strategic war plan (the SIOP) well into the 'seventies. The carriers had been withdrawn from the alert force, not because of perceived obsolescence, but because the alert mission limited their movement: they were wanted more for tactical operations, which required flexibility.

Carrier operational flexibility is still a major problem. The carriers are so important – and so powerful – that they have become a major symbol of US national power. As such, their movements and locations take on considerable political significance. On average, only one in three can be continuously deployed abroad, so that a force of fifteen supports five forward-deployed. In the early 'sixties that meant two in the Mediterranean and three in the Far East – one always had to be available to strike the Soviet Far East, and at least one to strike Chinese targets. This was the SIOP deployment, as the carriers were the main US nuclear force in the Far East. The deployments survived the withdrawal of the carriers from the SIOP, and in countries like Japan the ships in the Far East came to be associated with US interest in the region. Thus the withdrawal of a Seventh Fleet (Far East) carrier for operation in the Indian Ocean in 1979 (in connection with the Iranian Hostage crisis – also a political deployment) had major political consequences. Much the same might be said of the temporary withdrawal of one of the two Mediterranean carriers for the same duty. Changes in such deployment patterns require very high level political approval, yet they prevent militarily realistic operations. For example, US naval tactical doctrine requires that two, three, or

even four carriers operate together in wartime. Yet, without changes (reductions) in peacetime forward deployments, it is almost impossible to concentrate that many for exercises.

Both services spent substantial sums on strategic defense, partly because it was assumed that the Soviets were developing attack capabilities roughly in parallel with the United States. For example, as the US Navy developed a submarine-launched strategic cruise missile (Regulus), it became interested in defending the United States against a postulated parallel Soviet weapon. In the mid 'fifties, SOSUS, the US underwater surveillance system, was largely justified on this basis. Contemporary British observers feared that the growing US fascination would greatly reduce the US contribution to NATO open-ocean ASW defense.

Massive retaliation was limited, however, in its application. For example, it did not keep the Soviet-backed Viet Minh from winning in Vietnam in 1954. In 1955, the Chief of Naval Operations, Admiral Robert B. Carney, ordered a long-range naval plan. He formed a Long Range Objectives Group (LRO), which developed a US equivalent of the Royal Navy's Radical Review conclusions. The LRO was concerned primarily with the impact of new technologies, including nuclear 'plenty'. It concluded that, with the prospective development of a Soviet thermonuclear arsenal, neither superpower would be able to engage in major war. Future wars, then would be confined to the periphery of Eurasia, where Soviet proxies, like the Viet Minh, would attack US allies. The future of the Navy lay in its ability to fight them. Its strategic strike forces would most usefully function, not as part of everyday wartime operations, but as a peace-keeping deterrent. Polaris was the natural consequence of this reasoning. Its cost, in turn, had to be borne by other strike systems much more integral to the fleet and to its ability to fight a wide range of wars such as aircraft carriers and the new jet seaplanes. These implications were not explicitly drawn at the time, but they were inescapable.

NATO requirements in turn tended to moderate radical shifts in US and British national strategy because, once chosen, NATO strategy was extremely difficult to change. NATO began as a political organization with little military content, relying largely on the US nuclear deterrent. However, the outbreak of war in Korea seemed to presage a Soviet land attack in Europe, and NATO was transformed into a military alliance with its own integrated command structure. In accordance with the new, less heavily nuclear US and British thinking of the time, it included large conventional land forces, backed by tactical nuclear weapons. US and British land and sea forces pledged to NATO at this time (1952) could not easily be withdrawn later when national strategies changed.*

Then, as now, the central question was the proper balance between NATO land and sea forces. The central problem is a lack of defensive depth; there is too little land to trade for time in a protracted but dynamic war. That is why early war planners had to look to the Pyrenees for a line of resistance. It is also why NATO tends to emphasize forward defense, ie, a strong defense on the German border, rather than any sort of defense in depth – and why the problem of land defense is so difficult. Proponents of maritime strategy have, therefore, argued that NATO's defensive depth is the sea; that as long as the Soviets cannot win without gaining control of the sea as well as the land, NATO can survive.

It could be argued that, given its lack of defensive depth, NATO required very strong standing land forces to stop a Soviet offensive in time. However, those forces could not continue to fight for any substantial length of time unless they could be reinforced – by sea. Thus control of vital sea lanes of communication became a prerequisite for any sustained NATO land defense, but substantial land forces (the cost of which might preclude the purchase of sufficient naval forces) were a prerequisite for the initial viability of the alliance. When the initial force building plan was formulated at Lisbon in 1952, it was argued that the existing NATO navies were already too large, hence too expensive.

In contrast to its problems on land, NATO has important naval geographical advantages. As long as it controls most of its land territory, NATO controls the 'choke points' through which Soviet naval forces must come: the Greenland-Iceland-Norway gap in the north; the Danish Straits leading to the Baltic; the Straits of Gibraltar, the Strait of Taranto, and the Turkish Straits leading into the Mediterranean. In the Pacific, Japan blocks access to the fleet base at Vladivostok and the Aleutians very nearly block the submarine base at Petropavlovsk. Possession of the choke points suggests a trade protection strategy: the barrier, which wears down Soviet forces (particularly submarines) every time they try to pass through, going or coming. Submarine barrier operations were an important part of US and British ASW thinking from the early 'fifties onwards.

NATO was never able to raise enough troops to give it a real sense of security. In the mid 'fifties, when the Soviets had relatively few nuclear weapons, it could be argued that NATO nuclear weapons were effective equalizers, and therefore that an effective balance did in fact exist. However, as the Soviets acquired a large nuclear arsenal, the sense of insecurity returned. The US strategic advantage eroded after about 1965, as the Soviets built up a force of ICBMs of their own, capable of being launched relatively rapidly, and hence difficult to destroy pre-emptively. Although

the United States retained a considerable numerical edge, its ability to destroy the Soviet Union without suffering significant damage in return had gone. It was no longer possible to use US strategic weapons to deter a Soviet attack in Western Europe. The US government therefore led NATO into a Soviet attack by conventional means. If that failed, it would 'send a signal', threatening large-scale escalation by using limited numbers of nuclear weapons. If the Soviets replied in kind, NATO would (in theory) escalate to larger numbers of nuclear weapons, and ultimately to strategic nuclear weapons used against the Soviet Union itself. This type of strategy raised several disturbing questions. To what extent would the NATO governments find themselves deterred by the thought of Soviet nuclear retaliation? As the French asked during the 'sixties, would the United States be willing to accept destruction as the price of the ultimate level of escalation, merely to keep the Soviets from seizing Western Europe?

In 1985, the US government was trying to persuade its NATO allies to go one step further, and accept the possibility that nuclear threats are no longer effective when both sides posess large numbers of weapons, and therefore that the conventional defense must be capable of stopping a Soviet non-nuclear attack on its own.

This is very close to coming full circle, which is why the 1945-55 period is so interesting. Nuclear weapons were once scarce and hence unlikely to be used, or at least to be effective. Now they are scarce in an operationally useful sense, given the extent of deterrence. That is not to deny their importance. Their presence will certainly have a major effect on national strategy on both sides. For example, the tacit threat to Soviet ballistic missile submarines, carrying an important fraction of Soviet strategic nuclear firepower, lying in their northern sanctuaries, might be a dominant element of NATO ASW. Similarly, the sheer existence of nuclear weapons makes it difficult to imagine 'unconditional surrender' as a realistic war aim, since a government faced with such a demand might be impelled to commit suicide by using its strategic weapons.

Quite aside from NATO, Britain was responsible for the security of a global Commonwealth and Empire. The threats to that security were by no means limited to armed attack by the Soviet Union; they included internal instabilities or various kinds, and also territorial demands by neighboring states. Moreover, the mercantile origins of the British Empire survived in the British naval policing mission in areas such as the South China Sea. It was essential that trade routes be protected against such threats as piracy in peacetime, as well as against submarine and air attack in wartime. For this reason, the Royal Navy always had a limited-war mission on a global scale. One consequence was that Britain always had to maintain forces on several foreign stations, for what was at one time called the Imperial policing role. In that sense the cruiser on her

---

* The Royal Navy sometimes argued that the British naval command position within NATO would be lost unless Britain continued to contribute heavily to such organizations as the Strike Fleet. That participation in turn would allow Britain a voice in US decision-making.

distant station, rather than the battleship in a concentrated fleet, was the truest naval symbol of Empire.

In this sense the British debate over the future gun armament of the cruiser (see Chapter 5, ie, over that portion of her battery which would be effective in limited war, is a good symbolic summary of British postwar strategy. The US attempt to build a new gun cruiser, the strike cruiser of the 'seventies, suggests the strong parallel between classical British and modern American problems in reconciling the hot and cold war aspects of global power.

The central dilemma of postwar strategy, then, was how to deal simultaneously with two very different problems. Standing forces had to be able to fight off (or deter) a large-scale Soviet attack while at the same time fighting a series of minor wars in the Third World, all at a price low enough to permit continued Western political freedom and economic growth. Although NATO was a regional (European-centred) alliance, the two major maritime powers, Britain and the United States, had to think in global terms. The current US maritime strategy, for example, can be viewed as an attempt to combine the maximum degree of tactical concentration with sufficient flexibility to deal with global contingencies. It is the latest attempt to solve a problem which Britain never really could completely solve, within her limited resources.

France faced the US-British dilemma in an even more acute form, since she was a continental state and therefore could actually be overrun by Soviet armies. (The experience of 1940 is relevant here.) Moreover, like Britain, she emerged from World War II with a large overseas Empire. Even forty years later France retains responsibility for much of the defense of her former colonies. Thus she has adopted much the same posture chosen by the British in 1953-54 and in 1957, although the proportion of defense spending on strategic deterrence has been higher. French spokesmen generally argue that a Soviet leader cannot be sure that the French threat, however suicidal, will not be carried out, and that this uncertainty is an effective deterrent even against a non-nuclear Soviet attack.

This policy choice actually lies outside the period of this book, since France had no nuclear weapons of her own until 1960. At that time, with her forces integrated into the NATO command structure, she had to rely on the overall NATO (US-British) nuclear arsenal. Once she had her own weapons, France could withdraw from the NATO military structure, concentrating much of her naval resources on ballistic missile submarines. The remainder has gone into an intervention force built around carriers and amphibious ships, representing a capability which Britain virtually abandoned with the retreat from East of Suez.

*   *   *

Throughout the postwar period, the central issue of naval strategy was what role navies could play against the land power of the Soviet Union. The central new fact of naval warfare was the enormously increased role of naval aircraft, both carrier- and land-based. It was not merely that carriers replaced battleships as the central elements of seapower. They changed the reach of seapower. For the first time, a fleet could directly affect events deep inland, by striking with its carrier-based aircraft. Thus freedom of action at sea could be equated with freedom to strike at land targets from an unexpected direction, a possibility which dominated postwar American naval development.

At the same time, since it was virtually independent of foreign sources of supply, the Soviet Union was essentially immune to the classic naval weapon: blockade.

That left two traditional Western naval roles. The first, and, many would argue, the most important, was sea control. Throughout the postwar period, the Soviets maintained strong submarine and naval bomber forces. Whether or not they were assigned to attack NATO sea lines of communication, they clearly represented a deadly threat. The Western alliance would survive militarily only if its naval forces could avoid or otherwise neutralize potential Soviet anti-shipping (sea denial) forces.

The other basic traditional naval role was projection of force into the land. For example, carrier aircraft and amphibious forces could fall upon an enemy's flanks, and so affect the outcome of a land battle. Moreover, given their limited numbers, most NATO land-based tactical aircraft would necessarily be concentrated on the central front in Germany. Sea-based carrier strike forces would have to provide most of the early air support for the strategic flanks of the Alliance, in the North Sea and on the Black Sea and the Mediterranean.

Carriers were clearly expensive, and some have always argued that this necessary division of labor merely proves that the flank nations (Norway, Greece, Turkey) are sources more of weakness than of strength. That would be to ignore the role of geography. Soviet seizure of Norway would open the United Kingdom, the essential resupply base, to intense air attack. It would also make submarine operations (against the vital North Atlantic supply line) much easier. In the south, continued NATO access to the Middle East has always been considered vital. That in turn makes control of the Mediterranean important. Moreover, free Soviet access to southern Europe (including Italy) would outflank the central front.

Even so, it has often been argued that naval force projection would be difficult at best in the face of massive Soviet anti-carrier forces (bombers and submarines) operating close to their home bases. The central naval issue, then, has been the tension between sea control and force projection, the latter including the ability to strike directly at the Soviet Union.

Throughout the postwar period, the US Navy argued that the apparent distinction between sea control and projection was illusory: sea control could be achieved only through the exercise of power projection against the submarine and bomber bases, a tactic which came to be known as 'attack at source'. This idea, that sea control and strike warfare are inextricably mixed, was little understood outside the Navy; most observers associate sea control almost exclusively with convoy operations. It lost currency as local ASW and AAW weapons became more effective, and as the strategic focus of the Navy itself changed from the mid 'fifties on. Because it was rarely expressed, 'attack at source' tended to be forgotten, and the distinction between sea control and projection was a major theme in the US naval strategy of the early 'seventies. However, by the late 'seventies the relationship between offense

and defense had come closer to that of two decades before. 'Attack at source' is now once more the basis of US naval strategy.

'Attack at source' was justified by the likely cost of the alternative, the classical sea control forces (convoy escorts) needed to deal with jet bombers and fast submarines attacking convoys in the open ocean. War experience showed that at sea, land-based anti-ship bombers could be countered effectively only by defensive aircraft controlled by the threatened fleet or convoy. Ideally, that meant sea-based aircraft; at the least it meant land-based aircraft controlled by specialized ships. In either case, considerable numbers would be needed. Moreover, several new technologies (such as all-weather naval fighters and ship-to-air missiles) would be needed to counter jet bombers and stand-off missiles. Even then, it could be argued, from the kamikaze experience of 1944-45, that countermeasures at sea could not suffice. The US

The US Navy declined in relative importance after World War II because, for the first time, an enemy could deliver a crushing intercontinental strike by air, bypassing the ocean barriers. During the 'fifties the US Navy adjusted to this new circumstance by developing its own contributions to the national deterrent and to the national air defense system. The radar picket (converted destroyer escort) *Lansing* is shown off the coast of Oahu, Hawaii, in November 1963, slightly more than a year before the system of radar pickets was dismantled. [*USN*]

Navy had found that it was much better to catch the bombers on the ground, before they could strike.

'Attack at source' was hardly a new idea. It corresponded to the 'cutting out' attacks used to destroy blockaded 'fleets in being' during the age of sail. They in turn had been vitiated by improvements in shore fortifications. In World War I, for example, the large British Grand Fleet was occupied in containing the weaker German High Seas Fleet. Britain was, therefore, unable to use her superior sea power to turn the strategic flank of the Central Powers.

Strike aircraft, however, could penetrate harbors. For the Royal Navy, they became the ideal means of dealing with any future 'fleet in being'. A British Harbour Attack Committee pursued the question between wars. Although its proposed special weapons were never used, the attack on Taranto, which crippled the Italian Fleet, was the natural outgrowth of its studies. Similarly, the Japanese Navy sought to cancel out the US deterrent strategy (in effect, a 'fleet in being' threatening Japanese naval operations in east Asia) at Pearl Harbor.

Once the finite enemy bomber force had been destroyed, the seagoing force gained enormously in freedom of action. This victory would become more and more decisive as it became more and more difficult to replace destroyed anti-ship bombers, ie, as their capabilities and sophistication increased, and their numbers and production rate declined. From a strategic point of view, then, the engagement between seagoing fleet and land-based bomber fleet came more and more to resemble the classic decisive engagement between battle fleets. The destruction of the Soviet bomber fleet, then, came more and more to be one element of a struggle to control the sea. That is certainly the current US view.

Very large wartime forces had been required to

deal with a force of relatively unsophisticated submarines, which had spent much of their time on the surface. Total naval resources would inevitably be limited; those expended on ASW would have to come out of those available for sea lane air defense or for force projection. Admiral Sergei Gorshkov, the architect of the modern Soviet Navy, once remarked that every wartime German U-boat sailor had tied down a total of a hundred Allied airmen and seamen.

Wartime Allied ASW strategy combined escorts (both ships and aircraft) directly protecting convoys with offensive (hunter-killer, or HUK) forces (employing carrier- and land-based aircraft). The latter were directed primarily by a combination of code-breaking and high-frequency radio-direction (HFDF) finding*. HUK and convoy represented alternative strategies, the merits of which would be argued out postwar. The convoy strategy focused on raising the cost of each submarine attack, ultimately killing off the most aggressive submarine commanders and deterring the remainder. This attrition strategy was costly: postwar plans envisaged as many as eight to twelve escorts to be provided simultaneously for each of many convoys, for a total of several hundred in the Atlantic alone. Note that the number of escorts was virtually unrelated to the number of active submarines.

The offensive HUK strategy was attractive because it required much smaller numbers of ships and aircraft, with a much smaller attendant drain on manpower. However, HUK tactics required some means of detecting submarines at long range, so that aircraft could be vectored against them. By 1945, the Germans had already begun to counter HFDF with very short duration (burst or 'squash') transmissions (Kurier). Although Allied

* Convoy escorts also used HFDF as a long-range (30 mile) submarine detector.

A worsening financial pinch forced Britain to concentrate on a cold war strategy. Classic gun-armed cruisers, such as *Newcastle* (shown in August 1958, returning home to pay off after her last commission) therefore remained valuable as a means of policing the Commonwealth and other British spheres of influence. She and her sister ship *Birmingham* were refitted in 1950-52, receiving a modern dual purpose fire control system (Mark VI), a new bridge, and new radar. Note the 277Q height-finder forward on the lattice mast installed at this time, and the YE aircraft homing beacon on its separate pole mast aft. The former mixture of 2-pounder, 40mm, and 20mm anti-aircraft guns was replaced by a uniform battery of 18 40mm Bofors guns in single and twin mounts. Modernization also included air conditioning. [CPL]

land-based technology was barely keeping pace, Kurier could defeat ship-based HFDF – including the type aboard HUK group escort carriers. Surely the Soviets would quickly incorporate Kurier into their own submarine fleet. It seemed unlikely that Allied code-breaking successes would easily be repeated against the Soviets. Even so, HUK and its ASW aircraft were so valuable that the Western navies were loath to discard them. They went so far as to plan to send aircraft out to search the areas around 'flaming data', reports of ship sinkings. From about 1957 onwards, large fixed underwater sensors, such as SOSUS, would make HUK a primary Western ASW tactic.

There was also a complementary offensive concept, 'attack at source', ie, attack in areas in which U-boats had to be concentrated. British bombers mined the approaches to U-boat bases. Allied aircraft patrolled a major U-boat sortie area, the Bay of Biscay. Allied bombers struck the German submarine building yards, as well as their operational bases in France and Norway. The Germans built massive concrete submarine pens specifically to counter these attacks. In 1945, the US Navy sought a carrier bomber (which became the AJ-1 Savage) armed with an 8000-pound bomb capable of penetrating just such targets in a future 'attack at source' campaign.

The Soviets were expected to exploit such German developments as the fast battery submarine (Type XXI) and the Walter submarine (Type XXVI), which were beyond the capabilities of existing convoy escorts and ASW aircraft. The maritime powers were faced with an uncomfortable choice. They could modernize their war-built ASW fleets, ultimately replacing them with new escorts better fitted to fight the fast submarines. The sheer cost of this undertaking, however, would preclude them from maintaining projection or Third World forces. Designed for mass-production, the new escorts would probably not be suitable for alternative projection or Third World roles such as shore bombardment. Wartime experience had already shown how expensive even the cheapest escorts could be to man and maintain in sufficient numbers. Nor was it entirely clear in 1945-55 that surface escorts could ever hope to defeat the new submarines. That consideration alone made alternative strategies (HUK and attack at source) attractive, even mandatory.

Worst of all, in adopting a convoy strategy, the maritime powers would have to maintain large numbers of otherwise useless escort ships whether or not the Soviets chose to use their sea denial forces in wartime. The Soviets were thus presented with the possibility of using a new version of the classical 'fleet in being' strategy, in which a weaker fleet ties down a stronger one. Given the potential for Western use of superior sea power around the periphery of any Soviet land attack in Europe, this cannot have been an attractive prospect. 'Attack at source' promised to preclude it, by eliminating the 'fleet in being'.

Alternatively, if the Soviets did choose to attack the sea lanes, 'attack at source' would greatly reduce the load on Allied convoy forces, perhaps making up for the advantages enjoyed by the new submarines.

Postwar Western ASW added another alternative to convoy tactics. Submarine and aircraft barriers based on the favorable geography of the Western alliance, athwart the paths Soviet submarines had to take into the open ocean. The major expression of this tactic was the development of special ASW submarines, whose passive sonars could detect transiting Soviet submarines. Ranges were initially so short that the US Navy planned to station hundreds of such submarines just outside Soviet base areas. As sonar range improved, the ASW barriers could be withdrawn to the choke points, and the numbers greatly reduced.

HUK had political implications, since to some extent at least it substituted ASW aircraft for escorts. Britain, responsible for the security of the shallow North Sea and Channel, developed a shallow-water equivalent of the US deep-water SOSUS system, CORSAIR, at about the same time. In the US case, both long-range shore-based ASW aircraft and sea-based ASW forces were part of the Navy. In Britain, however, the Royal Air Force controlled shore-based aircraft. Although it had not yet been tested, CORSAIR became the basis for an argument (during the Radical Review of 1953-4) for large reductions in British convoy escorts (and, incidentally, in British aircraft carriers, which were assigned largely to ASW duties).

The chief symbol of 'attack at source', both in 1952 and 30 years later, was the Strike Fleet Atlantic, which was to be formed upon the outbreak of war, to move north into the Norwegian Sea. British naval strategists sometimes described the Strike Fleet as the direct successor to the Grand Fleet of World War I, providing the distant cover behind which otherwise defenseless escort craft and mine-sweepers could operate. Its missions would include direct air assistance to the NATO armies on the ground, as well as strikes at source.

'Attack at source' ideas naturally aroused Air Force opposition both in Britain and in the United States. Surely long-range bombers could achieve much the same results. The reality was more complex. The bombers would have many other urgent tasks. Moreover, many of the submarines and bombers would not be caught at their bases. They would be flushed, and the carrier strike force would have the combination of offensive and defensive weapons required to deal with them (particularly with the bombers) both at base and at sea.

The US Navy felt politically powerful enough to face down the US Air Force, and to adopt 'attack at source' as its central doctrine. It even sponsored the development of an atomic bomb specifically to deal with reinforced-concrete submarine shelters.

By way of contrast, the Royal Navy ended the war far weaker than the Royal Air Force. By 1949, British naval policy was to concentrate on classical convoy protection, using carriers to provide both fighters (against Soviet bombers and reconnaissance aircraft) and anti-submarine aircraft. This decision was not altogether popular, as many British officers considered offensive action the heart of any successful naval strategy.

Internally, the British policy decision was justified on an economic basis: money was tight, and carriers and their aircraft were expensive to operate. As a result, the first-line Fleet Air Arm was reduced to only 168 aircraft, including a cadre of only 36 strike bombers. In 1948, the US Navy argued that it would take 200 strike aircraft to achieve useful results in a single attack. Britain had wasted the best of her (very few) prewar pilots in Norway. Better to plan for a wartime build-up (based on the prewar strike cadre). British naval air mobilization plans therefore showed a steady post-outbreak growth of strike squadrons, the proportion of strike to fighter and ASW aircraft actually reversing after the beginning of mobilization. A force of about 600 first-line aircraft would be built up, about half of them strike bombers, within 18 months. In theory, too, the standing and ready reserve convoy forces would achieve sea control during that initial period. Early offensive operations would be limited to submarines and, perhaps, surface craft. For example, the postwar British midget submarines were designed partly to lay nuclear mines in the primary Soviet naval base, Leningrad.*

This official view was not altogether popular. Mobilization would be slow and who could guarantee that the war at sea would not be lost within 18 months? Certainly the prompt offensive actions taken against the Italians in 1940, when the Royal Navy had been at a considerable numerical disadvantage in the Mediterranean, had contributed disproportionately to effective sea control in that vital area.

However, the overt abandonment of 'attack at source' did preserve the strike component of the Fleet Air Arm from excessive RAF wrath. After 1952, the Royal Navy had an additional potent argument, in the form of British commitments to NATO. They included a two-carrier contribution to the Strike Fleet. Indeed, for the first two weeks of the war, the two British carriers would be the main elements of the Strike Fleet. Thus, when questioned during the Radical Review, British naval leaders could argue that to eliminate naval strike aircraft (as the RAF wished) would be to renege on an important national obligation – which, moreover, would give it a degree of control over US operations. This last argument later figured prominently in the British strategic debate: British nuclear forces were integrated with those of the United States precisely because that integration gave the British some say in wider Western decisions.

Thus, the relatively narrow politics of British inter-service relations, which controlled the future of the British carrier force, were closely connected to the much larger British post-1945 political theme of trying to retain great power status, despite a series of terrible economic blows, which were not limited to the destruction caused by World War II. Many Britons similarly associated Empire with great power status, and the determination to retain an expensive Empire also shaped postwar military and naval policy, both in the large and in such details as cruiser and destroyer armament. More than 30 years later, with the Empire all but gone, the great power requirement remains, in the form of the British nuclear deterrent, soon to be carried by Trident submarines. Great power strategic status is expensive, and some believe that this time the price will be the near-abandonment of conventional British sea power. If that happens, it will mirror what the United States nearly did in 1949-50, at a time when the Soviet Union was far weaker.

Quite aside from these broad considerations, war experience in carrier operation had considerable strategic implications. Unlike battleships, carriers could not be concentrated in unlimited numbers. Their strike aircraft had to join up to attack, and the larger the strike, the longer the joining-up process, and the less remaining endurance time there was left for the strike itself. Similarly, the larger the strike, the longer to recover from it. In defense, there was a natural limit to the number of individual fighters a carrier could usefully coordinate. Beyond that point, more fighters would cause confusion; friendly-on-friendly ('blue-on-blue' in current parlance) battles might even let more attackers through. Both in Britain and in the United States, then, the wartime conclusion was that four carriers formed the most effective tactical unit; six was the maximum capable of working together effectively. For example, Task Force 58, the massive fast carrier task force, was organized into four-carrier task groups.

Thus it was natural for postwar navies to be divided into several carrier forces which could operate in very widely separated geographical areas. The US Navy planned four carrier strike groups, keeping one ready at all times on each coast, for ready intervention or strategic deterrence. On a smaller scale, France planned to operate both a home and an overseas (colonial) fleet. By way of contrast, prewar navies had tried to concentrate their battle fleets to achieve local superiority. It was true that very large battle lines (as at Jutland) presented command and control problems of their own, but the numbers available after World War I never approached this limit. Each additional battleship added firepower at a very limited cost in coordination.

The natural division of carrier assets promised

---

* These submarines were initially justified as a means of training British harbor defenses. The formal shift to 'attack at source' dates from about 1952.

to solve the classic naval problem, of how to deal with (possibly simultaneous) worldwide problems using a battle fleet limited in numbers by finances. The British never really solved it. Since the late eighteenth century, Britain had been both an Asiatic and a European power. Her central policy had been to avoid simultaneous threats in both theaters, always appeasing a threat in one while fighting in the other. Alliance between the two threats, then, had always been particularly troubling. The 1894 alliance of France and Russia presented just such a threat; Britain had to choose between this European/Asiatic threat and the purely European threat of the Kaiser's Germany. At this time Japan, the growing Asiatic power, was an independent factor, although clearly she might ultimately want to seize the British Asiatic Empire.

In naval terms, this meant that in peacetime, Britain always had to maintain fleets in home waters, in the Mediterranean, and in the Far East (the China station), plus lesser numbers of ships on other foreign fleets; the lesser station forces, primarily to police the Empire and to protect British interests in a turbulent Third World. The problem was difficult, even given the wealth of pre-1914 Britain. It could, however, be solved in

the traditional manner. Britain was able to concentrate her navy against a one-theater threat, the Kaiser's new High Seas Fleet, having withdrawn most of her Far East and Mediterranean fleets, under the cover of appropriate treaties with France, Japan, and Russia.

After 1918, with the British alliance with Japan abrogated, Britain had once more to face naval problems as both Asiatic and a European power. She could not afford to maintain a strong peacetime fleet in the Far East, and had to reject a 1933 proposal to move the three battle cruisers to Singapore. The best the Royal Navy could do was to concentrate most of the battle fleet in the Mediterranean, where it could quickly 'swing' to join the Home Fleet, but where it was also somewhat closer to the Far East. There was never enough British seapower, then, to face simultaneous threats both in Europe and in Asia, as in World War II.

The prewar United States, concentrating almost entirely on Japan, was able to maintain a single concentrated US (Pacific) Fleet almost up to the outbreak of war. In 1945, however, the United States found itself by far the most powerful country in the world, with the sort of

The heaviest-gunned ships were much too expensive for the cold war intervention mission. As early as 1949 the then First Sea Lord, Admiral Fraser, decided to allow the guns and fire controls of the laid-up battleships to 'rot' pending a decision as to whether they should be rearmed with guided missiles. *Duke of York,* his flagship at the North Cape in 1943, is shown awaiting breaking up at Faslane, March 1958, with the maintenance carrier *Perseus* in the background. The war-built battleships enjoyed a brief revival of interest in the early 'fifties, as the Soviets built up a substantial cruiser force, but they were scrapped under the 1957 White Paper, which, from the Royal Navy's point of view, in effect, consolidated the ideas developed during the Radical Review of 1953-54. *Vanguard* and the two French battleships followed two years later. Only the US Navy was rich enough to maintain such ships, to lay down heavy fire against shore positions. [CPL]

simultaneous European and Asiatic commitments previously held only by the previous global power, Britain. Moreover, in prewar British terms, she could no longer use diplomacy to avoid a two-theater naval war. The new enemy, the Soviet Union, was already present in both Europe and Asia, not to mention the vital Middle East. As a result, the United States gradually came to appreciate that strong naval forces would have to be maintained both in European and in Asiatic waters: they ultimately became the Sixth and Seventh Fleets. That division was easier because of the nature of carrier operations, not to mention the vast increase in carrier striking power brought about by the atomic bomb.

Unlike battleships at their peak, carriers never combined ultimate offensive and defensive power. Under the appropriate circumstances, a battleship could still surprise and sink a carrier, as in the case of HMS *Glorious* off Norway in 1940 and USS *Gambier Bay* off Samar in 1944. Nor was it clear that small numbers of carriers could always concentrate enough weapons to sink modern battleships. After all, it took the entire striking power of Task Force 58 to sink the Japanese *Yamato* in April 1945. This consideration explains why early postwar US, British, and French fleet planners all expected to support future carrier task forces with fast battleships. As late as 1955, the design of the US fast carrier escorts (which became the *Farragut* class) included anti-ship torpedo tubes specifically to deal with possible enemy surface attackers, as off Samar.

Given its wartime experience facing heavy German raiders, the Royal Navy was perhaps particularly alert to this problem. Its postwar concentration on anti-bomber and anti-submarine weapons left it without very many anti-ship (strike) aircraft or modern air-launched anti-ship weapons. The Soviets, however, presented a two-fold threat in the north with fast gun-armed cruisers as well as submarines. If ASW-oriented carrier aircraft were really unsuited to deal with the cruisers (which, with no more battleships, were equivalent to battleships) then the carriers might well find themselves in jeopardy. It was not so much that the Soviet cruisers were formidable in themselves, as that, as survivors of an earlier age, they had largely outlived the countermeasures that earlier age had provided. In the late 'forties, then, the Royal Navy seriously contemplated modernization of the surface fire control systems of its cruisers. It later justified guns in missile cruisers on much the same theory: without an effective anti-ship weapon, it could not maintain the ASW/AAW power of its carriers. Soviet submarines and aircraft were a far more efficient threat to shipping, but the British feared that cruisers, like the *Tirpitz*, could uncover shipping to their attacks.

This was still a valid fear in 1982, in the Falkland Islands. The two British carriers were the primary ASW and AAW shield of the invasion fleet. Their specialization in that role precluded (at the time)

any substantial anti-ship capability. Nor do the British appear to have trusted ship-launched Exocets in the Task Force to deal with the relatively well-protected *Belgrano*, whose 6in guns, immune to electronic countermeasures, could surely have dispatched the two carriers. It was therefore essential to sink her, even though most of the world saw her as a relic.

The US, French, and Dutch navies also operated substantial forces of long-range seaplanes and land-based patrol bombers. Both in the United States and Britain the question was often raised whether land-based aircraft could not ultimately replace the relatively expensive carrier-based types. The fundamental answer turned out to be that the chief limitation of non-carrier aircraft was (and remains) limited endurance on station. They could, therefore, scout and attack ships (and submarines), but they are ill adapted to defending ships at sea. A defender must remain continuously on station, against the possibility of a surprise attack; it cannot realistically rely on intelligence or early warning.

In World War II, for example, Allied long-range maritime bombers could escort convoys only by flying relays, each airplane remaining on station for only a limited period (several hours) of time. Although the bombers were extremely useful (primarily because they forced shadowing U-boats down), they could not concentrate rapidly to counter an unexpected attack. Their bases were just too far away. At 200 knots, a bomber would require eight hours to reach an embattled convoy 1600 miles away, in mid-Atlantic. Similarly, a bomber which used up its limited stock of weapons early in a patrol could not be relieved except as scheduled. These limitations explain why escort carriers, which accompanied convoys and therefore could deal with sudden contingencies, were so useful.

Much the same questions still remain. How important is it to provide expensive defensive (ASW and anti-air) aircraft to accompany seaborne forces? How much can land-based aircraft do? These questions were particularly sensitive for navies which did not control their associated land-based maritime patrol aircraft, most notably the Royal Navy.

One answer is that land-based aircraft are most effective when they can attack ships or aircraft or submarines at sea without reference to defending a particular task force or convoy. Certainly, long-range land-based American, British, German, Italian, and Japanese aircraft were effective ship-killers. Postwar, the Soviets developed a naval bomber force along much the same lines. Thus the efficacy of the long-range anti-ship or ASW bomber depends upon an external factor, an efficient means of detecting the target at very long range. For the Western Allies, that meant SOSUS and its equivalents. For the Soviets, it meant land-based HFDF and, later, satellite-based radar and direction-finding systems.

2 THE SHAPE OF THE FLEET

Fleets changed after 1945 to reflect the new technological and strategic realities, most notably the primacy of the carrier. Both the US and the British navies relied on a combination of ready (active) and reserve (mobilization) forces, the latter including most of the numerous single-purpose escorts needed to fight a latter-day Battle of the Atlantic. Both planned active fleets built around carrier task groups. In both cases, too, although the shape of future fleets was clear on paper as early as 1945-1947, the reality changed much more slowly, as governments were extremely reluctant to invest heavily in new or rebuilt warships. Thus the fleets of this chapter are more representative of changing ideas (and of plans) than of actual commissioned forces.

The most modern existing tonnage, the result of wartime mobilization, largely reflected prewar and early wartime concepts, since mass-production generally required that designs be frozen. Thus Britain, going to war in 1939, had adopted designs limited by the existing treaties even though those treaties had lapsed. There was no hope of changing designs. This particularly affected new cruisers, which through the war were modified versions of treaty ships limited to 8000 tons (standard). Because the treaties lapsed in 1939, the US Navy was able to develop larger ships (albeit still much influenced by their treaty-restricted forebears), whose designs were frozen in 1940-41. Thus the US *Essex* class carrier displaced 27,500 tons (standard), and the US *Cleveland* class light cruiser, 10,500. The United States, blessed by a much larger industrial base, was also better able to incorporate wartime ideas in some of her production classes, perhaps most notably the *Midway* class aircraft carriers, the large *Baltimore* class heavy cruisers and the *Fletcher*, *Sumner*, and *Gearing* class destroyers. By way of contrast, the Royal Navy ended the war with classes corresponding to several major wartime designs either unbuilt or incomplete. From a postwar point of view, treaty limits tended to limit modification to fit ships to radically new requirements, or for the new weapons and aircraft.

This contrast between the two navies was particularly evident in aircraft carriers. Britain began to mobilize in 1937, and by 1939 the Royal

Navy had ordered six 23,000-ton carriers with armored hangers. During this time the US Navy ordered only two ships, the *Hornet*, which repeated the much earlier *Yorktown* (CV 5) design, and the small *Wasp*. However, the prewar mobilization program filled British yards capable of building large ships, and little further acceleration was possible after 1940. Consideration was given to ordering two fleet carriers under each of the 1941 and 1942 programs, but instead four ships (which became the *Ark Royal* class) were ordered under the 1942 program. Three larger fleet carriers, the *Malta*s, were included in the 1943 program. However, only one ship was actually laid down in 1942; the yards were just too full. At the end of the war only two of these seven ships survived the inevitable cut-backs. They were, moreover, the only truly post-Treaty British carriers. Their extra 10,000 tons of displacement brought much larger hangar spaces (for much larger air groups). Perhaps more significantly,

At the end of World War II, the carrier was clearly a dominant striking weapon, but it was by no means clear that battleships were entirely obsolete. That was particularly the case for a Royal Navy, very limited in its carrier-based strike power. Here *Vanguard*, the last British battleship, steams with the last of the World War II cruisers, *Superb*, September 1950. [CPL]

Quite aside from the battle fleet, the Royal Navy was responsible for policing a vast Empire and Commonwealth. *Kenya* is shown at Portsmouth, October 1949. Note the large (and immobile) fleet in the background. Throughout the postwar period, the active Royal Navy was considerably smaller than the total number of ships on its Navy list. Until 1957, then, British naval policy relied on manpower mobilization and ship activation to make up the considerable gaps in its active order of battle. *Kenya* served as Far East flagship, relieving the heavy cruiser *London*, in 1950-52. After a long refit (1953-5), she was flagship on the America and West Indies station, where she had served before the Far East. These were essentially colonial assignments, for which she was well suited. [CPL]

they were designed from the outset to operate much larger and heavier aircraft. The 1936-39 carriers were designed for a weight limit of 11,000 pounds (at take-off), which was considerably exceeded in wartime service. The 1942-43 ships were designed for 30,000-pound aircraft. In 1945, the Royal Navy was testing a 22,000-pound strike aircraft, the Fairey Spearfish, far beyond the capacity of its prewar ships.

The Admiralty was well aware of the need for more carriers. Limited by warship yard capacity, it ordered a series of austere light fleet carriers, built largely to merchant ship standards: the ten *Colossus* and six *Majestic* class of the 1942 program, and the eight *Hermes* of the 1943 program. Only eight of the first series could be completed by 1946. By that time they were obsolescent, and the similar *Majestic*s were never completed for British naval service. Instead, limited postwar resources went into the completion of four of the much more sophisticated *Hermes* class, to operate 30,000-pound aircraft.

By way of contrast, with no satisfactory production design available in 1940, the US Navy was forced to develop a new one. It became the very successful *Essex*, eleven of which were ordered in 1940. More followed in 1941-43. US large warship yard capacity proved immense, and 23 were completed during or immediately after the war. Another USS *Oriskany*, was suspended and stripped to become the prototype for postwar

reconstruction. Note that the US equivalent to the British light fleet carrier, the fast quick-production ship, was a converted cruiser hull, the *Independence*, nine of which were completed in 1942-43, in time to full the gap between the prewar ships and the *Essex*es. Part of the penalty was that an *Independence* was much less satisfactory, as a carrier, than a British light fleet ship.

The late 'thirties and the 'forties were a time of very rapid aircraft development, so that the four years separating the British armored deck carrier (*Illustrious*) and the *Essex* were quite significant in terms of carrier-imposed limits. Thus, virtually unmodified *Essex*es successfully operated the early US naval jets, but that was never really an option for the prewar-designed British fleet carriers. They had to be rebuilt or discarded.

Both countries built large numbers of destroyers during the war. However, the Royal Navy chose to mass-produce a much-modified version of its last prewar type, the J class, whose 1690-ton design had been influenced by the pre-1936 limit of 1850 tons. The United States Navy did build an equivalent *Benson-Gleaves* type, but most of its wartime destroyers were based on an entirely new design, the 2100-ton *Fletcher* of 1940. The American ship was, therefore, much larger and hence much more susceptible to postwar modification. Moreover, the US Navy had adopted dual-purpose (both high- and low-angle)

The potential for cruiser modernization was limited in any case. In 1945, with her three Mark 6 directors, *Superb* was the only British cruiser with a modern anti-aircraft armament. Photographed off San Diego on 11 July 1955, she has only one, aft; the other two (abeam her forefunnel) are marked by empty pedestals. At this time, morever, she still retained her obsolete 2-pounder pom-poms. At this time *Superb* was flagship of the America and West Indies station. Never modernized, she was placed in reserve in 1958 and broken up in 1960. [*USN*]

destroyer guns as early as 1933. The Royal Navy considered arming its destroyers with such weapons at about the same time, but found the inherent compromise unsatisfactory. As a result, it did not develop a destroyer armed with a true dual-purpose main battery until 1941, and such ships (the *Battle* class) did not enter service until the end of the war. The effect of postwar cancellations, then, was to deprive the Royal Navy of most of its next-generation destroyer force, whereas most of the planned US large destroyers were actually completed.

There could be little thought of scrapping the recently completed, if obsolescent, wartime ships. In 1945 the Royal Navy, for example, assigned its large warships a life of 20 years, plus ten more after a major refit or modernization ('mid-life refit', in current parlance). Destroyer lifetime was 16 years. On this basis the large prewar and war construction programs would last the Royal Navy into the 'sixties.

However, existing anti-submarine ships could hardly face the new fast submarines, which would surely enter service in substantial numbers within a few years. Existing British carriers could handle neither the new heavy strike aircraft, nor the new jet fighters. Existing British submarines would have to be modernized. Moreover, existing British anti-aircraft fire control systems, obsolescent even in 1939, would have to be replaced throughout the fleet.

Given these severe problems and an equally severe shortage of money, the Admiralty compromised. ASW obsolescence was clearly the most immediate problem. The solution was large-scale interim conversion of existing destroyers not needed for fleet screening, coupled with a program of new frigate design and prototype construction. Modernization of the existing fleet carriers and completion (to modernized designs) of two wartime fleet carriers (*Eagle* and *Ark Royal*) and four wartime light carriers (the *Hermes* class) would be the next step. All would be able to

handle the new generation of aircraft. Cruiser modernization received a somewhat lower priority, since existing unmodernized ships could still be useful in the Third World. Given the size of the war program, destroyer and cruiser replacement could be delayed until the late 'fifties.

Aircraft design was changing rapidly, and modernization was not an option. Given their 1957 planning horizon, the British chose to defer the expense of mass replacement by drastically shrinking the Fleet Air Arm. There was, in any case, little point in buying large numbers of interim aircraft when the new carriers capable of operating them would not enter service for some years. US Naval strategy did not admit this option, partly because the United States did not accept the British view that hostilities would not break out before 1952 at the earliest. As a result, by 1949, the US Navy planned a total force (including, it is true, second-line types and land-based aircraft) of over 14,000*. The expense of maintaining so large a force was part of the explanation of the major cut in US carrier strength from 1949 onwards.

Responding to a direct request by Winston Churchill, the Royal Navy began work on its postwar plans in March 1944. The Prime Minister wanted to establish the Navy's rationale before any claims for a future world security organization (hence for weaker British forces) could be made.

The First Sea Lord argued that the position of the British Empire as a world power depended on the extent to which it could operate as an integrated organization. That in turn required that it control the sea lanes linking its units. This rationale was entirely independent of any assumption as to particular postwar enemies. Certainly the Soviet Union had not yet been

* By way of comparison, the Royal Navy had 144 front-line aircraft in April 1951. However, that force was supported by a total of 771 front-line aircraft held as stock, and by 1302 training and ancillary types. On this basis the front-line strength of the US Navy was about 2000 aircraft.

identified as a postwar problem. It was, in any case, unrealistic to make such specific assumptions, as the fleet structure determined in 1944 might remain for 20 or 30 years. The early plan for a postwar fleet is, therefore, a measure of requirements. Later plans show how far short of the requirements the fiscal reality fell.

The active postwar Royal Navy would consist of station forces based on particular home and overseas bases, to protect sea communications, support local British interests, train, and show the flag. Mobile self-supporting battle forces would move rapidly to reinforce the station forces without detracting from the local (presence) station forces elsewhere. In addition, the Navy would maintain submarines, auxiliary forces (mine craft, escorts, coastal craft), and amphibious forces.

Both at this time and in 1945, the Admiralty would maintain the need for a balance of carriers and battleships. The carriers were valued for their long strike range and for their ability to provide fighter protection, the battleships for their shorter-range striking power, particularly when the air power of an enemy force had been neutralized. Cruisers would be needed for reconnaissance in non-flying weather, and to deal with light enemy forces. Moreover, carriers had little gun power. The consort cruiser was, in effect, the carrier's guns, and one would have to be attached to each carrier.

The postwar fleet unit would be the carrier task group (battle fleet): a maximum of four carriers, each supported directly by a light cruiser, with two battleships (each with an accompanying heavy cruiser) in close support. In this British parlance, a heavy cruiser was a large one, armed either with 8in or 6in guns (before the war 'heavy cruiser' denoted an 8-inch gun ship). Sixteen destroyers (two flotillas) would provide an all-round screen. To make this battle fleet self-sufficient, it would be supported by a destroyer tender, a heavy repair ship, an aircraft repair ship, and a fast tanker. The minimum fleet unit would be the battle squadron, half a battle fleet. An April 1944, Staff Review eliminated the distinction between cruiser tyres, and increased the destroyer screen to 18 ships (adding two flotilla leaders).

This was very much the structure advocated by the British Pacific Fleet in 1945: four carriers with a 12-destroyer screen (led by a cruiser), with eight more destroyers for 'extraneous duties' and four destroyers as plane guards. Two cruisers and two battleships would provide anti-aircraft cover, and two cruisers would act as radar pickets. However, in 1945, the British Pacific Fleet commander required an elaborate logistical support force, comprising a flagship, at least four escorts (plus those arriving with tanker groups), two ammunition ships, one stores (victualling) ship, one radio maintenance ship, one ocean rescue tug, two replenishment carriers, one escort carrier to provide a combat air patrol, and one escort carrier to provide a fleet requirements unit (eg, target towing services).

This group in turn, would be supported by a shuttle service between the advanced anchorage and the service area. It would include tankers sufficient for two-day turn-around at the base, and to arrive in the service area on the last day of a previous refuelling, each group supported by three escorts, underway replenishment carriers, replenishment ammunition supply issue ships, and refrigerator ships to top up the store ships. The depot and accommodation ships would lie at the advanced anchorage. This scale of operations, typical of wartime US fast carrier tactics, was never really acceptable to a much less prosperous postwar Royal Navy.

The British postwar mobile force would consist of one battle force in home waters, and another divided between the Mediterranean and the Indian Ocean/Australian area. A tabulation made in March 1944 showed one battleship on station in each of the latter two areas, to supplement the one in the local battle squadron. Each of the Home and Far East station forces would include two carriers and eight destroyers (six heavy cruisers on the home station, 12 in the Far East).

The active fleet, then, would include six battleships/battle cruisers, 12 carriers, 22 heavy cruisers, 12 light cruisers, 56 destroyers, 32 frigates (four squadrons of eight each, on the stations), 36 submarines, 24 minesweepers (one flotilla per station), and 32 coastal craft. It would be backed up by a much larger reserve (including ships being modernized), including six battleships, ten carriers, eight heavy and eight light cruisers, 60 destroyers, 158 escorts, 50 submarines, and 100 minesweepers. Sufficient amphibious forces would be maintained for a full divisional lift (two brigade assault basis) in Home waters, with brigade lifts in India and Australia for Dominion training. No amphibious forces would be maintained in the Mediterranean, which would have only garrison troops. This large (and expensive) amphibious force was pared to a nucleus of landing craft in home waters when the Staff reviewed the postwar plan in April 1944.

This was a huge force, but quite in keeping with existing British naval resources. In 1945, for example, the Royal Navy had four modern battleships (with another, *Vanguard*, being completed, and with two more planned) and a fast modernized battle cruiser (*Renown*) plus four adequate older battleships (two modernized *Queen Elizabeths* and two *Nelsons*); six modern fleet carriers (with seven more – four *Ark Royal* and three *Gibraltar* on order) plus 22 light fleet cruisers built or building. As for cruisers, the postwar program included three *Tigers* and six ships of a new design (*Minotaurs*) to be completed in 'slow time'. In 1945, the Commonwealth already possesed a total of 45 more or less modern ships: ten heavy cruisers, five *Leanders*, two *Arethusas*, six Towns, 11 *Didos*, and 11 *Fijis* and modified *Fijis*. Destroyers were in gross oversupply, at least in so far as the planned active fleet was concerned.

Even so, the 1944-45 plans could not be realized, because no postwar British government could afford the running or even the maintenance expense of so large a fleet. Nor could it provide enough men. In 1945, the Admiralty estimated a manning level of 220,000, including a 50,000-man Commonwealth/Empire contribution. This compared with a total of about 138,000 prewar, including the small Fleet Air Arm and the Dominion and Indian navies. Part of the reason for growth was much heavier manning of ships (for example, for more anti-aircraft guns and for more, and more complex, aircraft). Part of the increase was also a much expanded shore establishment to support the more complex postwar Navy.

The next step down was for the Admiralty to accept limitation to two main fleets (1945), a minimum set because to concentrate all tactical training into one fleet would abolish flexibility of outlook and competition. Economics dictated that one fleet be based in Britain and the other abroad but not too far away, which meant the Mediterranean. Similarly, effective training would require that each fleet include one of each of the two basic naval units, the heavy squadron and the lighter escort force, which had fought in the two primary British all-arms naval campaigns, the Malta and the Russian convoys.

Thus postwar heavy squadrons would be modelled on the Mediterranean Force H, light squadrons on the Home Fleet destroyer groups escorting the Russian convoys. This permanent organization would break up the traditional fleet pattern of battle line, carriers, squadrons and flotillas.

The single purpose escorts which had fought the Battle of the Atlantic were virtually excluded from this organization. War experience had shown that a minimum of ten escort groups were required for the North Atlantic route alone, with another 50 for British coastal convoys, a total of 480 frigates and corvettes. However, these small ships were expensive to man and to maintain in peacetime. Thus, only small numbers of escorts would be maintained in peacetime for training, most being laid up in reserve.

The heavy squadron would include a minimum of two carriers (for operational efficiency, and to provide a second deck in case of accident). Prolonged night operations would require a third. At least one battleship would counter heavy enemy surface units. Two or three cruisers would scout and screen in non-flying weather (or in the absence of aircraft). More numerous than battleships, the cruisers might perform much the same duties. Efficient anti-aircraft support required that the number of cruisers plus battleships exceed the number of carriers by at least one ship. The 1945 fleet structrure showed heavy squadrons each comprising two battleships, two fleet carriers, a cruiser squadron (five ships), and three destroyer flotillas (eight destroyers each).

Each main fleet would also include two light carriers, an escort group (eight ships) and one submarine flotilla (ten craft). However, the Home Fleet would have an extra escort group and 15 more submarines, plus ships for trials and training (two light carriers and three cruisers). Heavy and light squadron composition was studied further in 1946-47.

The Admiralty argued that station forces would help revive British overseas trade. The South Atlantic cruiser squadron had been re-established after World War I specifically to preserve a British commercial presence in South America, and trade had indeed followed the flag there. Quite apart from any requirement for Empire security, it therefore intended to maintain limited British naval forces on a global basis. Cruisers and escorts would be required on all foreign stations, whereas carriers would normally be restricted to those areas where Naval Air Stations were available and weather conditions suitable for flying training.

Cruisers would maintain Commonwealth security and also show the flag: four on each of the South Atlantic, East Indies, and Pacific stations, and two in African waters. Canada would contribute one light fleet carrier and two cruisers to Commonwealth defense; Australia and New Zealand, one carrier and three cruisers. Each of these two Dominion navies would also include an eight-ship destroyer flotilla and an escort group. In addition, there would be four escorts on each foreign station (eight in the Pacific, which would also support a ten-ship submarine flotilla). Thus active British Commonwealth naval forces would include eight light cruisers, 32 cruisers, seven destroyer flotillas, seven escort groups, and 45 submarines. These figures were slightly increased in the fall of 1945 (ten light carriers, eight destroyer flotillas – ideally four Weapons and four Battles, and a total of 60 escorts).*

The peacetime fleet would include sufficient assault lift for one brigade. First-line aircraft strength would be about 500. On mobilization, the fleet would require about 1300 first-line aircraft, and a total of about 400,000 to 500,000 men (compared to a peacetime total of about 220,000); about 600,000 would be required after 18 months.

A more sophisticated fleet organization study of May 1946 described the fleet screen in some detail. By this time the British had digested the US lesson of Okinawa. Pickets were needed to extend the

---

* The two classes mentioned were the only ones with modern dual purpose main batteries and directors. In 1945, the Royal Navy had built, building, or on order, two flotillas of 1942 Battles, three of 1943 Battles, and two of 1944 Battles (which became the *Daring* class). There were also two flotillas of 1943 Weapons and one of 1945 Weapons (the abortive G class). There were also some Australian ships on order, and some classes exceeded the numbers required for flotillas, as additional war losses had been expected. Of this total of more than 80 ships, only four and a half flotillas (two 1942, one 1943, and one 1944 Battle class and half a flotilla of 1943 Weapons), 36 ships, was completed.

range of fleet air defense, particularly as future aircraft would be so much faster. They therefore planned a screen of six Fleet Air Defense Escorts (FADE) 40 to 70nm from the fleet proper. They might be either cruisers or specially fitted destroyers.

Destroyers were needed offensively as a striking force, defensively for AS and AA protection. Twelve destroyers would suffice as a circular screen for a force of six heavy units. However, greater numbers might well be needed in the face of concentrated submarine attack, or in particular against fast submarines (which might call for inner and outer AS screens). Destroyers would also be required for other duties, and some would always be unavailable. The heavy squadron would, therefore, require a total of 24 destroyers.

This heavy squadron (one battleship, two carriers, two cruisers, six FADE, and 24 destroyers) was suggested as a suitable basis for peacetime organization.

These figures in turn formed the basis for discussions of specialization in destroyer and cruiser design. The great question was whether, as in the past, a single destroyer class, or even a single type of hull, could be effective in all four future fleet escort roles: anti-aircraft, anti-submarine, anti-ship, and air direction.

Destroyers had already grown alarmingly in wartime, from about 1700 tons (for the large prewar J class) to about 2700 tons in the *Darings*, which many already considered too large. Early studies of aircraft direction requirements, moreover, suggested that the minimum FADE would be a small cruiser. It appeared that the anti-aircraft/anti-surface role would impose a destroyer displacement of about 3000 tons, which was considered just too large for successful submarine hunting. Given the very short ranges of her weapons and sensors, the hunter would have to maneuver very sharply. A 3000-tonner would therefore be limited to hand-off tactics unless sensor (sonar) and weapons ranges could be considerably extended. She would be too large to detect and counter attack enemy submarines entering or penetrating the screen. Thus early British discussions of fleet composition envisaged separate anti-submarine, anti-aircraft, and FADE classes.

It was assumed that two anti-submarine destroyers would suffice to hunt and sink an intermediate (eg, Type XXI) submarine with a submerged speed of 17 knots. Four would probably be needed to contain and sink the 'ultimate' 25-knot submarine. anti-submarine destroyers would therefore be organized in hunting groups of four each. It remained to devise a proper balance between anti-submarine and anti-aircraft destroyers within the limited total available.

This was a matter of some debate, beginning with a 1947 proposal (by the Director of Plans) that the heavy squadron include four hunting groups. Since that would leave only eight anti-aircraft and

anti-surface ships in the force, with insufficient concentrated anti-aircraft fire, the Director of Plans retreated to three hunting groups (12 anti-submarine destroyers). The AA and anti-surface units would, similarly, be organized into three flotillas of four each; the FADE ships would form a flotilla of their own.

As discussion continued within the staff divisions of the Admiralty, pressure mounted to emphasize anti-aircraft firepower. The Director of the Torpedo/Anti-Submarine Branch and the Director of Gunnery both agreed that the screen might be limited to a single hunting group, as long as the other destroyers had some limited capability for screening. However, in the face of severe submarine opposition, as much as 25 or 50 per cent of the screen might have to consist of

By the mid 'fifties the Royal Navy could concentrate a small but modern carrier fleet. Here the large light carriers *Albion* and *Bulwark* steam in company with the larger *Eagle* off Malta, October 1956, shortly before Suez. The aircraft are Sea Venom night fighters and Seahawk day fighter-bombers. [CPL]

specialist anti-submarine destroyers. Otherwise, it might be well to limit the heavy squadron to the four-ship hunting group. These destroyers might not even lie in the screen. Instead, they could occupy pouncer positions from which they could take advantage of submarine detections by the screening destroyers. The Director of Operations argued for at least two hunting groups, three ships each (although two or four each might be found preferable). That made for a minimum of six anti-submarine destroyers out of the 24.

Like the heavy squadron, the light squadron could be seen in embryonic form in the 1945 fleet proposal. It was envisaged as a combination of a close escort (anti-submarine and anti-air) and a support force, which could strike offensively against submarines and aircraft, and against surface attackers of moderate size. The support force could operate either close to the convoy or at some distance.

Light carriers would provide reconnaissance, fighter cover, and anti-submarine search and strike. War experience showed that two were needed to provide the air support to counter heavy submarine and air attacks. At least one cruiser would be needed to deal with enemy surface raiders or cruisers, and to provide anti-aircraft support for the carriers. The support force escorts would hunt down submarines. They would be organized into two four-frigate hunting groups, and a third four-frigate screen for the light carriers to remain when the hunters were detached. A light squadron, then, might consist of two light carriers, a cruiser, and 12 escorts.

Convoys would also require close escort, the balance between anti-aircraft and anti-submarine depending on the situation. For example, about 20 frigates would probably be required to deal with fast submarines, with others for aircraft direction. By this time the Royal Navy had already begun to develop a family of postwar frigates for anti-submarine, anti-aircraft, and air direction. Very large numbers would clearly be needed to wartime, and the common hull envisaged in 1946 would simplify production.

By this time, British economic realities had made themselves felt. For example, newly-completed destroyers had to be laid up in 1947 due to a manning crisis. Much of the nominally active fleet had to be immobilized in 1948 to save fuel. In the fall of 1948, the operational fleet included two battleships, four light fleet carriers, 16 cruisers, 34 destroyers, 25 frigates, 26 submarines, and 12 minesweepers. However, the Navy was able to maintain other ships in commission for training, experimental, and special assignments: two battleships, three fleet carriers, three light fleet carriers, two cruisers, 18 destroyers, 18 frigates, eight submarines, and two minesweepers. Reserve forces included one battleship, three fleet carriers, an escort carrier, 11 cruisers, 65 destroyers, and 136 frigates. The active ships were widely spread among fleets and stations. For example, the Home Fleet consisted of only one cruiser and four destroyers.

The next stage of long-range planning was the Nine Year Plan, first formulated in February 1948. Most of the fleet was to consist of ships already in existence: six fleet carriers, six light fleet carriers (one on loan to Australia), five battleships, the 20 best cruisers (eight 5.25in and twelve of sixteen existing 6in cruisers), two monitors, three fast minelayers (one, *Ariadne*, converted into a FADE), 54 destroyers, 217 frigates, 51 submarines (of which 12 T-class would be converted to fast battery drive*), and 60 ocean minesweepers. Of the frigates, 59 would be converted destroyers. A total of four 6in cruisers (beyond the 20) would be retained pending decisions as to their disposal. Similarly, six more ocean sweepers would be retained in a low category of preservation.

Despite large concellations in 1945, many ships were still either suspended or actually under construction: two fleet carriers (the *Ark Royals*), seven light fleet carriers (four *Hermes* under construction, three *Majestic* class suspended), three cruisers (the *Tigers*, to be completed much later to a new design), eight destroyers (*Daring* class), four frigates (prototype anti-aircraft and aircraft direction ships of the 1945 program, and the last two Bays), and two experimental submarines (the hydrogen-peroxide powered *Explorer* and *Excaliber*). All were to be completed.

* This was the standard British phrase for the combination of streamlining, greater battery capacity, and more powerful motors to give higher underwater speed, as in the US Guppy program. It was often abbreviated FBD.

Moreover, three of the existing fleet carriers were to be modernized to handle all existing aircraft. Three existing light fleet carriers (and the *Majestics* under construction) would be modernized to be able to handle 'trade defense' aircraft (Gannets and Sea Venoms). The existing Canadian and Australian carriers might or might not be modernized.

This was a very substantial fleet. The demands of economy would be met by avoiding much new construction or modernization. New construction was limited to two new FADE, frigates (two follow-on anti-aircraft, three follow-on aircraft direction, and four ASW frigates), submarines (six fast diesel-electric, six hydrogen peroxide), eight midget submarines, 12 motor torpedo boats, 24 seaward defense (harbor defense) boats, and two fast oilers. Later, in 1948, the program was amended to show construction of ten new submarines, and conversion of eight T-class.

Although superficially not ambitious, the combination of completing virtually all suspended ships and modernizing others was quite expensive. In 1949, Admiral Edwards, Assistant Chief of Naval Staff (ACNS), proposed that cruisers and destroyers all be replaced by a new type of cruiser/destroyer or light cruiser armed with 5in guns (see Chapter 5). The Royal Navy would build 50, of which 30 would operate in peacetime (compared to ten large and four small cruisers, and 34 destroyers). Limited British finances also had radical political consequences. All three services found themselves under intense pressure to reduce spending. A Government study by Lord Harwood, for example, proposed a naval re-alignment, in which the carrier force would be sharply reduced (from its already low estate), the cruiser force cut to 12 ships and effort concentrated on frigates and minecraft. The Royal Navy was able to argue that, ton for ton, small ships cost far more to build, man, and maintain, and the Harwood proposals died.

The Royal Navy had to concede for the first time in its history that its forces no longer sufficed to protect British trade routes. Its future plans would have to assume American participation from the beginning. The US Navy would provide half the forces required for the control of sea communications in the Atlantic and in the Mediterranean, and all of the forces required for control of sea communications in the South Atlantic and Pacific. Australia and New Zealand would be responsible for the Indian Ocean.

This prospective American contribution was equated to substantial cuts in the planned war fleet: eight light fleet carriers, five cruisers (the large ones), eight fleet air direction escorts, 48 frigates, and 12 submarines. In addition, nine cruisers, 39 frigates, and 12 submarines could be disposed of to save money which might otherwise be required for repairs. Note that, of these ships, only five of the eight FADEs had not been included in 1948 fleet plan.

The final 'revised restricted fleet plan 1949' was

somewhat smaller than these figures might indicate. Of the five battleships, only *Vanguard* would be maintained. No further money would be spent to maintain guns and fire controls of two of the four *King George V* class. Their hulls were considered valuable primarily for ultimate conversion to guided missile ships. Two of the existing six fleet carriers, *Formidable* and *Indomitable*, would be scrapped when the two *Ark Royals* entered service. The three suspended *Magnificents* would be disposed of, and all six remaining war-built light fleet carriers stricken when the four larger *Hermes* class were completed. The remaining *Majestics* would not be completed. Of the four large fleet carriers to be retained, three were to be fully modernized to operate modern aircraft; the fourth would be modernized only for deck landing training.

Of the 18 surviving cruisers, three would be scrapped when the three new *Tigers* were completed. Three existing 8in gun cruisers would be scrapped at once, and three more (6in or 5.25in) when major refits were required. No FADE conversion would be undertaken. The new submarine building program would be abandoned, leaving 51 existing and two experimental new boats (four T-class converted to

fast battery drive). Of the 59 destroyers de-rated to frigates, only 15 would be converted, the others retained in their original condition as a mobilization reserve. A later version of this fleet plan showed 27 frigate conversions.

Most new surface ship construction was postponed to the latter part of the program, in 1957–58, when one large cruiser and four destroyer/cruisers might be ordered.

On the other hand, the new fleet plan did show considerable emphasis on mine warfare. It added a new ocean minesweeper and 110 coastal and inshore minesweepers, as well as 16 mine locators (minehunters) to counter pressure mines.*

British tactical concepts were also scaled down. In October 1949, a British study (presumably reflecting current policy) showed a carrier task force composed of three aircraft carriers, four cruisers, and only twelve (rather than 24) destroyers.

Limited in its active peacetime carrier force, but faced with enormous wartime requirements, the Royal Navy sought throughout the early postwar period to keep more carriers in service in subsidiary roles. By 1954, *Glory*, a war-built light fleet carrier, could no longer operate modern naval aircraft. She could, however, function as an escort carrier or trade protection carrier in an emergency. After operating in Korea in 1951-53, she served in 1954 as an aircraft ferry and trooping carrier. She is shown in Malta, September 1954. The cocooned aircraft on her flight deck are Avengers, with Seahawk fighters abaft them. [CPL]

* Minesweepers formed so large a proportion of this and later programs because modern sensitive mines would probably defeat the small civilian craft which, in the past, had been converted in such large numbers as wartime sweepers.

TABLE 2–1: EMERGENCY BUILDING PROGRAM (1953–54)

Type	Staff Requirement	Time on Slip (months)	Building Period (years)
CV	2 (—)	36	5
CVL	4 (—)	27	4
CRUISER	4 (—)	15	2½
DESTROYER	4 (4)	12	2
FIRST-RATE A/S FRIGATE	9 (11)	12	2
SECOND-RATE A/S FRIGATE	50 (56)	10	1½
THIRD-RATE AND COASTAL FRIGATES	35 (47)	8	1
A/A FRIGATE	24 (28)	12	2
A/D FRIGATE	12 (14)	12	2
SUBMARINES	24 (24)	18–12	2½–2
OCEAN SWEEPERS	64 (82)	8–10	12–14 months
BOOM VESSELS	30 (30)	8	1
LST (D)	10 (10)	—	—

The numbers in parentheses show a proposed alternative program in which ships taking more than two years to complete were abandoned in favor of smaller units. It was based on the following equivalence:

	CV Slip	CVL Slip	Cruiser Slip
DESTROYER, FIRST-RATE FRIGATE	6	2	2
SECOND-RATE OR COASTAL FRIGATE	6	4	4
OCEAN SWEEPER	8	6	4

In the event of war, the existing fleet would be supplemented by an emergency program, including carriers and cruisers. Table 2–1 (see below), the emergency program of 1953-54, was typical. Note that, as of 1950, the only existing designs for large warships were distinctly dated. The carrier would have to be a repeat *Ark Royal*. The cruiser would probably be a repeat *Dido*. In 1950, when full mobilization seemed imminent, the Admiralty decided that mobilization cruiser(s) would be armed with the existing production twin 4.5in gun (Mk VI) in place of the 5.25in which armed existing ships of this type.

Few of the disposals envisaged in 1949 had been carried out when the outbreak of war in Korea halted them altogether. Large-scale US assistance became available, and by October 1950 the First Sea Lord, Admiral Fraser, was proposing to bring the date of full fleet modernization forward to 1955. He could still offer only a minimum balanced

fleet, insufficient to meet the demands of a major war, or even of stated NATO requirements. On the other hand, he could put the existing ASW frigate and mine craft design into series production, on the theory that war requirements in both categories were enormous. In July 1951, the Admiralty proposed to continue building these ships at their current rates for three years.

The effect of the 1950 decision was to collapse the protracted frigate programs previously envisaged into the 1950-51 building program, which then included six (rather than two) Type 12 (*Whitby*) class, twelve Type 14 (second-rate A/S: *Blackwood* class), five Type 41 (*Leopard* class, anti-aircraft), and four type 61 (*Salisbury* class aircraft direction type). All six fast battery submarines (which became the *Porpoise* class) were also included in this initial program. The planned figure of 27 full frigate conversions of war-build destroyers was retained, but more were to be carried out earlier in the program (12 as opposed to eight). Minecraft numbers actually would be increased: 36 rather than 25 inshore sweepers, and 30 rather than 28 coastal sweepers. This program effectively filled the yards, so that a further acceleration ordered in 1951 showed very little new construction before the 1954-55 program.

By that time, the small cruiser or cruiser/ destroyer of earlier long-range programs had been downgraded to a 5in destroyer (see Chapter 6 for details), and two new small cruisers had been added to replace the single large cruiser projected earlier. Persumably they were the lineal successor to the mobilization cruiser (the improved *Dido*). A 5in version of this design is described in Chapter 5.

During the summer of 1951, the British Chiefs of Staff studied further armament measures, which would bring their forces up to the requirements of the (then) NATO Medium Term Plan. The naval element of this plan was predicted on completion by 1957-58, since replacement of existing fleet units would have to begin after that date.* Requirements could not be stated in advance, because several research programs would reach maturity only about that time. At this time it was estimated that NATO as a whole would require the addition of 32 destroyers or first-rate ASW frigate equivalents, 144 ocean escorts, and 459 coastal minesweepers to meet the Medium Term Plan. Similarly, there was a deficit of 259 carrier aircraft. The existing British rearmament plan would contribute a total of 38 escorts and 134 minesweepers to NATO. A planned naval air expansion to 300 first line aircraft would contribute 50 to NATO strength.

The Admiralty planners also sought fleet expansion to meet British requirements outside NATO. Finally, they argued that several large ships would have to be designed (and, perferably, laid down) as mobilization prototypes: a fleet carrier, a large or small cruiser, and a new destroyer. The carrier and the cruiser seemed particularly important. Moreover, they could not be built rapidly after the outbreak of war. Their inclusion in the rearmament program conveys some of climate of hostility sensed at the time. The Admiralty program also included third-rate frigate prototypes (Types 17 and 42) for emergency mass production, a prototype guided missile ship (for convoy protection), and modern floating docks.

In 1952-60, then, the Admiralty hoped to order:
— one fleet carrier
— six first-rate A/S frigates (Type 12)
— 32 ocean escorts
— 12 submarines
— 235 minesweepers
— 17 auxiliaries

— 128 miscellaneous small craft.
Conversions would include:
— two *Colossus* class modernizations to support declared NATO requirements
— four T-class submarines to fast battery drive
— one maintenance ship (*Girdle Ness*) to missile trials ship
— one aircraft repair ship or carrier as a replenishment carrier.

Note that no definite missile ship program had as yet been formulated. As for the three suspended *Majestic*s, one might be converted into a missile ship, one transferred to the Royal Canadian Navy, while the future of the third remained uncertain. In fact, no missile conversion was ever undertaken (see Chapter 5), one ship ultimately being completed for the Indian Navy. The remaining ship of the class, HMS *Leviathan*, was ultimately broken up.

The 1951-55 £4700-million plan is described in Table 2–2 (see below). It was clearly over-ambitious, and by the end of 1951 cuts had been ordered in the prospective 1953-54 program. Under the Global Strategy defense review, the number of new frigates was cut by 40 per cent, and eight new floating drydocks (considered essential for fleet logistical support) were cancelled. Fleet Air Arm expansion would stop in 1954 at 250 rather than 300 first-line aircraft. During 1953, too, the projected modernization of two fleet carriers was abandoned. The prospective date of ordering the two prototype emergency production coastal frigates (Types 17 and 42) was pushed further and further back (as their size and cost increased), from the 1952-53 program (as envisaged early in 1951).

The revised rearmament program was then stretched out to complete in 1958, under a new £1610-million plan first formulated in January 1953. This in turn was subject to the Radical Review. First, the heavy carrier initially contemplated was replaced by a medium or light carrier; if necessary, her aircraft would be tailored to her size. In July 1953, construction of the ship was put off from a planned laying-down date of 1957 to 1958. Second, in September, the 5in gun cruiser/destroyer was abandoned. Later, the entire program was stretched out, so that the plan as of May 1954 (described in Table 2–3) extended through the 1959-60 program.

By this time, one large missile cruiser was originally planned, a second being added to replace the four 5in cruiser/destroyers. The big missile cruiser survived as a project for another three years.

The major question was whether priority was to go to a fleet missile ship or a missile convoy escort. Note that in Table 2–2 the missile prototype is listed among the escorts. By mid 1954 the British long-term fleet plan (beyond 1957) called for a total of four fleet missile ships and ten convoy missile ships. The convoy prototype would be laid down in 1957 (to complete in 1961), and subsequent ships would be ordered in classes of three, spread

* For example, under the £4700-million plan, the fleet would be modernized (ie, would attain sufficient ASW strength) by 1958-59, assuming continued spending through 1955-56. Fleet strength would peak in 1958-59, declining after that unless further large programs to replace wartime tonnage were undertaken.

TABLE 2–2: THE 1951-55 £4700-MILLION PLAN

Program	1951–2	1952–3	1953–4	1954–5
NEW SMALL CRUISER	—	—	—	2
DESTROYER	—	—	—	4
TYPE 12 FRIGATE	—	—	—	4
TYPE 14 FRIGATE	—	—	—	10
TYPE 17 FRIGATE	—	—	1	—
TYPE 41 FRIGATE (A/A)	—	—	—	2
TYPE 42 FRIGATE (A/A)	—	—	1	—
TYPE 61 FRIGATE (A/D)	—	—	—	2
MISSILE ESCORT	—	—	—	1
FAST SUBMARINE	—	—	4	4
X-CRAFT (MIDGETS)	—	—	4	—
OCEAN SWEEPERS	—	—	5	—
COASTAL SWEEPERS	—	10	30	30
COASTAL MINEHUNTERS	—	—	10	15
INSHORE SWEEPERS	—	—	30	30
LONG FPB	—	—	4	8
SHORT FPB	—	13	4	8
SEAWARD DEFENSE	—	8	8	8
BOOM DEFENSE	—	6	6	6
FLEET TANKERS	—	4	4	3
FREIGHT TANKERS	—	3	—	—
UNDERWAY REPLENISHMENT	—	1	—	—
CONVERSIONS/MODERNIZATIONS				
FLEET CARRIER	—	—	1	1
LIGHT CARRIER	—	1	1	—
CRUISERS	—	1	2	2
CRUISER MINELAYERS	—	—	1	1
DESTROYER MODERNIZATION	—	1	4	8
TYPE 15 FRIGATES	1	6	6	—
TYPE 16 FRIGATES	1	2	6	5
TYPE 62 FRIGATES (A/D)	—	1	5	6
FRIGATE MODERNIZATION	1	7	14	26
T-CLASS CONVERSION	1	1	3	—
S-CLASS MODERNIZATION	4	5	—	—

out so that all ten would be in service by 1970. The lessons gained from operating the Seaslug prototype ship, HMS *Girdle Ness*, would be incorporated only in the second full class (ships five, six, and seven).

By 1970, only three gun cruisers, the three *Tigers*, would remain, leaving an enormous warm war gap. On the other hand, it appeared that Blue Slug, a projected anti-ship missile, and very much a paper project, might be available for operational use as early as 1962-64, so that even ships armed only with missiles would be able to deal with enemy surface ships.

Serious rearmament had to include massive weapon and munition production, quite apart from warship and airplane production. The situation in April 1951 is shown in Table 2–4. In December 1952, it was reported that, although production of weapons was about twice that in 1948, production of munitions was running at about eight or even ten times the 1948 rate (with telecommunications equipment, presumably including radar, at about seven times the 1948 rate). However, the requirement was so massive that it was estimated that, after the Global Strategy cuts, as of March 1956, the Fleet would have only one week's ammunition supply afloat and another week's ashore. Matters must have been considerably complicated by mass replacements of existing weapons, since such replacements greatly reduced the value of remaining stores of ammunition. In this sense the shift from guns to missiles was particularly disastrous for all navies, since, in many cases, a fleet might be reduced to two or possibly only one 'shipfill': barely enough missiles to fill all of its magazines once.

Given a clear intention to rebuild, it was possible for the Royal Navy to resume the earlier planned series of scrappings, with the fleet carrier *Formidable* in 1952.

The 1951 plan for 1953 fleet deployments is typical of actual British peacetime practice at this time. The Mediterranean Fleet was still considered the central British strategic reserve or 'swing force', and it also operated in the area best suited to all-year training. The foreign stations were also still important: America and West Indies, East Indies (including the Persian Gulf), South Atlantic, and the Far East. Each required one or two cruisers plus frigates (with four C class destroyers in the Far East). Their long endurance made frigates preferable to destroyers on the stations. Note that the stations absorbed six of the 11 active British cruisers.

That left very little for the two main fleets: one fleet carrier (*Indomitable*), two light fleet carriers (one *Hermes*, one *Colossus* class), two cruisers, 12 destroyers and eight frigates in the Home Fleet; one fleet carrier (*Eagle*), one light fleet carrier (*Colossus* class), three cruisers, 12 destroyers, and 11 frigates in the Mediterranean. Another fleet carrier was operational for trials, and a *Hermes* class light fleet carrier for deck landing training. Further ships, including 15 frigates and 30 submarines, were assigned to training duties.

In 1953, on the eve of the Radical Review, British war planning assigned the two operational fleet carriers to a task group which would cover SACLANT Scandinavian convoys. They would provide fighter and ASW support, as well as 'attacking at source', supporting NATO land forces, and attacking surface raiders. At this time, SACLANT planning estimates showed six escorts plus a light carrier (with 75 per cent jets) for each

---

NOTES: The two fleet carriers would have been *Implacable* and *Indefatigable*: *Victorious* was already in hand. The two *Colossus* class modernizations were projected to provide spares while fleet carriers were being modernized with steam catapults, so that the Royal Navy would be able to meet its D + 6 commitment to supply two operational fleet and four operational light carriers, plus a third fleet carrier for trials and one as a spare. In this scheme, *Indomitable* would be modernized as deck landing training carrier. One version of the program shows a steam catapult installed aboard the maintenance carrier *Unicorn* under the 1954-55 program. The cruisers *Royalist*, *Sirius*, *Phoebe*, *Diadem*, *Liverpool*, *Glasgow*, *Belfast*, *Swiftsure*, and *Superb* would be fully modernized; *Sheffield*, *Birmingham*, *Newcastle*, *Newfoundland*, *Cleopatra*, and *Euryalus* would receive 'large repairs'. This program would have extended through 1957-58.

Full modernization would extend to 25 destroyers: eight *Agincourt*, four *Trafalgar*, eight Ca, one Ch, two Co, and two Cr. Another 25 would receive interim modernization: eight *Armada*, four *Trafalgar*, seven Ch, six Co. Modernization of the 12 newest destroyers, the eight *Darings* and the four Weapons, was addressed only later. This program, then, would cover all surviving fleet destroyers. A version of the program extending through 1957-58 showed a total of 27 type 15, 18 Type 16, and 12 Type 62 destroyer conversions to frigates, including ships ordered under earlier programs. ASW modernization would be extended to 19 *Loch* and 24 *Castle* class frigates, and AA modernization to 24 *Black Swan* and 21 *Bay* class frigates (in many cases using US 3in/50 guns supplied under MDAP).

Beyond 1955, a new carrier would have been ordered under the 1955-56 program, and a new large cruiser at the same time. In one version of the program, only the prototype of the small cruiser would have been built under the 1954-55 program, four others following in 1955-56. All four new destroyers would have been built under the 1954-55 program, as shown in this table.

In this version, the program showed six or more type 12 frigates (two in 1955-56 in addition to the four shown), 20 more Type 14 (ten in 1954-55, ten in 1955-56), six more Type 41 (two in 1954-55 as shown, then two more in each of 1955-56 and 1957-58), and four more Type 61 (two in 1954-55 as shown, then two in 1955-56). The Type 42 prototype would be moved forward to 1954-55. In this version the submarine program was moved ahead a year (none in 1953-54, four in 1955-56). The first five ocean sweepers would be followed by 20 in 1955-56. Further additions were also projected for lesser craft.

TABLE 2–3: THE £1610-MILLION PLAN, MAY 1954

Program	1954-5	1955-6	1956-7	1957-8	1958-9	1959-60
CARRIER	—	—	—	1	—	—
GW SHIP	—	—	1	—	—	1
FAST ESCORT	1	—	—	—	3	—
TYPE 12	2	—	—	—	—	—
TYPE 14	1	2	2	2	2	—
A/S COMMON HULL	—	1	2	—	—	—
TYPE 41	—	1	1	2	2	—
A/A COMMON HULL	—	1	—	—	—	—
TYPE 61	1	2	—	3	—	—
OCEAN SWEEPER	1	—	5	5	5	5
CMS I	(117)	15	15	20	—	—
IMS I	(99)	12	—	—	—	—
FAST SUBMARINE	2	—	—	—	—	—
1953 SUBMARINE	1	—	3	5	3	3
LONG FPB	—	—	2	3	3	—
MEDIUM FPB	—	2	4	3	—	—
BDV	3	3	2	2	2	—

NOTES: In this table, the carrier is medium-sized rather than the large type originally desired. As of 1954-55, six Type 12, 12 Type 14, five Type 41, and four Type 61 frigates were under construction, together with six fast battery drive (FBD) submarines. CMS and IMS are coastal and inshore sweepers, respectively. BDV is a boom defense vessel.

Four cruisers were to be modernized: *Royalist*, *Belfast*, *Swiftsure*, and *Superb*. The full destroyer modernization program showed only four ships (all Ca class) in 1954-55. Interim modernization was planned for 14 in 1954-55, 11 in 1955-56, and four in 1956-57, the last two years including Weapon class ships. The Type 15 frigate program was to have ended with six units in 1954-55 and one in 1955-56. The common hull frigate (Common in the table) was the functional successor to the type 17 and Type 42 prototypes of earlier programs. Note that the missile ship had moved from the frigate or escort to the cruiser category (compare Table 2–2). The fast battery drive submarine conversion program was to have ended with three T-class boats already in hand, but 18 more submarines (14 A and four T class) were to be streamlined.

fast or slow Scandinavian convoy, plus six escorts for the gap between Britain and Scandinavian fighter cover. However, the Royal Navy could provide only four escorts per convoy, and the carrier issue was unresolved. The British light carriers would more likely be needed to provide fighter and anti-snooper cover to the west of the United Kingdom.

In the Atlantic area, for example, SACLANT requirements were based on eight through-escorts per convoy, plus two more escorts in focal areas, and a total of ten support groups, each consisting of a light carrier and three escorts. However, existing NATO resources were equal only to one through-escort per convoy, two in focal areas, and five support groups. In the Channel, the estimated requirement was three escorts per convoy, plus 15 three-escort support groups: available forces could support only one escort per convoy and 12 two-ship support groups.

The Royal Navy had to define those forces 'vital to UK survival' (during the first six weeks of war) at the outset of the Radical Review. The D-Day force included two fleet carriers (for the strike fleet) and three light fleet carriers (for support forces), plus 22 cruisers, 25 destroyers, 55 frigates, and 42 submarines. After the first six weeks, 19 destroyers and 23 frigates would be added, but the bulk of the frigate force (142 ships) could be mobilized only much later. Similar considerations applied to the battleships, the remaining four fleet carriers, four light cruisers, 13 cruisers, 18 destroyers, and one submarine.

The earliest version of the £1610-million fleet plan covered only the period through 1957-58. However, under the force of the early part of the Radical Review it was restructured, and by May 1954 it showed the program through 1959-60 (see Table 2–3). The major changes were the reduction of the carrier from 50,000 tons to about 35,000. It

TABLE 2–4: WEAPONS ON HAND, APRIL 1951

	Aboard Ships /Outfit	In Store	Required
TORPEDO MK 8	500	2500	4500
MINES	—	41,500	74,240
SWEEPS	250	—	900
OIL FUEL (MILLIONS OF TONS)	—	3.6	4.4 interim (3.53) 5.5 final (3.54)
BOFORS GUNS	1400	3400	5900
BOFORS MOUNTINGS	973	2767	3740

would be ordered in 1957 for completion in May 1962, with staff requirements due in the fall of 1954. The large and small cruisers of earlier programs were replaced by a missile cruiser, the prototype to be ordered in 1956 for completion in 1960 (with a second unit to be completed in 1963). At this time, the future of the suspended light fleet carriers *Hercules* and *Leviathan* was still under discussion.

Four special-purpose fast escorts replaced the general purpose cruiser/destroyer of earlier programs. The first units were to be fast ASW escorts, but later an anti-aircraft version would be built on the same hull. By late 1954 this concept had been superseded by a more austere general-purpose escort, the improved *Daring*. Meanwhile

a DNC study showed that a minimum missile capability could be achieved on an even smaller hull, and in 1955 this austere system was married to the improved *Daring* to become a missile destroyer. By that time each clearly showed about half the missile capability of a cruiser, so the total force contemplated in May 1954 (two cruisers and four fleet escorts) does translate into the eight *County* class missile destroyers actually built.

The program as described in Table 2–3 was far beyond British means. The Admiralty first sought to cut immediate expenditures by stretching out the frigate program, selling two unnamed Type 12, two Type 14 (*Palliser* and one other), and two Type 41 (*Panther* and one other then unnamed) to India. In each case these losses were to be made

The Martin P6M Seamaster was conceived as part of a dispersed naval strike force, supplementing carrier task forces. Martin won a 1951 Bureau of Aeronautics design competition, followed by a contract in October 1952. The prototype flew on 14 July 1955. Although it was always described as a minelayer, Navy documents such as the Long Range Objectives report listed it as part of the Navy strategic strike force. The difference may have arisen with changes in Navy outlook from 1951 onwards. Payload was very large: over 30,000 pounds, compared to about 20,000 for the standard contemporary Air Force medium bomber, the B-47E. Performance compared with that of contemporary land-based bombers. For example, with four J75 engines (as in the production version), the P6M-2 was rated at 584 knots at sea level. Gross weight was 175,000 pounds, and range 2000nm. The rotary bomb bay could be loaded while the airplane was in the water. The P6M program was cancelled to free money for Polaris missile and submarine development and production. [USN]

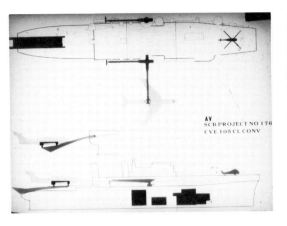

LSD SEAPLANE TENDER

The Seamaster was a huge airplane and its tenders had to be able to bring it aboard for major servicing. These sketches, reproduced from contemporary Bureau of Ships slides, show two alternative approaches. The converted escort carrier (CVE 105) would have a stern ramp with a special slide up which the airplane could be brought. A similar scheme was envisaged for an existing seaplane tender, which was converted under the FY56 program. Alternatively, the LSD could flood its stern well, and the airplane could dock that way. Both schemes show very long servicing booms, necessary in view of the great size of the airplane. [USN]

up under a later program.* Four of eight planned Ch, Co, and Cr interim modernizations were cancelled at once, as were the six planned Type 15 and all the submarine streamlinings.

The five ocean minesweepers were cancelled**, the coastal mine craft reduced to 137 and the inshore units to 91. Some of these cuts could be explained on the basis that minehunting techniques were as yet undeveloped. The eight projected long-hull fast patrol boats were cancelled. Twenty-one minesweepers motor launch (MSML) conversions were cancelled, leaving 25 completed. Similarly, 25 conversions of existing motor minesweepers (MMS) were cancelled, leaving 30 completed.

These were not yet very drastic cuts, and they did not go nearly far enough. The Admiralty had to make strategic choices. The Director of Plans outlined them in an internal paper circulated in the spring of 1954. If war was unlikely for the next five or ten years, then conversion and

* In fact, no Type 12 were sold, nor were any of the original twelve type 14. The planned 1956-57 Type 41, Panther, was cancelled in the 1957 Defense Review, as was the 1956-57 Type 61, Exeter. A sixth Type 61 was re-ordered as a Type 12 and then as a Leander. A sixth Type 41 was sold to India, two more being built to Indian account, as were two Type 12 and three Type 14. The British Type 14, 41, and 61 programs terminated at, respectively, twelve, four, and four ships. The 1954-55 and 1955-56 programs each showed five modified Type 12 frigates, which became the Rothesay class, one of which (Hastings) was sold to New Zealand, which then bought another. Australia bought six improved versions as her River class. Three more units planned under later programs were re-ordered as the first Leanders. The 1955-56 estimates originally provided the first three general purpose frigates (Type 81, Tribal class), with four more following in 1956-57 (early reports showed four in 1956-57). The frigate program then lapsed altogether. Two missile destroyers were authorized in 1955-56, two in 1956-57, then two in 1964-65 and two in 1965-66. Frigate construction resumed with the Leander class general purpose ships developed from the Type 12: three in 1960-61, three in 1962-63, three 1963-64, three 1964-65, two in 1966-67, and two in 1967-68.

** The ocean minesweeper was also useful as a coastal escort. Based on the wartime Algerine, it was armed with a single Squid ASW mortar. Cancellation was partly on technical grounds, as it was argued that its steel hull could not be sufficiently well degaussed to avoid modern magnetic mines. Note that several Algerines were rearmed with Squids during this period.

modernization of virtually all existing hulls was unrealistic. Similarly, if hot war was unlikely, then the large new frigate programs contemplated under the £1610-million program contributed little.

The Type 14 and the mass-production common hull were both abandoned in favor of a second-rate, general purpose frigate, which became the Tribal, or Type 81. A 1955-65 new construction program, drawn up in the aftermath of the Radical Review, showed 28 of these sloops, as well as 20 of the most flexible class, the Type 12 (Whitby). Construction of the other types was to stop with the units actually on the slip: 12 Type 14, five each of Types 41 and 61 (one of each later being cancelled). All frigate construction stopped for a time after the 1957 defense cuts, only seven sloops (Tribal class frigates) actually being built. Instead, when construction resumed, it concentrated on a general purpose version of the Type 12 hull, which became the Leander (26 built, compared to six Type 12 and nine modified Type 12).

This was a painful choice. It effectively ended any British effort to provide full air defense for convoys, since no convoy missile ships (which would be ineffective in cold war, but so important in hot war) would be built. Nor would convoys enjoy sufficient aircraft direction facilities. In future, the Royal Navy would be able to contribute a carrier task force to NATO (for hot war), but most of its resources would go into cold war missions (sloops and general purpose frigates).

Money was very tight. Proposals for savings included extending submarine life (for training) from 13 to 16 years. The planned full modernizations of the cruisers Belfast, Swiftsure, and Superb were reduced to limited conversions similar to those of the Newcastle, Birmingham, and Newfoundland. Further Type 16 (limited) destroyer conversions were cancelled, together (ultimately) with the type 62 destroyer aircraft direction conversions. Although the new construction anti-aircraft frigate program was insufficient, it could be increased. Coastal and inshore minesweeper production might be cut pending progress in countermeasures to the pressure mine.

Two new technologies, the surface-to-air missile and the VTOL airplane, promised radical changes in cruisers and carriers. The missile would make the individual cruiser much larger and more expensive, but (see Chapter 3) it would also sharply reduce the value of the cruiser in warm war or in anti-ship operations. On the other hand, the VTOL promised to make small carriers viable again, particularly if the chief strike weapon were a small atomic bomb.

By 1965, large SAMs would be effective at up to 30,000 yards, and a new lightweight anti-missile SAM (15,000 yards) would probably be carried by small fleet anti-aircraft escorts, displacing perhaps as little as 2000 tons. A visual-link, short-range missile (effective at 5000 yards) would be available for merchant ship and auxiliaries.

Perhaps the most important feature of the 1965 era, as visualized by the Royal Navy in 1954, would be the sea-based ballistic missile.* The Director of Plans wrote that 'a ballistic rocket capable of firing from a submarine off North Russia, in the Black Sea, or in the Persian Gulf would have such immense strategic advantages in the 1965-70 era that we should certainly try to attain it'. Even so, aircraft would still be the primary means of strategic attack. Carrier-based strike aircraft would complicate Soviet air defenses by forcing them to defend against all possible routes of approach.

At this time the British expected that hydrogen peroxide (HTP) submarines would be in service in some numbers by 1965. Nuclear submarines might exist, but would be so expensive that few would be in service. The reality was that HTP submarines never entered service, and nuclear submarines existed in considerable numbers by 1965. Increased underwater endurance and better listening devices would make submarines more useful anti-submarine platforms. X-craft (midget submarines) would be able to lay atomic mines in

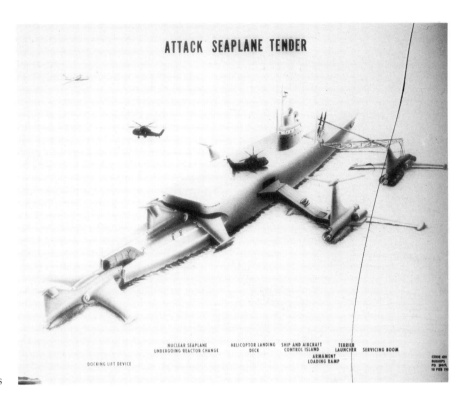

ATTACK SEAPLANE TENDER

NUCLEAR SEAPLANE UNDERGOING REACTOR CHANGE · HELICOPTOR LANDING DECK · SHIP AND AIRCRAFT CONTROL ISLAND · TERRIER LAUNCHER · SERVICING BOOM · ARMAMENT LOADING RAMP · DOCKING LIFT DEVICE

harbors for 'attacks at source'.

CORSAIR (the long-range submarine detector) and 'sniffers' (airborne devices to detect snorkel exhausts) would restore the effectiveness of anti-submarine aircraft, both land- and sea-based.

All large ships would probably be equipped with anti-torpedo devices, with a lightweight version for merchant ships and escorts.** New propellers would increase the silent speed of escorts.

The combination of these developments would shift the burden of anti-submarine protection from convoy escorts to a combination of interception in transit (by submarines and ship, aircraft, and helicopter hunters), 'attack at source', and torpedo countermeasures.

Given all of these developments, submarine attacks on convoys would be substantially less profitable. The Soviets would probably turn to air attacks. Protection would be based on VTOL fighters flying from the smallest possible carriers, surface-to-air missiles, and attacks on airfields.

Mines would continue to be important. Countermeasures would not change very much: shore-based air defense to stop minelaying bombers; detection of minelaying submarines by shore listening stations; accurate mine detection and location; improved means of mine destruction; and limited sweeping by ships and helicopters.

By the late 'fifties, the US Navy was seeking very advanced technologies for strike warfare. The US government was developing nuclear aircraft powerplants. This drawing, from a February 1956 Bureau of Ships slide, shows a proposed combination of the two: an attack seaplane tender to service nuclear-powered seaplanes. Sketch designs for such a ship, itself nuclear-powered, were actually drawn up at this time. The seaplane engines would have been chemically boosted for higher speed, using hydrogen fuel which the tender could produce by breaking down sea water. The twin Terrier launcher forward would give the ship a degree of self defense, as it tended its portion of the dispersed naval attack force. The vertical line is a crack in the original glass slide. [USN]

---

* Missiles would have been extremely expensive. In February 1955, the Superintendant of the Admiralty Gunnery Establishment assumed a 750nm weapon (capable perhaps of 1000nm in future) would weigh 90 tons, and could be 90ft long with a diameter of 96in. He considered 750nm a maximum range, based on a required accuracy of 250 to 2000 yards. At this time, the Royal Aircraft Establishment (Farnborough) had abandoned plans for a 2500nm missile, and was working on a 1600nm single-stage weapon using three land stations (about 100nm apart) for initial guidance (accurate distance measurement for engine cut-off). The DNO suggested the development of the best possible weapon would take about 20 years, and that a weapon based on existing technology could be ready in 12, for an eight-year useful life. The oxidizer and fuel would be HTP and kerosene or liquid oxygen and alcohol. In fact, the first Polaris missile (with a 1200nm range) weighed 28,000 pounds, with a length of 336 inches (28ft) and a diameter of 54 inches. Accuracy (CEP) was probably about the 2000 yards that the Admiralty considered the maximum acceptable, and warhead yield was half a megaton. An earlier proposed (abortive) Jupiter-S missile would have weighed 160,000 pounds, closer to the British estimate, but with a range of about 1500nm. Polaris became operational in 1960, about four years after the project began. The key difference between British estimates and the actual US weapon was probably warhead weight, a lightweight weapon having been promised (by Dr Edward Teller) in the summer of 1956.

** At this time the Royal Navy favored a concept called *CAMROSE*, which was to fire a salvo of 50-knot proximity-fuzed torpedoes in the direction of an incoming torpedo. As a concept, it succeeded *RULER*, a rapid-fire gun which put explosive charges in the predicted path of the torpedo. Neither ever reached prototype stage. Note that, unlike the usual towed noise-maker, *RULER* and *CAMROSE* actually would have destroyed incoming torpedoes.

Given the huge estimated requirement for escorts in a future war, the US Navy was fortunate in having many large destroyers suitable for conversion. *Robert A Owens* is shown newly completed, with two Weapon Alfa ASW rocket launchers (the large turrets fore and aft) and a trainable Hedgehog superfiring over her forward twin 3in/50. Plans initially called for three Weapon Alfas. Four fixed torpedo tubes in the after part of her deckhouse are not clearly visible. Note also the HFDF antenna on the stub mast on her after funnel. This was an interim configuration: the 3in/50s were to have been replaced by much heavier twin 3in/70s, which (just after World War II) were considered the most effective available anti-aircraft weapon. The *Owens* was not a mobilization prototype; she was conceived as the flagship of a hunter-killer (HUK) group (DDK), in effect a second-rate version of the big ASW cruiser (CLK) *Norfolk*. However, the Navy did plan to convert all surviving *Fletchers* to ASW escorts (DDE). The DDK were all redesignated DDE on 4 March 1950, and the *Norfolk* was designated a large destroyer (DL) as completed in 1953. [*USN*]

The surface ship problem would eventually be solved by missile attack, which might be possible in all weathers at ranges as great as 200nm.

Since the rate of wear-out of war-built ships would exceed any likely rate of construction, the fleet would probably reach its lowest level in 1965. The Director of Plans listed a possible 1965 fleet (with 1954 force levels in parentheses):
— Modern carrier (capable of operating
   all 1965 naval aircraft)   7 (0)
— Interim carrier (operates all 1954 aircraft 0 (5)
— Partially modernized carrier (some 1954
   aircraft)   0 (1)
— Unmodernized carrier (obsolete aircraft,
   helicopters)   5 (11)
— Battleships, cruisers   7 (13)
— Missile ships (4 convoy, 1 fleet)   5 (0)
— Destroyers/fleet escorts   20 (62)
— Anti-submarine escorts   65 (125)
— Anti-aircraft escorts   60 (83)
— Air direction escorts   15 (0)
— Ocean minesweepers   40 (64)
— Coastal and inshore sweepers   315 (200)
— Submarines   50 (57)
— X-craft   8 (2)
— Coastal craft   50 (54)
— There would be a total of 230 first-line naval
   aircraft.

The projected 1954-55 program included two new medium aircraft carriers (suitable for VTOL operation) and four convoy missile escorts. The carriers were needed to make up for the expected run-down of the modern carrier force (three fleet and four light carriers) after 1965; they could not lightly be dropped. However, three of the four convoy missile escorts could be replaced by two composite or two heavy gun cruisers or by six *Darings*.

Beyond the 1954-55 program the Admiralty sought a new light fleet carrier, eight missile ships,

12 fleet escorts, 53 anti-aircraft escorts, eight aircraft direction escorts, 35 anti-submarine escorts, 34 ocean minesweepers, 75 coastal and inshore sweepers, 36 submarines, three X-craft and ten coastal craft.

Most of the new mine countermeasures craft would be minehunters, whose construction had been deferred in hopes of clarifying the necessary techniques.

The projected fleet was by no means sufficient to meet tactical requirements. It was dictated by expected resources. Escorts would be the worst deficiency.* Nor was it the only possible 1965 fleet. One alternative (March 1954) was to build four new VSTOL carriers (two completed and two still under construction in 1965), leaving seven modernized (*Victorious*, the two *Ark Royals*, and the four *Hermes*) and five unmodernized conventional carriers. The modernized full-size carriers would operate high-performance attack aircraft. Converted merchant ships (the modern

---

* The financial problem affected not only new construction but also the operation of the fleet itself. From 1945 onwards the Royal Navy suffered from chronic undermanning, due in part to the need to maintain a much increased shore establishment, and in part to the much greater complements of individual ships, as compared to their prewar equivalents. This problem was masked by the mobilization for Korea, but 48 ships had to be laid up in 1953-54. In 1955, it was expected that 19 more would be withdrawn in 1956, and 17 more in 1957-60, quite apart from any new reductions. This situation had been tolerated because the Navy could hope to mobilize a large reserve fleet to meet its wartime requirements. However, the new strategy implied the loss of the reserve fleet. By 1965, the wartime and peacetime Royal Navies would be much the same except for a reserve of perhaps 200 minesweepers and 15 depot and maintenance ships. One argument raised at this time was that British warships were overmanned compared to their US counterparts.

equivalent of wartime MAC Ships) would be able to operate the same aircraft as the unmodernized ships, for trade protection. The new carriers would be paid for by foregoing modernization of the five interim ships envisaged in the alternative plan, and by reducing the number of guided missile ships from five to four.

These programs incorporated the new technology, but they also showed the rapid prospective decline of the gun in the Royal Navy, without any commensurate reduction in the warm war mission which required guns. By this time the Soviets had demonstrated their new gun cruiser, the *Sverdlov*, at the 1953 Coronation Review. By September 1954, the First Sea Lord, Admiral McGrigor, was asking whether it was really wise to omit gun-armed ships from the new construction program. Did the Royal Navy need something effective against a *Sverdlov*, with sea-keeping and endurance similar to that of existing 6in cruisers, and anti-aircraft weapons effective against 1960s aircraft? Or should it rely on a prospective missile to deal with the *Sverdlov*s, and concentrate on something much cheaper to shell Third World shores?

The existing *Daring* was clearly the minimum general purpose warship. Two *Darings* could be bought for the price of one heavy cruiser, and two or three for the same manning cost. The *Battle* class destroyer, at about a third the cost and manning level of a large cruiser, was now just too small for general purpose use. Indeed, the 1943 *Battle*s had just been proposed for conversion to radar pickets.

The choice, then, lay between an all-gun cruiser, a mixed gun/missile cruiser, and a modernized or converted battleship. In answer to a query by the Director of Plans, DNC had sketched a cruiser armed with four twin dual purpose 6in mounts (Mark 26, as in the *Tiger*s) and four twin 3in/70, on a displacement of 18,200 tons, with a complement of about 1200, and at a cost of £13 million. This could be compared with the abortive light cruiser (two twin 5in, close range weapons, Limbo, on 4750 tons, with a complement of about 550, at a cost of £5 to £6 million). The Director of Plans suspected that it would be better to build a new three-turret, 6in cruiser (with two Mark 26 forward and one aft, and three twin 3in/70) on about 16,850 tons, than merely to repeat the cramped *Tiger* design. Even so it was doubtful that any gun cruiser could deal with 1960's aircraft.

That left the solution actually adopted at this time (see Chapter 5): a composite design with guns forward and missiles aft. It would have to have at least two twin Mark 26 in order to be able to deal with a *Sverdlov*. The advantage of this choice was that cruisers passing out of service from 1962 onwards would be replaced by ships capable of effective bombardment and surface action, ie, suited for wars of all temperatures. The same could not be said for either the all-gun or the all-missile ships hitherto considered.

It would also be useful to build more general purpose ships, which would be improved *Daring*s.

The next stage of argument was the observation that the Navy would probably have to settle for a four-carrier fleet. On that basis, carrier replacement could be put off for a few years, and money released for surface combatant construction. Guns would continue to be important, not only for hot war, but for warm war shore bombardment and for cold war presence. A gun could fire a shot across the bow: an expensive missile could not.

By late 1954, these largely technical considerations had been combined with the Royal Navy's version of the new strategy, which was oriented far more to limited than to hot global war. The four convoy missile escorts had been abandoned altogether, together with most of the mine countermeasures program and much of the earlier frigate program.

The planned future (1965) Royal Navy emerged from the Radical Review with five missile cruisers. The other major new designs contemplated at this time were an improved *Daring* class fleet escort, a general purpose escort (sloop), and the new light aircraft carrier. Within two years a missile destroyer based on the improved *Daring* (the *County* class) had superseded the missile cruiser altogether.

*   *   *

In 1945-46 the US Navy planned a global peace-keeping force, based on five task forces (each comprising two large carriers, a fast battleship, two heavy and four light cruisers, and three destroyer squadrons, each of nine ships). In accordance with wartime US practice, each would be supported by a fast replenishment group, including escort carriers to supply replacement aircraft. Protracted carrier operations required that two carrier air groups be formed for each fleet carrier. For example, the brief FY49 (1948) naval build-up (prior to the deep 1949-50 cuts) envisaged the formation of 24 carrier air groups (of which only 16 were actually formed) to support 12 fleet carriers. This was an ideal. By FY51, the Navy was down to nine carrier air groups, to support seven carriers.

Overseas deployments gradually became permanent. In 1946, the US presence in Europe seemed transient, and there were three main fleets: the Fifth (Eastern and Central Pacific), Seventh (Western Pacific), and Eighth (Atlantic). However, the Mediterranean force soon became a fleet (the Sixth) in its own right, and the Fifth and Eighth Fleets were redesignated Third and Second. Short-term forward (Sixth and Seventh Fleets) deployment could be supported by similar forces in the two Fleets closer to home, but sustained peacetime forward deployment of one unit actually required a total of three: one deployed, one working up, one refitting.

In November 1947, the US Navy's General Board developed an agreed (Opnav, Atlantic, and

Pacific Fleets) view of the force necessary to fight a war in July 1955. It was never an official planning goal, but it reflects then current US naval doctrine and tactics. Four fast strike carrier task forces (sixteen carriers), would be supported by three fast logistics groups.

Each of the four carrier task forces would consist of one of the projected flush-decked (*United States* class) carriers, supported by a heavy *Midway* class carrier and two modernized fleet carriers (SCB 27A class). Since there were only three *Midways*, one task force would include three SCB 27As. It would be screened by seven heavy support ships (battleships and cruisers – in future, missile ships) and 24 destroyers. Near their targets, the fast carrier task forces would be supported by radar picket submarines (SSR). Since the submarines were much slower that the task forces, they would have to deploy in advance to the several target areas which each task force would strike in succession. The 1947 plan envisaged a total of 14 SSRs.

By 1947, moreover, the US Navy was actively developing a submarine-launched missile, which would become Regulus. The General Board assumed that a total of 19 missile submarines (SSG) would be available in 1955.

Each supporting fast logistics force would consist of two escort carriers, one fleet carrier (for heavy aircraft, unless they could be staged by way of land bases), four fast oilers, one ammunition ship, one stores (provisions) ship, one (general) stores issue ship, one aviation stores ship, and eight destroyers or destroyer escorts.

This striking fleet would be combined with sufficient fast (20 knot) lift for two Marine divisions consisting of 24 attack transports, ten attack cargo ships, 34 landing ships dock (or six LSDs and 28 20-knot tank landing ships), four command ships, 14 escort carriers, 36 destroyers or destroyer escorts, four battleships, six cruisers, and ten destroyer minelayers/minesweepers to clear a beach.

ASW would be a combination of HUK, escort, and submarine operations. For quick enough response to submarine sightings, HUK warfare would require a combination of shore-based and open-ocean units. As in World War II, there would be both ocean and coastal convoys. Each of six open ocean HUK forces would consist of a light fleet carrier (CVL), a heavy ASW ship (CLK, of the *Norfolk* class), and eight fast escort destroyers (DDE, converted fleet destroyers). Each of six fixed-area patrol/HUK forces would be similar, except that the carrier would be replaced by a land-based or seaplane patrol squadron. Thus, the 1955 fleet would require a total of 12 (plans reportedly called for 14) new heavy ASW command ships (CLK) and 96 DDEs. Ocean escort would require another 200 destroyers or destroyer escorts, while coastal escort would need 100 coastal escorts (PC) and 150 blimps. The fleet would also require about 150 minecraft.

The 1947 study estimated that a total of 252 submarines (exclusive of radar pickets and missile submarines) would be needed. The United States already possessed 178, of which 62 were to be converted to fast Guppy configuration. Fourteen more would be used for training. The others would be converted to support 100 small ASW submarines in forward areas: ten personnel transports (SSP), five cargo transports (SSA), and nine oilers (SSO(. The remainder of the 1955 submarine force would consist of 32 new, fast diesel-electric attack craft.

Of the ships envisaged in the 1947 paper, the four big carriers, the 12 *Norfolk* class CLK, the 20-knot amphibious ships, the fast submarines, the ASW submarines and the coastal escorts (PC)* were all new. Major conversion projects included the *Essex* modernization (nine required), the ASW conversion of existing *Fletcher* class destroyers (DDE), and the Guppy submarines. Although not explicitly included in the fleet plan, the fast task forces would include specialized flagships such as the new *Northampton* (CLC 1). Ideally, the carrier task force escorts would be the new *Mitscher* class (3650-ton) destroyers. At this time there seemed to be a real prospect of achieving an annual program of one heavy carrier, two SCB 27A conversions, two CLK, four 3650-ton destroyers, nine DDE conversions, 24 Guppy conversions and at least 12 SSKs. The reality was considerably bleaker. For example, the second CLK was never built, and the four 3650-ton destroyers were followed by the considerably less capable (and less expensive) *Forrest Sherman*.

These ideas were further elaborated. In 1949, for example, the Navy compiled the forces required to execute a 1957 war plan (DROPSHOT). It expected to operate two fast carrier forces in the Mediterranean, one in the Barents and Norwegian Seas, and one in the Western Pacific. Each would include a battleship, six or seven cruisers (including two or three anti-aircraft cruisers), 20 general purpose destroyers, four radar picket destroyers (DDR), and four radar picket submarines. There would be one fast carrier support group per carrier task force (ultimately with two in the Western Pacific). The idea of ferrying heavy aircraft aboard unconverted *Essexes* had been discarded.

The envisaged missile submarine force had been reduced to twelve (four in the Pacific, eight in the European area).

ASW requirements were developed in detail. On average, eight Atlantic and eight Pacific convoys would sail each month, and two would be at sea in the Mediterranean at any one time. A typical Atlantic escort group would comprise a light fleet carrier (CVL) screened by four destroyer escorts and supported by a four-DDE ASW surface attack unit (SAU). A Mediterranean group, facing

---

* The existing 173-foot, 21-knot PC was not considered fast enough to deal with even the intermediate Type XXI submarine. The new PC eventually materialized as the *Dealey* class ocean escort, although something much more modest seems to have been envisaged in 1947.

stiffer air opposition, would consist of two light fleet carriers, but only two destroyer escorts and two DDE. A typical Pacific escort group, facing weaker opposition, would consist of one escort carrier, two destroyer escorts, and two DDE. Allowing for refits the Atlantic would require six escort groups, the Mediterranean two, and the Pacific six, for a total of ten light fleet carriers, six escort carriers, 44 destroyer escorts, and 44 DDEs. Other figures showed much higher forces.**

In contrast to the 1947 study, each of nine HUK groups (at D + 6 months: three Mediterranean, three North Atlantic, one South Atlantic and two Far East) would include 12 destroyers or DDKs plus the carrier and CLK. This would allow two to operate continuously in the Mediterranean and the North Atlantic. They would be supported by eight fixed area patrol/HUK groups (two East Coast, one South America, one West Coast, one Azores, one Iceland, one Casablanca, and one Far East).

Supporting submarine forces would comprise 54 ASW submarines (SSK) in the Barents Sea (supported by 36 cargo submarines, SSA), 36 SSKs in the Mediterranean (12 SSAs), 18 SSKs in the Far East (18 SSAs); and 12 SSKs (12 SSAs) in the Black Sea, for a total of 120 SSKs and 78 SSAs. There would also be eight submarine personnel transports (SSP, presumably for special operations) in the European area, and six submarine oilers (SSO, for seaplane support, two in the Pacific and four in the European area).

This was in addition to base forces in the western Pacific and in the Far East (a total of three cruisers and twelve destroyers).

Also in 1949, the General Board submitted a projected 1951-60 building program, anticipating hypothetical requirements of a 1960 war. It envisaged a 50 per cent increase in US forces, eg, to six carrier task forces (two in the Mediterranean, two in the Barents and Norwegian Seas, and one

each in the western Pacific and Arabian Sea), supported by six logistics groups. Amphibious lift would support three rather than two divisions, and additional shipping was needed to transport the associated three Marine Air Wings. In modern terms, this translated as three Marine Amphibious Forces (MAF, or division/air wings) rather than simple divisions (which would have required less lift). Another new feature was the planned use of some of the less effective war-built escort carriers as helicopter ships to scout ahead of convoys.

By this time, too, the United States had begun to build up a continental air defense system, including a Navy offshore radar barrier between Argentina (Newfoundland) and Bermuda. Thus, the 1949 study included a combination of 12 radar pickets (DER, to maintain eight on station) and three escort carrier groups (one CVE, two DDEs, and four destroyer escorts: two groups would be maintained on station). Although the report does not say so explicitly, the CVE groups may well have been intended to deal with Soviet missile-firing submarines approaching launching positions off the US East Coast. That would certainly accord with later US ideas.

The big flush-decked carriers were not built, but a US war deployment plan of July 1952 showed three four-carrier task forces, one in the Pacific, one in the North Atlantic, and one in the Mediterranean. Supporting units would include one battleship and five or seven cruisers. The nine existing light fleet carriers (CVL) would be assigned to HUK groups.

The first report of the US Navy's Long Range Objectives (LRO) Group, submitted in December 1955, illustrates very different concepts of naval warfare. At this time naval effort was largely committed to the carrier-based nuclear strike mission, but the report (which looked to the 1960-70 period) envisaged a retreat from that strategy. The United States, facing a powerful Soviet nuclear force, would probably seek a tacit or overt agreement limiting the use of nuclear weapons. That in turn would limit the US ability to deter conventional attack, and the LRO saw a need for increasingly powerful non-nuclear striking forces.

None of this, however, ruled out the possibility that a nuclear war would actually have to be fought. Although the LRO observed that investment in offensive forces seemed to yield a higher return than similar investment in defensive forces, it also argued that increasing Soviet nuclear capabilities would increase Navy defensive responsibilities. Moreover, the Soviet submarine fleet was becoming more effective. Some minimal level of sea communications would have to be maintained, and striking forces might be unable to guarantee that level. In particular, because of their nuclear striking power, they might well be assigned non-naval objectives. This was the obverse of the old Air Force argument against Navy dependence on 'attack at source': the naval forces might find themselves occupied in attacking

** In NATO negotiations in 1950, the US Navy argued for a through convoy escort capable of obtaining a 50 per cent probability of detecting a submarine attempting to penetrate the screen of a 60-ship convoy. If four escorts could deal with one submarine, the minimum was set at the eight needed to deal with two. In threatened areas, a third quartet of escorts would be added, so that the convoy would maintain its minimum cover after the detachment of four ships to deal with one submarine. The Royal Navy argued instead for a through escort of two destroyers and four ASW frigates. Support groups in the approaches to the United Kingdom, however, would each consist of three ASW, three AAW, and one air direction frigate. There would also be a support group at Malta (four destroyers and four ASW converted destroyers) and another at Gibraltar (four frigates). In 1950, NATO regional force plans were added together, but the result was considered excessive. Instead, the NATO standing group adapted a US global study, which was considered a reasonable force level. It included two carrier task forces, one each in the Atlantic and the Mediterranean (each of six fleet carriers, five cruisers, and 40 destroyers). The remaining forces consisted of three battleships, 17 light and escort carriers, 23 cruisers, 297 destroyers, 512 escorts, 114 submarines, and 877 sweepers (not including inshore sweepers), plus shore-based aircraft.

In her ultimate escort configuration, the *Robert A Owens* shows two twin 3in/70s; the trainable Hedgehog has been removed as weight compensation. Note that the forward Weapon Alfa is off-center to starboard. The muzzles of two of her four torpedo tubes are visible on her after deckhouse, below and abaft the floater net trough. [*USNI*]

traditional strategic targets.

The LRO report, it should be noted, like the Admiralty planning study of 1944-45, was very much a requirements or objectives paper, and explicitly not a statement based on available resources. That came later and, as might be expected, it was far less buoyant. However, the LRO report is useful for its image of the way the US Navy perceived its future.

The LRO report divided the fleet into a series of striking forces (carrier, submarine, seaplane, and amphibious) and defensive forces (ASW and continental air defense).

As in 1947, the main striking force would be the carrier task groups. At a minimum, one task group and one reduced task group (two attack carriers and nine supporting ships) would be maintained in each of the two main fleets (Atlantic and Pacific), to be able to strike within two or three days of an alert. Elements sufficient to form

another task group within seven days would be maintained in each fleet. On the basis of the normal readiness factor of one in three (two in three or better in an emergency), the minimum objective would be five task groups.

Each strike group would consist of three attack carriers (CVA), one ASW support carrier (CVS), one missile battleship (BBG), four Talos (long-range) missile cruisers (CAG), three large missile frigates or light cruisers (DLG, armed with Terrier), and six destroyers. It would be supported by two radar picket submarines. Of the total of ten submarines required, eight would be nuclear-powered, hence capable of keeping up with the task group. The other two would be the two postwar units of the *Sailfish* class.

The most radical new element here was the presence of the ASW carrier within the carrier strike force. In 1955, the US Navy used its ASW carriers for open-ocean HUK operations, replacing

reconnaissance aircraft, six to 12 all-altitude attack aircraft, 20–32 low-altitude attack aircraft, and four early warning aircraft or helicopters. The CVS would carry four to six VTOL fighters, four early warning aircraft or helicopters, 24 ASW helicopters and 16 low-altitude attack aircraft. Given the abandonment of the long-range nuclear strike role, the future attack airplane (which became the A-6 Intruder) could be designed to operate from a relatively small carrier, such as a future 30,000-ton CVS. It would deliver either a small atomic bomb or 4000 pounds of conventional weapons, at ranges of about 300–800nm.

The LRO concept was based on three key technologies: long-range missiles (such as the air-breathing Triton) which could replace the existing heavy carrier bombers; effective long-range anti-aircraft missiles, which could replace many carrier fighters; and VTOL interceptors, which might operate from surface ships other than carriers. Thus the Triton-armed BBG would provide long-range strategic firepower, freeing the carriers for the tactical strikes which would become increasingly important in an era of limited warfare. Heavy attack bombers (VAH) would be phased out as long-range surface-to-surface missile and seaplane strike forces were phased in. Future attack carrier air groups would emphasize close air support (for limited war) and the precision delivery of conventional or small nuclear weapons at up to 1000nm. They would still be able to deliver nuclear weapons at greater ranges through in-flight refuelling. The carriers would also operate high endurance all-weather fighters, although surface-to-air missiles would take over much of the air defense load. The support carrier and missile cruiser aircraft (including helicopters and VTOL aircraft) would be responsible for some air interception, for airborne early warning and air control, and for task group ASW.

The BBG would rotate air control with the CAGs, and would provide primary inner zone air defense against high altitude attackers. The CAGs would provide inner or outer zone missile air defense, and would support VTOLs and helicopters for outer zone air defense. The DLGs provided last resort missile defense, and they and the DDs constituted the anti-submarine screen. The destroyers would also provide limited low-altitude air cover, using short-range surface-to-air missiles.

Surface-to-air missiles would be the primary means of killing high altitude attackers. The rate of fire would therefore be extremely important, which is why the US Navy shifted from single- to double-ended missile ships (cruisers and large destroyers) at this time.

Carrier task group air defense would be based on dispersion, to deny an enemy attacker the intelligence he needed. Dispersion (which required decentralized control) would also limit the efficacy of enemy nuclear attacks. Two CAGs, with their 100nm Talos missiles, could be spaced 75–100nm apart (on the circle 50–100 nm from task

earlier escort carriers (CVE). The standard carrier task group contained three attack carriers (CVA), and its main ASW weapon was its speed, allowing it to evade virtually any diesel submarine in its path. However, the LRO could expect the Soviets to develop nuclear or even closed-cycle submarines fast enough to engage task groups, which would then need much more sophisticated ASW defenses. In practice, the US Navy did not begin to assign one CVS to each carrier task group until about 1965. Note, however, that the LRO did not foresee the assignment of fast attack submarines in direct support of the task groups. Instead, it placed its faith in surface ship and helicopter sonar.

All carriers were to be armed with Tartar missiles (four launchers each) for self-defense. CVA air groups would comprise 16–32 fighters, four to six VTOL for interception in the inner low-altitude air defense zone, four to six photo

group center) to cover the two 90-degree sectors looking towards what would now be called the threat axis. Each would be able to search over a 200nm radius (with accurate height-finding at 150nm), and would control airborne early warning radars and VTOL fighters. Carrier-based fighters would occupy CAP stations on a 150nm circle. A third CAG or BBG within the main body would handle the opposite 180-degree (unexposed) sector, normally relying on a pair of early warning aircraft (75nm out) and maintaining radar silence.

The other two CAGs would maintain inner zone surveillance and air defense from within or on the flanks of the carrier formation. One (inner control ship) would control all air defense within the 75nm circle.

The task force would enjoy defense in depth against both high- and low-altitude attack or pre-attack reconnaissance. High-altitude aircraft would be intercepted by CAP fighters at 150–250nm (towards threat axis; 100–150nm away from threat axis). Then they would be engaged by the two threat-axis CAGs at 25–200nm, and by the unexposed CAG at 0–100nm. Finally, the three inner screen DLGs would engage at 0–25nm.

Low-altitude attackers would first encounter CAP fighters, then VTOL fighters (at 75–150nm towards the threat axis, and from carriers at 25–75nm in all directions). The screen would engage them at 0–25nm.

As a result, all mass attacks would be under continuous missile fire for 200nm (about 20 minutes at Mach 1). The boundary of the force would be pushed so far out that any low-level attacker trying to locate the main body would have to pop up within defensive missile range.

In contrast to the earlier studies, the 1960-70 fast task group screen in the direction of general advance consisted of only nine ships (three DLGs, six DDs), plus two to four carrier-based ASW helicopters. The LRO assumed that all ships of the task group would have long-range active and passive sonars able to detect submarines at very long ranges (eg, two convergence zones, 70nm), that the ships (other than carriers) themselves would be able to fire long-range (20nm) nuclear ASW missiles. Each forward sector air defense ship would be screened by one or two helicopters from its own deck, or from the carriers. Helicopters would also be maintained to attack ASW contacts beyond missile range.

The 1955 study did not describe logistic support forces in any detail. It seems noteworthy, however, that it did not include escort or converted fleet carriers to ferry replacement aircraft: the war would probably not last long enough for that to be important. As nuclear power was introduced, oilers would become less and less important, although ammunition ship requirements might actually increase. In any case, the underway replenishment force would include 'one stop' ships (AOR), some of which might be nuclear powered (AORN). The AOR had been proposed as early as 1946, but, as a controversial

item, it was not included in the 1947-49 long-range fleet programs. The total 1955 logistics support force included ships to support HUK groups and barriers: ten ammunition ships, six stores (provisions) ships, six (general) stores issue ships, 16 fleet tankers, five AORs, five AORNs.

There would also be two new strategic strike forces. As in the earlier studies, the Navy would operate a submarine missile force, which the LRO set at 15 boats by 1966 (23 by 1970), each capable of launching at least four Regulus II or Triton missiles. By 1966 or 1970, 1500nm ballistic missiles might be in service, but numbers and types of platforms were not yet clear. At the least, submarines would dissipate Soviet defensive efforts, and at the most they might help deter or fight a nuclear war. However, they would be expensive, and they would not contribute to limited war capability. the LRO therefore wanted to limit their numbers. This was prophetic for the large Polaris missile submarine program actually did crowd out Navy general purpose (limited war) forces such as carrier task groups.

From about 1951 on, the Bureau of Aeronautics had developed a new seaborne strike concept, in which a force of about 72 long-range jet seaplanes (the Martin P6M Seamaster) would operate from widely dispersed, moderately defended, self-supporting mobile bases in remote areas relatively secure from enemy reconnaissance and attack. Their roles would include the traditional seaplane function of long-range reconnaissance, but mining and strategic nuclear attack would be more important. The seaplanes in turn would require their own base ships: large tenders (two new AVA – seaplane tenders, attack – and two tenders coverted from existing ships), auxiliary tenders (four AVPs, redesigned AVLs, or light seaplane tenders), and refuellers (six converted submarines and six converted light cargo ships, AVO rather than AKL). This would have been a substantial investment, and its scale goes some way towards explaining how Navy investment in Polaris missile submarines required the cancellation of the P6M program.

The 1947 20-knot amphibious lift requirement – two full marine divisions – had been reduced to the assault elements of two marine divisions and their air wings. However, there was also a new element: for vertical envelopment, the force would have to include sufficient helicopters to be able to lift the assault elements of 1⅓ division/air wing. That came to a requirement for four (new) amphibious flagships, six fast attack cargo ships, eight attack transports, 16 (new) amphibious helicopter carriers (LPH), 24 landing ships dock (LSD) and 16 landing ships tank (LST). The LPHs could double as small ASW carriers, and the attack cargo ships and transports could be converted from existing (postwar-built) Mariner cargo ship hulls. A new LST would be needed, since existing types (of which 24 had been built since World War II) could not make anything like the required 20-knot speed. In addition, beach reconnaissance

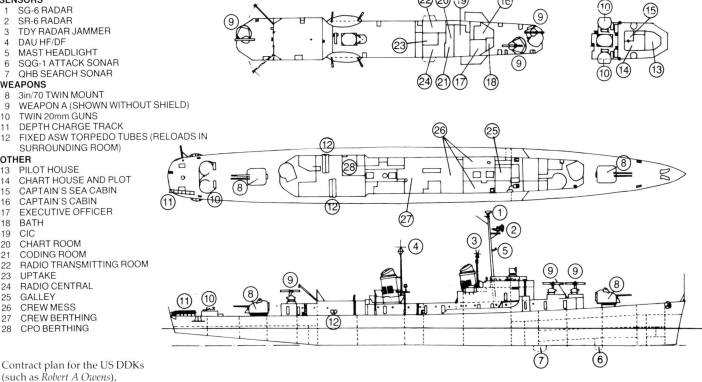

SENSORS
1 SG-6 RADAR
2 SR-6 RADAR
3 TDY RADAR JAMMER
4 DAU HF/DF
5 MAST HEADLIGHT
6 SQG-1 ATTACK SONAR
7 QHB SEARCH SONAR

WEAPONS
8 3in/70 TWIN MOUNT
9 WEAPON A (SHOWN WITHOUT SHIELD)
10 TWIN 20mm GUNS
11 DEPTH CHARGE TRACK
12 FIXED ASW TORPEDO TUBES (RELOADS IN
   SURROUNDING ROOM)

OTHER
13 PILOT HOUSE
14 CHART HOUSE AND PLOT
15 CAPTAIN'S SEA CABIN
16 CAPTAIN'S CABIN
17 EXECUTIVE OFFICER
18 BATH
19 CIC
20 CHART ROOM
21 CODING ROOM
22 RADIO TRANSMITTING ROOM
23 UPTAKE
24 RADIO CENTRAL
25 GALLEY
26 CREW MESS
27 CREW BERTHING
28 CPO BERTHING

Contract plan for the US DDKs
(such as *Robert A Owens*),
undated, but about 1947. Note
the unshielded Weapon Alfas
and the four fixed torpedo tubes.

and underwater demolition would require the
construction of eight new fast transports (27-knot
APDs, formerly converted destroyer escorts) and
six new personnel-carrying submarines (ASSP).

This was a large program, particularly given the
existence of numerous slow amphibious ships: 15
amphibious flagships (AGC), 36 attack cargo
ships, 75 attack transports, 82 fast transports
(APD), and 21 LSDs. Some of these ships,
supplemented by merchant hulls and by the 24
existing slow LSTs, would transport the follow-on
elements of the two marine divisions and air
wings.

Defense included both strategic defense of the
United States (against air attack and against
submarine-launched missiles) and classical
defense of shipping. As the British had feared (see
Chapter 1), it would be difficult for the US Navy to
build separate forces adequate for both. The LRO
sought to accomplish both tasks by means of a
series of barrier lines which submarines and
bombers would have to pass. The barriers closest
to Soviet bases would tend to keep submarines out
of their ocean patrol areas, and the barrier system
in general would tend, over time, to kill off the
patrolling submarines in the open ocean. SOSUS
was already under test, and the LRO expected
SOSUS-directed shore-based aircraft ultimately to
replace some of the barrier ships.

The strategy was predicated on new technology
that would permit each barrier ship to control a
relatively large ocean area: very long-range active
sonar (LORAD), improved long-range ASW
weapons (both aboard ship and aboard ship-

launched helicopters), and long-range air search
radars backed by long-range ship-launched
missiles (primarily Talos).

The outermost (distant) barrier would consist of
50 ASW submarines.

The outer (ocean) picket line, stationed just out
of range of Soviet tactical air attack, would consist
of 35 to 40 surface ships (PBG, replacing existing
DERs) designed to detect bombers and
submarines at long-range. They would use
helicopters against the submarines, and would be
armed with Terrier (including an ASW version),
for limited self-defense. The PBG would also have
a secondary convoy escort role. It might be a
converted Victory ship, and it would cost about
$20 million. It would support three to four
helicopters.

The next line would consist of outer offshore
pickets, to control shore-based interceptors. Those
based in the Atlantic (12 CVHGs) would also be
fitted to counter low fliers using a combination of
Talos missiles, VTOL fighters, and helicopters for
early warning and control. The Pacific would
require 12–15 PBCs. The CVHG would be used
primarily for the Newfoundland–Bermuda barrier,
but it would also be useful for convoy escort. It
would support 16 helicopters and VTOL fighters,
as well as a 100nm missile (Talos) and long-range
active and passive (LOFAR) sonars. It was
conceived as a conventional 18–20-knot, 10,000-
ton ship, although CVL conversions were also
considered. The cost would be about $40 million
(compared to $160 million for a BBG conversion).
The PBC would operate in the outer offshore

Pacific barrier and, as a YAGR replacement, in the inner barrier. It, too, would have a secondary role as convoy escort. In effect, it would be a PBG without Terrier, at a cost of about $15 million.

Finally, inner offshore pickets (16–26 PBC or YAGR) would control shore-based interceptors. All pickets would be capable of long-range submarine detection and kill. The surface ship barriers, moreover, would be supplemented by airborne early warning aircraft on alert.

The barriers would be supplemented by mobile HUK groups (built around helicopter carriers), which would also cover important forces and convoys; by ASW submarines, and by surface escorts. However, escort requirements would be minimized, as only relatively few submarines would be able to break through the barriers. Thus, the LRO expected the US Navy to build about 75 new, fast ocean escorts, equipped with both missiles (such as Terrier) and long-range sonars. They would be about the size of the existing *Forrest Sherman* class destroyer.

For all its exotic descriptions of new kinds of pickets, from an air point of view this was really much in line with the existing arrangement: forward barrier submarines supported by DERs and then by an inner barrier of converted Liberty ships (YAGR). The LRO wanted the entire system, to be in place by 1965, which, ironically, was when the barrier system was dissolved because it was irrelevant to the new Soviet strategic threat, the ballistic missile. The really new feature was the emphasis on detecting and killing Soviet ballistic missile submarines en route to firing areas off the US coast.

Also new was the requirement that all attack submarines be suitable for ASW employment, since ASW would be so clearly their primary mission (50 out of a total of 74 attack submarines would operate in the distant barrier, and others would back up the barriers). The LRO argued that the classic submarine mission, attacking enemy shipping in areas under his own air control, would not be worth the cost of maintaining a large attack submarine force. However, some attack submarines would still be needed for this and such other missions as mining vital areas, air–sea rescue (in support of carrier forces), reconnaissance and peacetime ASW training.

Of the new technologies involved in the 1955 study, VTOL was surely the greatest disappointment. Without it, the screening ships could not contribute very effectively to long-range, low-level air defense, and the decentralized task group could not easily be formed. Nor could the carriers shrink in size and cost. In 1955, the heavy attack bombers imposed a lower limit on their size, and the LRO hoped that replacement of such aircraft by missiles might lower the carrier size limit. After 1955, however, the long-range carrier fighters grew to the point where they represented much the same problem.

Although the LRO sought a new naval strategy, it was well aware of fiscal limitations. It could still derive comfort from the vast numbers of ships left over from the wartime building program, including (until about 1965, it hoped) about 600 destroyers and detroyer escorts. Moreover, as new BBGs and CAGs were built or converted from existing large hulls, existing missile ships would become available for other duties, such as supporting amphibious ships. By 1970, all ships built before 1942 (except the two *North Carolinas*) would be unserviceable. Of post-1942 ships, the small light carriers, the converted escort carriers, the two worst fleet carriers (*Franklin* and *Bunker Hill*), all the anti-aircraft cruisers, all the fleet submarines, the World War II mine craft and the patrol craft would have to be discarded.

The principal lesson of this (and later) long-range studies was the critical need for destroyers which faced bloc obsolescence. Thus, the 1955 report urged the retention of 150 to 200 war-built destroyers – which explains why the FRAM program was begun three years later.

The other two major Western navies, the French and Dutch, were in a very different position. Neither had benefited from war construction. Each had suffered badly, and each was left with a mixture of prewar, US, British, and German ships, pending postwar replacement. Each also shared the British problem of combining general war and Third World (colonial) forces.

The French Navy of 1945 was still quite powerful, but most of its ships were obsolescent, and many of them were badly worn by wartime service far from bases and spare parts. The only carrier, *Bearn*, was obsolete. Of two modern battleships, one was incomplete, and some proposed converting her into a carrier. Three light cruisers and three large destroyers remained in good condition, out of an enormous prewar fleet. Even though France had suffered badly during the war, the new French government was determined not merely to reconstruct but, like the British, to pursue simultaneously all of the important elements of military technology – including new warship construction.

The postwar fleet would consist of three carrier task forces (Atlantic, Mediterranean, colonial) plus four ASW escort groups, an amphibious flotilla (60,000 tons), coastal forces (motor torpedo boats, pocket submarines, and minesweepers), 60 long-range submarines, and 12 colonial avisos (sloops). Each carrier group would consist of two carriers, a battleship, four cruisers, and 12 fast escorts. Each escort group would consist of a small carrier and about 12 escorts (for a total of 50). The fleet would return to about its pre-1940 size (750,000 tons compared to 700,000 in 1940, or 400,000 in 1945).

This ambitious plan was soon cut by about half. By using existing ships the Navy could avoid any requirements to build battleships or cruisers, although clearly it needed carriers. It would operate two task groups, each built around one of the two modern battleships, with one heavy and one light carrier (to be built) and a dozen escorts (half of them ex-German or ex-Italian at this stage). Two escort groups would be organized around the escort carrier *Dixmude* and the aircraft transport *Commandant-Teste* (which would be converted into an escort carrier), plus ex-Allied frigates. Coastal defense would be the responsibility of 24 small craft (vedettes), 12 ex-German midget submarines, and a hundred aircraft. There were 30 submarines and 30,000 tons of amphibious shipping. Even this program would have required 222,500 tons of new construction, over a dozen years. The reconstruction program was finally fixed in 1949. It added 72,000 tons of ships to replace those reaching retirement age, and another 28,000 tons under construction, for a total of 322,500 tons.

By this time, France had joined NATO. She was also deeply involved in Vietnam, and so could not afford the planned program. As early as 1946, the war in Indo-China required six cruisers, two aircraft transports, six frigates, 16 avisos, and major amphibious and support units. US MDAP aid could pay for ships, but only for those required to fight the kind of war NATO envisaged. A planned 28,000-ton carrier had to be abandoned, and even a 14,000-tonner seemed too difficult, Instead, France obtained a former British light fleet carrier (*Colossus*) and then, under MDAP, two US light fleet carriers. Of the high seas forces envisaged in 1945. France was able to build two anti-aircraft cruisers (one a redesigned ship laid down before the war) and 18 large destroyers (*Surcouf* class). She planned a total of 73 ocean escorts: 13 ocean-going E50/E52 class (*Le Corse* and *Le Normand* classes; 18 were actually built, and two more cancelled), 40 austere mass-production units (E54, a French equivalent of the British Type 14), and possibly 20 larger dual purpose units (colonial avisos and frigates).

There was always a tension between French national concerns (including colonial security) and her NATO obligations. NATO could not formally support the wars either in Indo-China or in Algeria, although it certainly did provide considerable informal assistance. Funds were tight, and even though MDAP paid for much of

Opposite: Both major navies tried to modernize existing escorts, so as to preserve the value of the very large wartime investment they represented. *Loch Ruthven*, shown in December 1961, was the prototype modernized British ASW frigate. The visible elements of modernization were replacement of the earlier single 4in gun by a twin 4in, and replacement of the earlier 2-pounder pom-pom by a twin 40mm gun aft. The former twin 20mm on her bridge wings were replaced by single 40mm, for a total of six 40mm guns. Note, too, the 277Q stabilized surface search radar atop her mast, and the UHF 'candlesticks' at either yardarm. Not visible are her new sonars: Type 162 in place of the former acoustic sweep (SA) gear, 147F, and 144Q2 (later 164) in her main dome. Her FH4 HF/DF was raised (for greater range) and HDWS (Type 974) installed. An STD director was installed as well. The radar office was enlarged, and the former wheelbase converter into a CIC. Six other ships were modernized in 1952-54: *Loch Fada, Loch Alvie, Loch Insh, Loch Fyne, Loch Lomond,* and *Loch Killisport.* A much larger modernization program was planned, but it could not be carried out (see text). [*USNI*]

the purely NATO construction, operating those ships cost scarce men and money. From about 1955 onwards, with the draining war in Indo-China over, France could increasingly favor what some called her national fleet over the NATO ASW/anti-mine fleet. She built two fleet carriers and planned another, and she abandoned the austere E54 entirely, in favor of the *Commandante Rivière* class 'aviso-escorteur', of which she built 9. The national program in turn was scaled down as money was drained by the Algerian War and by the French nuclear weapons program, the latter increasingly important as General de Gaulle turned his country away from reliance on NATO for her defense. Almost 30 years later, it seems symbolic that the replacements for the NATO frigates of the early 'fifties are avisos (A69 class) designed primarily to protect the seaward approaches to the French ballistic missile submarine bases, ie, to protect what the French consider the guarantee of their national independence.

Early postwar Dutch planning was based on three small task forces each comprising of a light carrier, two light cruisers, eight destroyers, and a fleet train of a fast tanker and a fast depot ship, to be built up over a decade. The first light carrier was purchased from Britain in 1948. Two small cruisers already existed, with two more incomplete on the slip. Similarly, the Dutch Navy bought four destroyers from the Royal Navy in 1945, soon ordering 12 more from Dutch yards. Each carrier would be provided with an air group of 20 fighters and 15 attack aircraft, and the Navy would also operate three squadrons each of 12 four-engine reconnaissance bombers, and six squadrons each of 20 twin-engine attack bombers. This was a World War II US fleet in miniature. Its most unique feature was the design of the new destroyers, which concentrated on anti-aircraft and anti-submarine weapons to the virtual exclusion of traditional anti-ship features.

In 1949, the Netherlands joined NATO. With the loss of the East Indies, it no longer needed its traditional overseas fleet. However, it was now integrated into an Alliance requiring powerful trade protection forces. The heavy ships already built or planned could not be disposed of, but new ASW and mine warfare craft could be ordered. In 1951, then, the fleet plan was modified to show one carrier, the two new cruisers, 12 destroyers, 12 large frigate, five small frigates, seven coastal escorts, six submarines, 65 minesweepers, six patrol boats, and a net-layer. These figures did not include a variety of older ships, such as three ex-British destroyers, many of which remained in service through the 'fifties. Early US assistance included six frigates and six coastal frigates (updated PCEs), while five coastal ASW craft (updated US submarine chasers) were built in the Netherlands. Except for the larger ships, the full 1951 force levels were never reached. For example, six new *Leander* class frigates were ordered from 1963 onwards to replace the former US ships, not to supplement them. On the other hand, as the early general purpose ships wore out, they were replaced by types better suited to the NATO general war (specialized ASW) mission. Thus the two cruisers were succeeded by two large missile destroyers, the 12 postwar destroyers by 12 Standard frigates, and the six small coastal escorts are to be replaced by M class frigates. The total of six submarines has been met and has remained stable for many years.*

---

* Two of the original 12 Dutch Standards were sold to Greece, and replaced by guided-missile armed versions of the design. A total of eight M class frigates is on order, with four more planned; they will replace both the small US-built coastal escorts and the British-designed *Van Spejk* class frigates. Finally, only four submarines are currently in commission (1986).

3

NEW WEAPONS TECHNOLOGY

Technical developments in weapons and sensors, rather than any changes in naval strategy or in world politics, were the most striking features of early postwar naval warfare. They literally shaped postwar surface ships. Aircraft (including aircraft control) and submarine technology will be deferred to later chapters, but this one includes the new generation of early postwar anti-ship weapons, developed before it became apparent that the Soviet Navy was effectively a missile/bomber force. British developments will be emphasized because American weapons have been described elsewhere in considerable detail (*US Naval Weapons*, Conway Maritime Press & Naval Institute Press, 1983). Mines are reserved for a later chapter.

The new radars and sonars and the new weapons they directed were reactions to faster and more agile aircraft and submarines, armed with longer-range weapons of their own: jet bombers with stand-off missiles and deep-diving fast submarines with homing (and later nuclear) torpedoes. The other major new weapon was the pressure mine. Each of the new anti-ship weapons threatened to overcome the advantages which the Western navies had achieved in wartime: the victories of the carrier task forces, the victory over the U-boats, the big amphibious landings. Each had first appeared in German hands during the war, and thus each had already led to active wartime programs, which formed the basis of the first two generations of postwar sensors and weapons.

Stand-off bombs and homing torpedoes were particularly terrifying because they changed the terms of defense. A reading of wartime anti-aircraft and anti-submarine experience suggests that success, in the sense of negating an attack, was most often achieved by making it too dangerous for the attacker to approach to within effective range. In the case of an airplane, so much fire was thrown up that the bombardier flinched as he approached the target, or the pilot bombed from too great an altitude. Using a guided missile, he could remain outside gun anti-aircraft range, yet still achieve better accuracy than most conventional forms of bombing.

The Germans introduced the FX-1400 guided

bomb and the HS-293 glide-bomb anti-ship missiles in 1943-4, one of their first victims being the Italian battleship *Roma* in September 1943. By 1945 the US Navy had its own anti-ship missile, the Bat, and both Britain and the United States were developing successors. Although it was manned, the Japanese rocket-propelled Baka had a very similar tactical significance. The Japanese Kamikazes also shared missile characteristics, at least from the point of view of the target.

Submarines acquired effective stand-off weapons at about the same time. The Germans introduced both an anti-ship (anti-escort) homing torpedo, T-5 (Zaukoenig, or Wren) and a pattern-runner which circulated within a convoy until it encountered a target, hence did not have to be aimed at any particular ship. Like a homing torpedo, a pattern-runner could be fired from long range. However, unlike a homer, it could not be jammed, since it did not work on any external signature until it actually hit its target. It could be countered only by being destroyed physically. Much the same can be said of a torpedo guided, not by an internal seeker, but by a guidance wire, or of the later nuclear torpedoes. Before the end of the war US submarines in the Pacific were using anti-ship homing torpedoes.

The technological threats were not abstract. They seemed urgent. The Soviets had captured the futuristic German naval weapons, and would surely decide to mass produce them. For example, it was widely understood that, even given huge numerical superiority, the Allies had come close to defeat in the Battle of the Atlantic, fighting against the old generation submarines. It appeared that the first of the new type, the Type XXI and Type XXIII, had easily evaded British screening ships in 1945. In one case a Type XXI commander had made a dummy attack on a British heavy cruiser without being detected. Those who believed that Stalin had maintained his army could easily imagine that he would soon mass-produce German-type submarines, the plans of which his troops had captured in 1945. As in the case of the Soviet land army, the reality was more prosaic. The Soviets certainly wanted to exploit their scientific booty, but the new systems were difficult (and, presumably, expensive) to develop, and even the simplest, the fast Soviet submarine, did not appear until 1950, in the form of the WHISKEY class submarine, which took some years to appear in significant numbers. The first Soviet anti-ship stand-off missile, KOMET (AS-N-1), probably did not enter service before about 1956. This delay was fortunate for the West. Although the two leading Western navies poured their limited resources into their own new generation of weapons, little entered service before the mid 'fifties. The new technology was just too difficult to rush.

The postwar sensors (radars and sonars) had to deal with fast, highly streamlined targets, and in some cases (missiles) with much smaller targets than those of the past. Streamlining reduced radar (bomber) or sonar (submarine) reflecting cross-section, and hence the probability of detection per pulse or per ping. This was compounded by high speed, which reduced the number of detection opportunities as the bomber or submarine swept past the radar or sonar. Weapon systems needed some minimum time within which to react to incoming threats. The faster the threat, the longer the detection range corresponding to that reaction time. This was entirely apart from the longer range required to deal with stand-off attacks (by missile or by submarine-launched homing torpedo).

To be effective, defending weapons (or fighters) had to be aimed (directed) on the basis of target tracks, permitting prediction of future target position. That in turn required a sequence of detections. The fewer or less definite the detections, the less precise the track and hence the

worse the fire control or intercept solution. That is why postwar US radars rotated (scanned) at about three times the speed of their wartime predecessors, in order to multiply the number of detection opportunities and so preserve tracking accuracy in the face of higher target speed.

Sheer speed also greatly reduced the attacker's exposure to the defense. Hence the defense had to be able to achieve more per unit time, either by firing faster (as in the case of the new generation of anti-aircraft guns) or by making each shot more effective (as in the case of anti-aircraft missiles and homing torpedoes). For example, a jet bomber attacking at sea level at a speed of 450 knots would be visible for only 25 seconds, and would spend only two seconds within range of a wartime weapon such as a 40mm gun.

The anti-aircraft and anti-submarine weapons can be divided, crudely, into two categories: ballistic and homing. In anti-aircraft fire, guns were the ballistic weapons, surface to air missiles the guided ones. Although both were developed in parallel, the ballistic systems were simpler and therefore formed a first generation. In the US Navy, for example, automatic 3in/70 and 5in/54 guns, developed from about 1945 onwards, were specified for the first postwar generation of ships. The Project Bumblebee missiles, Terrier and Talos, were more complex and took longer to develop; they formed, in theory, a second generation. In fact the most ambitious gun mount, the 3in/70, was so complex mechanically that it entered service at about the same time as Terrier. In ASW,

The British 5.25in gun, as illustrated aboard *Euryalus* (24 January 1952, off Malta) was the starting point for the most important (but abortive) postwar British naval gun project, the 5in medium calibre dual purpose gun. It began as a late wartime attempt to devise a superior 5.25in, for a cruiser designed in 1944 but then abandoned before the end of the war. Note that, nearly six years after the end of the war, *Euryalus* is still equipped entirely with wartime radars and with prewar fire control systems. For example, although she has a single-calibre dual purpose battery, she has separate surface and anti-aircraft directors. The latter were still equipped with range-only radar, so that they could not be used for blind fire. *Euryalus* served in the Mediterranean in 1948-53, and in the South Atlantic in 1953-54. She paid off at Devonport in August 1954, and was broken up in 1959. [*MoD*]

the equivalents were, respectively, the postwar ahead-throwing weapons (Hedgehogs Mark 14 and 15 and Weapon Alfa in US service) and the homing torpedoes (such as Mark 37). Again, both originated almost simultaneously, and in fact the US Navy had an air-launched ASW homing torpedo (Mark 24) in service as early as 1943.

Again, very generally, the two types of weapon represent two choices of the division of the intelligent part of an overall weapon system between ship and weapon proper. At any given level of technology, it is easier to fit more intelligence in a large ship than in a small expendable weapon. At one end of the time scale, when all gunnery computers were immense analog devices of gears and cams, it was impossible to put anything more intelligent than a time fuze in a shell; guidance of any type was unthinkable. The next step was command guidance, in which most (but not all) the intelligence still resided in the ship. First-generation anti-aircraft missiles, such as Terrier and Seaslug, were command-guided (beam-riders). As electronics became more compact, missiles could become more intelligent, guiding themselves onto their targets. Modern naval anti-aircraft missiles such as Standard and Sea Dart steer themselves towards radar pulses reflected from their targets. At some further remove, one might imagine missiles guiding themselves by means of their own active radars, entirely without reference to further assistance from the intelligence aboard ship.

The new AMRAAM (AIM-120) air-to-air missile falls into this 'fire and forget' category*.

One advantage of putting more intelligence in the missile or torpedo is that it can respond better to target motion. How important that response is depends on time of flight. If the missile travels fast enough, the target cannot move very far, and there is little point in homing of any sort. Indeed, a homing mechanism may not be able to respond fast enough. That is why modern last-ditch defense systems generally employ guns (the ballistic solution) rather than missiles. However, the greater the range, the less the chance that initial target data will suffice. That is why the natural response to the bomber-launched stand-off weapon was the ship-launched guided missile. Much the same consideration applies to a very high-speed maneuvering target, since the target can move further (from the predicted point of impact) during the same time of flight. The key consideration here is how far the target can move during the 'dead time' inherent in a ballistic weapon – the time between the last ballistic input (upon which firing is based) and the time of impact or miss. This is more than just flight time, because generally there is some delay in

* On the other hand, the distance a missile can operate autonomously is limited ultimately by its 'field of view'; the inherently small antenna will probably limit active radars to terminal engagements for the foreseeable future.

Visiting the US naval base at Norfolk, the French anti-aircraft cruiser *de Grasse* displays both of the new French first-generation guns: the twin 5in/54 and the twin 57mm Bofors. Similar weapons armed the contemporary French destroyers and ocean escorts. [*USN*]

calculation and in transmitting gunnery data to the weapon.

Similar considerations obtain in ASW. A Limbo or a Weapon Alfa or a Hedgehog (or, for that matter, a depth charge track or thrower) was essentially a gun (ballistic) firing its weapon at the estimated future position of the target submarine. The deeper the submarine, the longer the delay between firing input and prospective impact, and the better the chance that the submarine could evade. Any attempt to fire a ballistic ASW weapon to a great range had to encounter the same limitation. Thus the combination of fast submarine and long-range (stand-off) torpedo had to make homing ASW torpedoes attractive.

The choice between the two solution was never entirely clear-cut. Generally, the ballistic weapon systems could reduce 'dead time' in three ways: by improving their computers, increasing muzzle velocity or its equivalent to reduce time of flight, and by increasing rate of fire to make up for a limited kill probability per shot. For example, in the Weapon Alfa system, the US Navy introduced an electronic target course predictor (the Mark 101 fire control system) which automatically aimed the weapon, a fast-sinking depth charge, and a fast-firing launcher. Similarly, the 'ideal' US anti-aircraft gun, the twin 3in/70, used the best available computer, achieved a muzzle velocity of 3400 ft/sec (compared to 2650 for the previous 3in/50), and fired about twice as fast as its immediate predecessor, the twin 3in/50.

Both the major Western navies chose to develop both ballistic and homing solutions in parallel; the ballistic systems were generally considered interim solutions which would ultimately be superseded by the more modern homing weapons. The reality did not always match, since the two types of weapons encountered quite different kinds of problems associated with quite different levels of technology. The ballistic weapons were largely mechanical (except for electronic fire controls in some cases), while the homing weapons relied heavily on electronics. Thus fast-firing ballistic weapons, such as the US twin 3in/70, or the British 6in Mark 26, or the US Weapon Alfa, turned out to be mechanically unreliable.

The homing weapons suffered from the problems of vacuum-tube electronics, both in their fire control systems and in their own guidance elements. Many postwar homing torpedoes, for example, had to operate at very low speeds because their homing mechanisms could not overcome higher levels of self-noise associated with higher speeds. That in turn limited their ability to counter fast submarines, since it is a rule of thumb that a homing torpedo must be 50 per cent faster than its target. Thus the Royal Navy, which for a time planned to arm its frigates primarily with homing torpedoes, had to abandon them and rely entirely on an earlier ballistic weapon, Limbo. Similarly, although the first postwar French frigates (E50 type) were armed entirely with ASW torpedoes, large Bofors and other ASW mortars (the ballistic weapon) soon appeared to supplement them.*

Missiles were a very sore point. The US Navy, faced with an extremely severe threat, had to plunge headlong into the new world of anti-aircraft guided missiles. By 1962 it had numerous batteries of Talos, Terrier, and Tartar missiles in service – and an internal Defense Department report denounced them all as worth little more than scrap. It took an expensive 'Get-Well' program to solve their problems, just in time for

them to perform effectively in Vietnam. The problem was always reliability rather than performance. Even in 1962, the missiles were quite adequate when they worked properly.

This was not a uniquely American problem. The British Seaslug was approximately equivalent to the US Terrier, derived from roughly the same technology base, on roughly the same schedule. It was no better (or worse) than Terrier, but never benefited from the sort of expensive 'get well' program which cured the unreliability of the American weapon. The reader may note that the one Seaslug ship in the Falklands, *Glamorgan*, was limited to shore bombardment duty, well away from any air threat, no matter how docile.

As for the chief source of the threat that the Western navies faced, the Soviets surely faced much the same sort of problems. The new technology promisd a great deal, but that promise might be met only intermittently. Like the Soviet Army of 1946, the Soviet Navy a decade later was outwardly impressive. However, its new weapons were probably even more unreliable than the counters just entering service with its rivals. In the West, it took two decades for the promises of 1946 to approach true fulfillment. At this time we cannot know (at least outside of the intelligence organizations) what the comparable time was (or, in some cases, perhaps yet will be) for the Soviet Navy.

Anti-Aircraft Guns

The anti-aircraft gun system included four elements: the gun itself, plus the detecting sensor(s), a coordinating or target assigning mechanism, and a fire control computer which directed the gun. Typically, targets were detected at long range by a search or warning radar, whose broad beam made for early detection (many pulses on target per scan) but only limited precision. Ultimately, they had to be handed over to a very precise radar or optical tracker which fed its data into a fire control computer. The Royal Navy typically interposed a narrow-beam target indicating radar, in effect a short-range air search set, between warning set and fire control. Although this was not US policy, late in World War II many US warships used their height-finding radars as target indicators. Postwar, however, US warships generally relied only on their air search sets – which generally had narrower beams than those in British service. British cruisers continued to combine target indicators (Types 293 and 992) with their postwar air search sets (generally Type 960).

The intermediate target assigning function was particularly important in confused air situations, when a ship might have to engage several aircraft at once. British wartime practice was to centralize this function under a target indicating officer, who would assign directors and guns to targets. Postwar, this idea was formalized as a Gunnery Direction System (GDS). The postwar standard was GDS 3, incorporating TIU Mark 3 (Target

---

* The French approach to torpedoes was distinctive. In March 1943, a Free French Navy constructor-Captain, Louis Kahn, proposed to the Royal Navy that existing unguided torpedoes be used as, in effect, ahead-thrown ASW weapons, set for a submarine's predicted depth and range. Their pistols could be pre-set for time (range) or they could be magnetically (proximity) fused. The Admiralty rejected this idea, claiming that development of such a weapon would hardly be simple. In effect, the usual setting for gyro-angle would have to be supplemented by a setting for down-angle as well. Kahn became a senior French naval constructor postwar, and his unguided anti-submarine torpedo, designated K2, was adopted. It was a very fast weapon (alcohol-oxygen driven at 50 knots) and was considered effective against fast submarines at ranges as great as 1000 yards. For greater ranges, the French developed a companion active-homing torpedo, designated L3 (L because it was the letter of the alphabet succeeding K). It was considered effective to about 3000 yards, and could also be fired by a submarine. Both could be fired from the same short torpedo tube. The next generation French surface ASW torpedo, L4, was designed to be carried by the Malafon missile, out to a range of 10,000 or 15,000 yards. L5 is the current ship- and submarine-launched anti-submarine weapon, using active homing. French submarine torpedoes are designated the same way: the number is sequential (in a series beginning with 12), the letter indicating the leading characteristic. Thus the first postwar weapons were E12 (passive anti-ship torpedoes, electrically-propelled, derived from wartime German torpedoes) and Z13 (pattern-running, ie, zig-zag). Later weapons in this series are the E14 and E15, Z16, and the wire-guided (filoguidée) F17.

Indication Unit Mark 3). The Type 992 radar was specifically designed to support it. It scanned at the very high speed of 90 rpm, and the operator could place a strobe over any target it displayed. The radar would then keep the strobe on that target, feeding range, course, and speed into the GDS. This early track-while-scan system was originally designed to maintain eight such strobes simultaneously. The full range of GDS included:

— GDS 1, visual only.
— GDS 2 TIU 2, with Type 293 radar: three or five channels (GDS 2* incorporated Radar Type 293Q, and was limited to three channels).
— GDS 3 radar Type 992, TIU 3, four or six channels.
— GDS 5 radar Type 293Q or 992, TIU 5, three or four channels.

Wartime US Navy practice was to divide guns and directors into sectors, relying on decentralized control. However, by 1945, it was clear that massive firepower would be required to deal with individual Kamikazes, and the decentralized system seemed much less attractive. At the end of the war, Bell Laboratories was engaged in a general study of the anti-aircraft problem, under the designation Fire Control System Mark 65. The laboratory concluded that the solution was an electronic device, which it called a Threat Evaluator and Weapon Assigner (TEWA), which could evaluate incoming threats and match them

with available director and weapon capabilities in some centralized manner. It might operate either automatically (as an ATEWA) or manually. In theory, the ATEWA would obtain its target data from a dedicated three-dimensional track-while-scan radar, analyze the data, and assign directors to specific targets. A simulated ATEWA was tested at Bell Laboratories between 1949 and 51. It could display up to ten raids and assign up to four available directors. The operational prototype, Mark 3, using the experimental SPS-3 radar, was installed aboard the command ship *Northampton* in 1953. Later versions controlled US gun/missile batteries: Mark 7 in the *Boston*s, Mark 9 in many other Terrier ships. Their successors were Weapon Designation Systems (WDS): Mark 1 for Tartar ships, Mark 3 for carriers armed with the Terrier missile, Mark 4 in *Leahy* class cruisers, Mark 8 in the first two *Belknap* class cruisers, Mark 9 (planned) in Typhon ships. With Mark 11 the WDS was merged with the ship's naval tactical data system computer to form a single combat system which could accept its data both from onboard and from external sources.

Director performance could determine the performance of the entire gun system. The US Navy was fortunate in its early choice of a series of gyroscope-based units which predicted target position on the basis of measured (angular) target speed. The Royal Navy, which termed such units 'tachymetric' (rate-measuring), unfortunately had

The Dutch destroyer *Friesland,* at the 1957 Jamestown naval review, displays the Bofors twin automatic 4.7-inch dual-purpose gun, which the US Bureau of Ordnance considered the best in Europe at the time. The same mount appeared in the Swedish and Colombian navies, and units salvaged from scrapped Dutch destroyers arm the current missile destroyers *Tromp* and *de Ruyter*. This class is also interesting in comparison with the US *Gearing* and the British *Daring*, all of which were about the same size and shared virtually a common propulsion plant. At this time, ASW armament was limited to a pair of triple Bofors mortars, forward of the bridge. Two ships were each fitted with eight fixed tubes in 1960-61, as in the Royal Navy. This project died, and the Dutch did not adopt a longer-range helicopter-delivered weapon in its place. A Lynx helicopter did appear aboard the new *Van Spejk* class frigates delivered in 1967-68. [*USN*]

Despite its complex appearance, the British twin 3in/70 Mark 6 (illustrated by a model in the Priddy's Hard ordnance museum) was relatively successful, arming Canadian frigates as well as British cruisers. It shared common ammunition and gun tube with the much less successful US 3in/70. Note the water-cooling tube attached to the gun proper, and the loading drum underneath. [*Priddy's Hard*]

A model of the British twin 6in Mark 26 at the Priddy's Hard ordnance museum does not hint at the complexity (or the delicacy) of the weapon. The shell case disposal chute of the left hand gun is visible. In service, the 6in Mark 26 was said to be good for no more than 20 seconds of continuous fire, before some stoppage occurred. [*Priddy's Hard*]

chosen an alternative system – in which aircraft speed was estimated – in the 'twenties, and had not realized its error until well into World War II. Thus, although on paper its anti-aircraft batteries were equivalent to those of the US Navy, in fact, they required expensive fire control modernization. Moreover, in 1945, the Royal Navy was faced with the painful choice between developing a new generation of dual purpose fire controls and paying scarce foreign exchange for US equipment. It had already obtained US Mark 37s for some of the Battle class destroyers and for the two *Ark Royal* class carriers and the battleship *Vanguard*.

The only existing modern British system was the power-stabilized Mark VI Director, which incorporated the narrow-beam Type 275 radar, capable of tracking a target in elevation, range, and bearing. Initially, it incorporated the unsatisfactory Fuze Keeping Clock (FKC) predictor (computer) of earlier British anti-aircraft fire control systems, but at the end of the war a satisfactory flyplane computer was becoming available for use with it. It was fitted to the *Daring* class destroyers after the war and later replaced the FKC in earlier ships.

Postwar, the Royal Navy sought to develop a new series of fire control systems. LRS 1, for long-range gunnery and missile control, became the basis of the Seaslug missile guidance system, just as the postwar US long-range gunnery radar, SPG-49, became the basis of the Terrier and Talos guidance sets. Cancelled as a gunnery system in 1949, LRS 1 was designed to deal with 750mph targets at ranges as great as 28,000 yards.

Postwar British systems were a mixture of the new Medium Range Systems (MRS) and modified versions of the wartime types, all controlling 40mm, 3in/70, 4in, 4.5in, and 6in guns. MRS 1 and MRS 2 were never completed; MRS 3 was conceived as a license-built version of the US Mark 56 radar-only dual purpose director. It was actually produced instead as MRS 3 Mod 1, with a predictor based on Flyplane. MRS 4 was to have been an alternative all-British system, and MRS 5 was a more advanced type with a Type 905 monopulse (rather than conically-scanned) radar. Neither entered service, MRS 3 proving successful in its two versions: Mod 1/SU2 and Mod 1/SU4, for, respectively, full AA and surface control of 4in and over; and for full AA and limited surface control of 3in and larger guns, at limited ranges.

MRS 6 was the wartime Mk VI director fitted with SEDC (Simple Electric Deflection Calculator) in place of the FKC, to control 4in guns. Production was very limited, and the US Mark 63 was substituted in several British cruiser modernizations. MRS 7 was an equivalent system fro 4.5in gun control.

MRS 8 was a short-range system to replace earlier 40mm directors, using the existing Type 262Q or 262R radar.

Two related systems were:
— FPS (Flyplane System) 3 Mark 6 director with

Flyplane Mark 3 predictor, for full AA and surface control of 4.5in, in frigates.
— FPS 5. Same but with predictor Mark 5, for 4.5in and 5.25in guns. It would have been installed, for example, in modernized *Dido* class cruisers.

As an indication of the efficacy of these systems, maximum blind fire ranges could be calculated on the basis of radar accuracy and an assumed two per cent single-shot kill probability. FPS with a Type 275 radar would be effective at 3500 yards. MRS 3 with a 903 radar was considered effective at 5000 yards, and the greater accuracy of the 905 radar would make for an effective range as great as 10,000 yards.

In 1945, the Royal Navy had an elaborate stabilized twin 40mm mount in service (STAAG, the Stabilized Tachymetric AA Gun), and sought something simpler, which became the STD (Simple Tachymetric Director) widely installed postwar. A new Close Range Blind Fire (CRBF) system (using radar Type 262) was broadly comparable in performance to the US Mark 63 system, ie, with a limiting aircraft speed of about 500 rather than the prewar 340 mph.

The STD was limited to visual control of Bofors guns and 4in twin mounts, comparable therefore to the wartime US Mark 51. It was to have been succeeded by a Tachymetric One Man (TOM) director for 4.5in and smaller guns, fitted with a Type 908 range-only radar, and therefore broadly comparable to the wartime US Mark 52.

The number and type of guns and the number of directors determined the number of available anti-aircraft channels, ie, the number of aircraft the ship could expect to engage simultaneously. For example, in 1955, the British considered two twin 4.5in Mark 6 or one twin 6in Mark 26 were each sufficient to deal with one target, so in theory each represented the gun element of one channel, and each would be provided with its own director, which might be visual only, or radar range only, or full radar blind-fire, with radar tracking.

Guns themselves could be divided into four categories: close-range automatic guns, such as the 40mm Bofors; the pure heavy anti-aircraft gun; the dual purpose destroyer gun, a 4.5 or 5in weapon; and a dual purpose cruiser gun.

The US Navy ended World War II with a 20mm free-swinging machine gun, a 40mm power-operated machine cannon, a variety of 3in/50 dual purpose and anti-aircraft guns, 5in/38 and 5in/54 dual purpose destroyer and secondary battery guns, and a new 6in/47 twin dual purpose cruiser gun.

The only major weapons under development were an automatic 3in/70, roughly comparable in weight to a twin semi-automatic 5in/54, and a rapid-fire single 5in/54 of similar size. The 3in/70 was expected to be the better anti-aircraft weapon, the 5in/54 representing a compromise between anti-aircraft and anti-ship capabilities. The 5in/54 had originally been conceived as a direct successor to the semi-automatic prewar and wartime 5in/38, for the new generation of battleships (*Montana* class) and carriers (*Midway* class). Only the latter were completed. By 1944, a lighter-weight twin mount had been proposed for a new class of anti-aircraft cruisers, which again was not built. Postwar, BuOrd proposed a single automatic mount, weighing about as much as the twin mount and firing about as fast, but requiring many fewer crewmen. It replaced the twin mount in the postwar destroyer design, which became the *Mitscher*.

Both the 5in/54 and the 3in/70 were mechanically complex, and neither was entirely reliable. The 5in/54 was test-fired in 1950, and it did see mass-production and service. The 3in/70 was not available for service until 1956, and it appeared aboard only eight ships: the command cruiser *Northampton*, the ASW cruiser *Norfolk*, the four *Mitschers*, and the ASW destroyers *Carpenter* and *Robert A Owen*. It was always considered to be a terrible maintenance problem, and had a bad reputation in service.

From a theoretical point of view, however, the 3in/70 was the ideal anti-aircraft gun. Early postwar US thinking was based on the concept of the lethal grouping sufficient to deal with one air target: four 5in/38 (two twin) barrels. Postwar studies suggested that each of the new gun mounts, the single automatic 5in/54 and the twin automatic 3in/70, would be about twice as effective as a twin 5in/38. If two twin 5in/38 were rated as unity, then two single 5in/54 were rated as 1.5, and two twin 3in/70, 2.2.

As for larger calibres, there was limited interest in a new dual purpose 6in/47, as the existing mount (scheduled for installation in the *Worcester* class) was not considered entirely satisfactory, BuOrd seems also to have considered an 8in anti-aircraft gun, mounted in triple or even quadruple turrets, for installation aboard a large anti-aircraft ship, such as the ex-battleship *Kentucky*. Interest in weapons of calibre larger than 5in seems to have waned after about 1946, the Bureau retreating to consideration of a higher-velocity 5in, such as a 5in/70.

The 40mm twin and quadruple mounts were being replaced, respectively, by single and twin rapid-fire 3in/50s. These weapons, modifications of the existing semi-automatic dual purpose 3in/50, had been developed on an emergency basis to deal with Kamikazes, as they were the smallest calibre which could support a proximity (VT) fuze. Ironically, with the failure of the new 3in/70, they became the standard medium anti-aircraft cannon of the postwar US fleet. They became available to the Royal Navy under the Mutual Defense Assistance Program (MDAP), and thus were incorporated in such postwar projects as the new ocean minesweeper, early versions of the Type 42 mobilization frigates, the Type 62 converted air defense destroyer, and even the big cruiser/destroyer. They actually appeared only aboard the rebuilt carrier *Victorious*.

The US Navy considered the free-swinging 20mm much too light to be effective, but retained a few for their morale value. They were to have been replaced by a new weapon, sometimes described as a 35mm (on the basis of one new gun for each twin 20), but little actual work appears to have been done.

The Royal Navy ended the war with a greater variety of weapons. The 40mm close-range gun was replacing the existing 20mm and 2 pounder pom-pom. At the next step up were single and twin 4in dual purpose guns, no longer considered effective against fast aircraft. The twin 4.5in gun was roughly equivalent to the US 5in/38. At the upper end of the scale, a triple 6in cruiser mount (Mark 25) had just been abandoned in favor of a twin rapid-fire dual purpose Mark 26. It would not enter service until almost 15 years later on the three *Tiger* class cruisers.

Unlike the US Navy, the Royal Navy ended the war confident of the efficacy of the 40mm gun. Thus a new 40mm/70 ('L70'), in a variety of single, twin, and sextuple mounts, was a fixture of many postwar British designs. It never entered British naval service (although it did serve in the British Army), so the wartime 40mm/60 soldiered on.

As an indication of the importance of the 40mm

COMPARISON OF WEIGHTS (TONS) OF CRUISER GUN MOUNTINGS
plus incidentals and ammunition (ex fire control)

	Mark XXII	Mark XXIII	Mark XXIII	Mark XXIV triple	Mark XXI Twin	Mark XXVI Twin	5in/70 MCDP Twin	5in/70 MCDP Twin
	Southampton	*Belfast*	*Fiji*		*Arethusa*	*Tiger*	V A (Barrow)	V (Elswick) design
REVOLVING*	146	182	161	168	91 tons	152	189	113
OFF-MOUNTING**	41	28	28	34	25	40	69	86
AMMO (excluding cases)	46 (200 RPG)	44 (200)	44 (200)	41 (200)	28 (200)	79 (400)	53 (500)	66 (500)
Total	233	254	233	243	144	271	311	265 tons

* Includes ammunition in mounting
** Roller paths, hoists, stowages, etc

L70 to the postwar Royal Navy, in the fall of 1953 DGD proposed that it arm not only the second- and third-rate A/S frigates, but also the coastal frigate (Type 42) intended primarily as a gun platform, to fight aircraft and hostile fast attack boats. At this time the 40mm/70 (or L70) was credited with an effective surface range of 5000 yards. Surely, standardization of armament was well worthwhile. DGD argued that its high rate of fire would surely make up for the limited lethal effect of each round. The proposal foundered because existing 40mm rounds were ineffective against the ½in and ¼in plating characteristic of small surface craft and even of submarine superstructures. The alternatives considered at this time were a 3.3in (adapted 17 pounder tank gun) developed for coastal forces, and a variety of 4in weapons (Mark 19, Mark 25, and Vickers Venture); the 4in was adopted for the coastal frigate because a true dual purpose (anti-surface and anti-aircraft) gun was demanded.

World War II had impressed the Royal Navy with the need to guarantee its source of ammunition supply by standardizing with the US Navy. The Royal Navy therefore selected the 3in/70 gun as its new anti-aircraft weapon, although it used a very different (and, ultimately, much more successful) mounting.

Particularly in the case of the larger weapons, the phrase 'dual purpose' requires some elaboration. It was not enough for a gun to be able to fire at both high and low angles. Effective anti-aircraft operation required a combination of a high rate of fire and high muzzle velocity, both of which favored a small shell. However, surface fire required a substantial shell, fired, probably, at a lower rate. Moreover, the heavier the shell, the longer it would retain its initial velocity, so the longer its effective range. It was generally agreed that 3in shells were too light for effective surface fire, and that 6in was too heavy for rapid anti-aircraft fire. A 5in gun seemed a useful compromise; hence the US 5in/38 and 5in/54, and the British 5in/62 project.

The surface fire requirement also explains why the US Navy rejected an all-3in/70 battery for its first postwar destroyer, the *Mitscher*. The 3in/70 was clearly the best prospective anti-aircraft gun, but the CNO, Admiral Nimitz, argued that it would be useless against a surfaced submarine.

Unlike the US Navy, the Royal Navy ended the war expecting to build a new generation of major gun-armed ships (see Chapter 5). They might as well mount new weapons. The principal candidates were the new twin 6in Mark 26, which was approaching service, and an entirely new medium calibre dual purpose gun, which became the automatic 5in.

The table below (1948) shows just how large the expected new generation of cruiser main battery might be. The two 5in/70 columns show alternatives under consideration at the time. They were twin rapid-fire mounts; the later cruiser/destroyer was to have been armed first with a

single version and later with a twin version of lower individual gun performance.

The new British 5in gun was actually an outgrowth of a wartime plan to develop a new 5.25in gun for a projected class of light cruisers. Treasury approval was granted in July 1943 for two mountings, to compare all-electric and electro-hydraulic operation. Rates of fire as high as 24 rounds per gun per minute were claimed, using a new arrangement in which shell and cartridge were manhandled from hoist to ramming position. The previous rate of fire, eight rounds per gun per minute, would be doubled in controlled fire; this was not considered feasible, at least at high angles of elevation, for anything larger than a 5.25in.

Although the 5.25in cruiser project died in 1944, development of the new gun continued, on the theory that the Royal Navy might build such a ship postwar, and that, without it, there would be no modern dual purpose gun larger than the 4.5in. It was also being considered for use in the new battleship then being designed, if it proved impossible to mount the planned six twin 4.5in on each side. Similarly, the heavy dual purpose gun survived the cancellations at the end of the war, as the only other large gun was the rapid-fire twin 6in Mark 26, for large cruisers. The new mounting was clearly better than the existing 5.25in and it would also be less expensive to manufacture.

However, it would fire only 50 per cent faster than the prewar 5.25in. The Director of Naval Ordnance and various inter-service committees proposed an alternative, to apply the 'automatic gun' (machine gun) principle to a medium calibre weapon. In theory, a 5.25in could achieve 90 rounds per minute, although 50 – a 300-per cent improvement – seemed more likely in practice. This presumed a fast enough supply of ammunition.

By this time, the 5.25in calibre was no longer very important, since a new gun would require a new shell and cartridge. A requirement was written and approved in October 1947, for a gun capable of harassing aircraft at 15,000 yards. Ironically, British and US experiments would soon show that maneuvering targets could be almost sure of avoiding damage at ranges beyond 3000 yards. Such results greatly damaged the case for a heavy anti-aircraft gun. It would be better to fire shorter-range rounds at a higher rate.

As in the case of the 3in/70, it might be extremely important to use an American type of shell, for wartime supply. The British knew that BuOrd was working on a medium-calibre gun of its own, probably a 5in/70, and by June 1948 they were looking towards standardizing gun and ammunition with the US Navy, perhaps even using the existing US 5in/54. By February 1949, both navies had gone far enough to fix the calibre of a new weapon at 5in. The British sought a single mount suitable for a 2500-ton destroyer, roughly equivalent in size and weight to the existing twin 4.5in. For a time they also pursued a heavier twin mount suitable for a cruiser (as in the table above),

Girdle Ness was converted to test the Seaslug missile. She is shown in Malta in December 1961. Note the triple launcher, which appeared in early British Seaslug ship studies, but not in the County class destroyers. The big lens-like radar above her bridge was the Type 901 missile guidance set; the dish below was for missile telemetry. Her foremast carried a Type 293 narrow-beam (target indication) radar, and she had Type 960 on her lattice mainmast, with Types 982 and 983 below it, forming the pair usually considered a minimum for fighter control. The small antenna atop her fore topmast is the IFF associated with Type 293. Note that in the later photograph she has the bar-like IFF Mark X antenna beneath her Type 960 long-range air-search set. [*CPL*]

but it was ultimately abandoned in favor of the twin 6in gun already under development.

It was later suggested that the Royal Navy had first selected the 5in calibre on the basis of anti-aircraft considerations alone, in hopes of developing an FSDS (fin-stabilized discarding sabot) round for it. When this was abandoned the 5in calibre was retained in hopes of standardization with the USN.

Further studies showed that the US 5in/54 would not develop sufficient velocity for effective anti-aircraft fire, and the Royal Navy selected a 5in/62 in November 1951. It was expected to be superior to the 6in gun which had been selected to arm the rebuilt *Tiger* class cruisers. Moreover, no alternative was likely to be available before 1960.

However, it was not entirely clear that the new gun was worthwhile for it was a the very edge of what a gun could achieve. To achieve any substantial improvement over existing 4.5in guns (2500 ft/sec), muzzle velocity would have to increase to 3200 ft/sec, which in turn would require a light shell, whose velocity would fall off so rapidly that the older weapon's shell might reach the target in a comparable time – and it was time to target, not merely initial muzzle velocity, which counted. Moreover, the lighter shell would not be materially more lethal than that of the existing 4.5in; the 5in AA shell would weigh 58 pounds compared to 55 for the 4.5in.

High muzzle velocity would heat up a gun barrel as shells were fired in rapid succession. Depending on cooling arrangements, the gun might be unable to fire except in short bursts. In 1955, the Director of Gunnery Division argued that the 5in, as then proposed, would last only 30 minutes, compared to 120 for the 4.5in Mark 6. Even if the 4.5in was only half as effective in its

first engagement, it would last four times as long.

Nor was it clear that this was the proper ratio of effectiveness. Gun direction and fire control systems might be the main determinants of success against aircraft. For example, in a saturation or stream attack (eg, five aircraft at five second intervals), neither the 5in nor the 4.5in would be able to engage more than one of the five aircraft. It would be relatively unimportant that the 5in achieved its kill slightly more quickly, since even a perfect gun would be limited to one out of the five aircraft.

By 1952, the single 5in gun was in trouble. The combination of 60 rounds per minute and a very high muzzle velocity, then 3400 ft/sec, seemed to require unacceptable complications, in the form of fixed ammunition and water cooling. The Director of Gunnery (DGD) proposed a solution: a simplified twin mounting, each gun of which might fire at 40 rounds per minute, two-thirds of the required rate. Two twin mounts would provide slightly less than the output expected of the earlier and even riskier single mount. DGD expected to develop a new slower-firing single mount (comparable in rate of fire, it would seem, to the US 5in/54 Mark 42) for destroyers, which would mount two of them. A medium cruiser might mount three or, more likely, four.

The twin mount was not without complications. At very high muzzle velocities, the gun tube itself would heat so rapidly that a limit of 100 rounds at a time would have to be imposed, after which 100 more rounds could be fired after a five-minute pause. In a simplified version of the mounting, the rate of fire would be reduced to ten rounds per minute after the first 40.

True dual purpose operation required two kinds of shell: HE, for anti-aircraft fire, and HEP (HE

Piercing) for the anti-surface role. HEP was expected to pierce 1in NC plate at the minimum striking velocity at angles up to 50 degrees from the normal, carrying at least five pounds (eight per cent) of explosive charge. The mounting would have to be designed to switch rapidly from one type of shell to the other, perhaps with very little warning.

Like other large-calibre, rapid-fire guns, the new 5in would take its shells from a ready-use hopper, which in turn would have to be emptied, by firing, before it could be reloaded with an alternate type of shell. Or, the hopper could be filled with a mix of both types of shell, selecting the appropriate ones for loading while it cycled. This would add complexity and weight, in a ship already very tightly designed. The longer the required sustained burst, the larger the hopper – and the longer the delay in switching. For example, a ship expecting a night surface encounter would have her hoppers loaded with HEP. It would take at least two and a half to three minutes (70-round hopper) before being able to fire one burst at aircraft and at least five minutes before being ready for a full scale attack (maximum warning of attack by low flying aircraft might be as little as one to one and a half minutes or even less).

As early as 1949, the 5in gun had become the basis of a radical cruiser/destroyer design (see Chapter 5). When the light cruiser was cancelled in September 1953, the gun followed.

At this time the British Army was developing its own Vickers-designed medium calibre anti-aircraft gun, a 5in/56, which was briefly considered as an alternative to the Navy's 5in/62. It died in the Radical Review.

It was not quite dead, however. The Royal Navy was still developing a missile cruiser. In the absence of a new medium-calibre gun, it would have to be armed either with the 3in/70, or the existing twin 4.5in destroyer gun, or with the much heavier twin 6in cruiser gun. Since the gun was needed partly for shore bombardment and partly to deal with enemy surface ships, the 3in/70 was clearly out. The 6in was very large, and seemed to drive ship size up unduly.

What of a revived 5in? A twin 5in could deal with destroyers and lesser craft, and it certainly seemed better than the much-maligned 4.5in. However, it would take too long to develop. Nor was there enough money, in 1955, to start a new major gun project. Guided missiles were desperately needed to deal with a rapidly escalating air threat, and, DGD argued, 'we will be fully extended, with the money and effort available, getting these into service in time.' The new gun would encounter its own teething troubles in a ship already burdened with the prototype anti-aircraft guided missile.

Perhaps worst of all from the point of view of economy, the twin 5in would probably weigh about twice as much as the existing twin 4.5in Mark 6, and therefore would be suitable only for a few large ships. The 4.5in would have to soldier on.

The 5in project was not entirely wasted. After the demise of the twin mount, Vickers applied some of the same design ideas to a new Army medium-calibre mobile mounting (the 5in/56) and then to a private-venture 4in naval gun. Both differed from more conventional guns in using through-trunnion loading: the breech was carried forward of the trunnions, the two ammunition hoppers behind it. DNO objected that this would make for greater inertia in the mounting (ie, for a longer rotating mass), hence for slower power elevation and train. Vickers' reply was that the through-trunnion scheme had actually originated with the Mark M, the two-pounder pom-pom so widely mounted in the prewar and wartime British fleet.

Although the new Vickers weapon was initially designed for export, the company hoped that it would be adopted for the Type 42 East Coast gunboat (Chapter 6). It used a standard British 4in Mk 16** gun (2650 ft/sec). With 56 rounds in hoppers elevating with the gun, Vickers claimed 50 rounds per minute (48 rounds per minute had already been achieved in the Army mounting, using a 4in gun). The Director of Naval Ordnance was skeptical; the existing twin 4in Mark 19 could be fired at 40 rounds per minute at elevations as high as 50 degrees, using a new 'Canadian [gun loading] drill'. The older mounting weighed two to three tons less, in fact, than Vickers claimed on paper. The Royal Navy therefore never adopted the new gun, although for a time it was being considered for the Type 42 frigate.

Vickers was more interested in the export market. Potential customers included Argentina (to rearm the cruiser La Argentina), Chile, Israel (for a 1200-ton frigate proposed by the Italian CNT yard), Peru, and Venezuela. Vickers planned to offer it as a dual purpose companion weapon to a conventional 4.7in gun in a 2600-ton destroyer it was designing for export. Ultimately, the new 4in

Girdle Ness embodied the missile handling system originally designed for the British missile cruisers described in Chapter 5, rather than the single-level (straight-through) system actually installed aboard County class destroyers. This photograph, of a scale model of the loading system (at Vickers-Armstrong Elswick, Newcastle), shows the below-decks tilting bucket which would carry a missile across from the ready-use space at the right. The arrow at the right indicates a chain rammer. When the bucket tilted, as here, a rammer underneath could carry the missile in it up to the launcher above (arrow at left). The magazine was below the ready-use space, at the right. [NMM]

This photograph of the model shows the magazines themselves, with the tilting bucket at the left. The missiles are stowed three deep and three across (for the triple launcher) in two magazines, forward and center, each on its own trolley. The lift, at the right, with the human figure on it, separates the forward and center magazines from an after magazine. Missiles are checked out in the lift space, and duds are sent forward of the tilting bucket into a discard space not visible here. Note that other early missile systems, such as the US Terrier in the first two US missile cruisers, also incorporated checkout spaces and some means of discarding duds without jamming the loading cycle. [*NMM*]

mount was bought only by Chile, and it formed the main (gun) battery of two Vickers-built destroyers of about 2730 tons standard: *Almirante Riveros* and *Almirante Williams*, each of which carried four of the mountings.

The other major early Western postwar gun developers were the Swedish firm of Bofors (which had been responsible for the classic wartime 40mm anti-aircraft gun) and the French Navy. At the end of the war Bofors was developing a 70-calibre version of its 40mm gun (the wartime weapon was 60 calibres), as well as a successor, a twin 57mm/60 machine cannon conceived as intermediate between the 40mm/70 and the usual 4.7in destroyer gun. It was also producing a 120mm (4.7in) twin cannon for destroyers, and a 6in cruiser gun.

The automatic 4.7in/50 was conceived in 1944 as a successor to the 57mm gun in the Bofors family of automatic weapons. Bofors tried horizontal and vertical fan feeds (as in the smaller gun) before setting on a swinging pendulum, largely to permit rapid shifts between different types of ammunition. It achieved 43 rounds per minute, but was quite bulky at 62 tons and, reportedly, noisy. Nor was it water or flash tight. Even so, in 1952 the US Navy's Bureau of Ordnance considered it the best long-range anti-aircraft gun in Europe. The twin automatic 4.7in gun was adopted only by the Swedish and Dutch navies. The Royal Navy considered it in about 1952 as an alternative to the twin 4.5in but rejected it as too expensive to 'anglicize'.

In about 1955, the Swedish Admiralty planned a single 4.7in automatic gun (60 rounds per minute) for future destroyers. Bofors adapted its existing army automatic gun (120mm/46, 75 rounds per minute), but Swedish defense policy changed away from maintaining major surface ships before any ships mounting it could be laid down.

At the end of the war, the French Navy possessed far too wide a variety of weapons. For example, a list prepared about ten years after the war showed two different 3.9in/45, a 3.9in/50, a new automatic 3.9in; two different 4.1in/45, a 4.7in/45, a 5in/45 (German), a 5in/54, a 5.5in/50, and a 5.5in/55, among others. The only escape was

to be found in standardization on a very few calibres: a 5in gun, ammunition for which the United States Navy could produce in quantity; a 100mm (3.9in) intermediate weapon suitable for frigates; and a 57mm anti-aircraft gun, using the Bofors mechanism in a new four-axis stabilized mount, the first in the West (other navies stabilized tri-axially).

The postwar twin 5in/54 was developed from a design originally intended for a 5.1in (130mm) gun. Unlike the US Mark 42, it was semi-automatic, so that two barrels were required for approximately the same rate of fire, about 36 rounds per minute in the French case. Thus it corresponded to wartime US projects for twin semi-automatic 5in/54s, or to the single semi-automatic mounts aboard *Midway* class carriers. Elevation was limited to 70 degrees to avoid any requirement for a gun pit, and so to reduce the deck penetration of the mount. Development was completed in 1951.

Only the automatic 100mm (1953) continued a traditional French calibre. It fired the same ammunition as the 1945 model gun mounted in the battleship *Jean Bart*, and it was developed in preference to a twin fully automatic 4.1in/60 (105mm) gun, which would have used German-type ammunition. Comparable in weight and power requirement to the twin 57mm gun, it was developed as a replacement. The larger calibre was attractive partly because it was suitable for shore bombardment as well as or anti-aircraft fire. The French Navy had to be able to fight cold wars quite as much as hot ones. A similar theme is evident in French ASW weaponry.

*   *   *

Anti-Aircraft Missiles

The missile differed from the gun, either existing or planned, in two vital ways. First, it was no longer truly dual purpose, in that it was no longer particularly effective against ship targets. For example, anti-ship capability in the projected US Typhon system (about 1963) was equated with the use of a nuclear warhead, whereas non-nuclear Typhons were considered perfectly effective against aircraft. Nor would missiles be useful in shore bombardment, at least outside a nuclear context. To replace guns by missiles, then, implied a larger shift in the capability of navies, particularly in the sort of minor peacetime naval operations in which the Royal Navy had specialized.

Second, the missile had very different limitations. Since it relied on aerodynamic controls, it was ineffective until it had accelerated to some considerable speed, perhaps at a range well beyond 2000 yards. It could, therefore, be argued that it became effective at just about the range at which conventional guns lost their efficacy. Beyond the point of minimum effective range, however, missile effectiveness generally increased considerably, limited only by the

accuracy of the missile guidance system and then, ultimately, by the exhaustion either of fuel or, in the case of a boost-glide missile, momentum. This consideration explains why virtually all modern close-in defensive weapon systems (such as the Dutch Goalkeeper or the US Phalanx) rely on rapid-fire guns. The only way to control a missile before it reaches high velocity is by placing vanes in the jet stream of its motor, and to date that has been done only to pitch vertically-launched weapons over to their cruise trajectories, not to maneuver them into targets.

Like gun weapon systems, missiles were limited in the number of targets they could engage simultaneously; one missile guidance radar (or channel) per target. Often, given limited expectations of missile reliability, each director would be provided with more than one missile launching rail, in which case it was one missile *launcher* per guidance channel. Saturation was therefore always a problem.

In the case of the British Seaslug, it appeared that the production rate of missile guidance systems would be so limited that to require two per cruiser (a 'double-headed' system) might preclude installations in a planned class of missile-armed convoy escorts. Such considerations go far to explain the British choice of single-ended area defense missile ships.* The US electronics industry suffered from no such limitations, and designs like the double-ended *Albany* resulted. In their case the number of missile guidance channels was limited by a combination of topweight and

* Most of the missile ship design studies (see Chapter 5) show only a single guidance radar, and the 'Counties,' which were the only outcome of the design program, had only one. However, note that their successors, the Sea Dart ships, all have two directors for their one launcher.

fear of electronic interference. For example, around about 1956 a proposed missile conversion of the large cruiser *Alaska* was abandoned because, due to expected interference between guidance channels, it would not have been able to accommodate more launchers or channels than a converted heavy cruiser half its size.

Perhaps most importantly, the missile changed the traditional balance between long-range fighter interception and close-in defense by shipboard weapons. At first, it was seen as a means of defending the fleet in weather so bad that fleet fighters would be unable to fly. After all, in 1945, carrier-based night fighters were still relatively rare. No fleet could operate aircraft on anything approaching an all-weather basis, and the worse the expected weather, the less the expected effectiveness of carrier fighters. To fight the Soviets in the north would be practically to seek out such unflyable weather. Hence the intense interest in anti-aircraft missiles, which could (in theory) continue to operate in even the worst weather.

The range of first-generation missiles, 20,000 (the US Terrier) to 30,000 (the British Seaslug) yards, was predicated on the effective range of wartime German anti-ship air-to-surface missiles, perhaps 10 nm (20,000 yards). This was still far less than the normal distance out to a combat air patrol station. However, by 1955, the US Talos was flying out to 100,000 yards (50 nm). It would soon fly 130,000 yards, and its developers hoped for a range of 100 nm (200,000 yards). In its final version, Talos achieved a range of 125 nm (250,000 yards). Terrier range was also expected to double. Ship-launched missiles might then fly into the fighter interception zone. Such performance was needed to match the first Soviet anti-ship stand-off missile, Komet. However, it suggested to some

Devonshire fires her Seaslug for the first time, May 1962. At this point the four wrap-around boosters are still attached to the missile. The high freeboard of the ship is largely due to the long missile stowage hangar worked under the weather deck. [CPL]

that a fleet might defend itself more by missile than by fighter. Fighters might be reserved for missions requiring them to investigate distant contacts, such as possible snoopers supporting submarine operations. Thus, the US LRO hoped to increase carrier attack firepower by replacing some carrier fighters with missiles. Alternatively, the sheer size of the carrier could be reduced, if big attack bombers and heavy fighters no longer had to be operated.

Similarly, quite early in the development of Seaslug ship designs, some British officers suggested that the missiles might ultimately supplant the carrier-based fighter altogether. If the carrier existed largely to provide fighter cover, the transition to an all-missile air defense might allow considerable savings.

In fact, missiles were not nearly so effective as had been expected. Not only did the United States retain heavy carriers, it reached the point where a fighter, the F-14, represented by far the greatest demand on carrier facilities. As for the Royal Navy, one of the surprises of the Falklands War was that the few carrier-based Sea Harrier fighters destroyed many more Argentine aircraft than did

ship-based missiles. Yet the Sea Harrier had been designed for long-range interception, precisely on the theory that missiles would account for most short-range fleet air defense requirements.

The predictions of the demise of the manned fighter really typify the 'fifties. It seemed that the new electronic technology could solve any problem, and that robot warfare was very nearly at hand. Murphy's Law had been repealed. Only after the magical new systems had entered service did it become obvious that they did not always perform as expected. Radars did not always detect targets, and missiles often failed to fire as expected. Perhaps the most celebrated incident of this type was a firepower display arranged for President Kennedy off the US East Coast in 1961, in which a propeller-driven target airplane flew towards the fleet. Three Terriers were fired in succession. By the time the third had missed, the drone was well within attack range. Reportedly, the President personally ordered the Navy to install 5in guns aboard ships previously intended for all-missile armament, such as the nuclear cruiser *Long Beach*. The fighters survived for much the same reason. When all else failed, their pilots

The box-like standard twin Seaslug launcher is shown aboard *Hampshire*, at the John Brown shipyard, March 1963. A blast door leading into the missile magazine is visible on the left. [*CPL*]

could still see and attack. Even now, in an age of much more reliable electronics, the US Navy values its F-14s because they can operate effectively even when communication to their radar control aircraft (E-2s) and to their carriers is cut off, either by distance or by jamming.

In a larger sense, in both countries, naval anti-aircraft missiles competed with other missile programs for a share of a very limited pool of specialized technical capability. Both countries were therefore forced to review missile programs on a multi-service basis, both to avoid duplication and to set priorities. The latter in turn were related to the evolving concept of modern warfare described in the previous chapter. In the United States, this occurred in 1949. In Britain, the Ministry of Supply, established in wartime to produce aircraft, appeared to be the natural choice for an overall missile development agency. Land-based air defense missiles, such as the US Nike, clearly came first. In neither country were they adapted for naval service, although the British Army considered buying Seaslug, the US Marines briefly adopted Terrier and the US Army came close to buying Talos.

The Soviets and the French, who have cross-service development and production organizations, actually do use the same weapons on land and sea: the French point defense weapon, Crotale Naval, was originally developed for land service. At the time of writing, moreover, the principal next-generation French naval surface to air weapon, SAAM, is being developed as part of a tri-service program. Most Soviet naval surface-to-air missiles are derived from land-based equivalents.

The early missiles presented severe ship design problems, not least because they (and their guidance and handling equipment) changed several times between the initial design stage and entry into service. After all, they represented the fusion of several new and radical technologies.

The US systems, Terrier and Talos, began development in 1944, as Project Bumblebee, which was conceived as a ramjet. In 1949, however, in view of the urgency of the fleet air defense problem, the solid-fuelled Supersonic Test Vehicle (STV) developed as part of the Bumblebee program was ordered developed into a weapon. It became Terrier, which actually preceded the planned Bumblebee missile (Talos) into service. The two missiles shared some guidance systems, but otherwise were quite different, and required quite distinct handling systems.

Seaslug was conceived in November 1943, presumably as a result of the painful lessons of stand-off attacks at Salerno. It was initially designated GAP, the Guided Anti-Aircraft Projectile. A firm design was expected by October 1946. However, in the postwar run-down of the Ministry of Supply, work was transferred from Westcott, where it had begun, to Farnborough. Many in the design team, including its chief, resigned rather than move, and work was virtually

suspended until 1948. Although it was scheduled for service introduction by 1956 under the postwar Ten Year Rule, Seaslug was only tested aboard the converted auxiliary *Girdle Ness* in 1958, and entered service aboard the County class in 1962. In 1954, the working party on the introduction of guided missiles into the Royal Navy had estimated that it would not enter service before 1960 or 1961, based on an average ten- to twelve-year development time, and dating the project from 1948.

Missiles affected a ship on three distinct levels: guidance (which often determined topside arrangement), stowage, and handling safety. The ship designers had to contend with a long series of unpleasant surprises and dead ends. For example, Seaslug went through three distinct types of propulsion. As of October 1945 it was assumed that it would be either a ramjet or a liquid-fuelled rocket, in either case with a cordite booster in tandem. The ramjet, which was soon rejected, at least presented no safety problem. However, it appeared that the rocket would use liquid oxygen and gasoline, both considered completely unacceptable for ship use. However, by 1949 these had been replaced by Kerosene and Red Fuming Nitric Acid, which were considered stable enough for missiles to be maintained, already fuelled, in magazine stowage as ready rounds. The missile was actually tested in this form, but operational rounds were solid-fuelled. The US Terrier was sold-fuelled from inception, since it began as a sold-fuelled Supersonic Test Vehicle for the Bumblebee (Talos) program; Talos, however, was a liquid-fuelled ramjet.

One reason the 1956 date could not be met for Seaslug was that dimensions could not be fixed in time. The earliest sketches showed a large bi-fuel, non-boosted rocket. Boosters were then added, and early in 1948 Seaslug was described as a boosted bi-fuel rocket, 20ft long, 16in in diameter, with a wing span of 4ft 10in (58in). However, there was some hope that it might shrink appreciably. The RAE, which was developing it, suggested a length of only 15ft, a diameter of 12in, and a wing span of 3ft, 7½in (43½in), which, unfortunately, turned out to be optimistic. Worse, to meet the required service date of 1956, launch and guidance methods would have to be fixed by January 1948. That February, a Seaslug re-assessment assumed that the best method of guidance and control could not be determined for at least another two years. The solution was to have industry (in this case, Armstrong Whitworth) develop a beam-riding Seaslug Mark II while work continued on what was hoped would be an optimum Mark III. By 1950, dimensions had been set once again: a length of 19ft, 6in, a diameter of 16in, and a maximum wing span of 63in. Of the all-up weight of 3700 pounds, 200 pounds would be warhead. This was substantially larger than the dimensions previously assumed. Even that, however, was not enough. By 1955, the missile (with a solid-fuel sustainer, inherently larger than the earlier liquid

The postwar British concept of ASW combined a medium-range mortar (Limbo) with longer-range torpedo tubes, firing a homing torpedo, BIDDER. Few ships were actually fitted with the planned torpedo tubes, however. *Blackpool*, a Type 12 anti-submarine frigate, shows six of her 12 tubes (four singles and a pair) in this photograph taken on 14 August 1958. Her Limbo is hidden in the well at the after end of her forecastle. She carries a high-frequency (radio) direction finder atop her foremast, with the small horns of a UHF/DF system below it. The big 'cheese' antenna is Type 293, for short-range air search; the small one, 974, is the high definition surface search (HDWS) navigation and periscope-detection set. The antenna in gymbals is 277Q, used as a stabilized surface search set aboard frigates. The horizontal bar on her short mainmast is an independent IFF antenna. 'Candlesticks' at her yardarms, fore and aft, are shortwave radio antennas. [*MoD*]

rocket) was expected to weigh 4200 pounds, with a length of 20ft. A year later, however, the Mark I missile was 21ft long with a 67in span, and missile stowage in the cruiser design had to be redesigned to match.

Stowage and launching systems had to be designed together to accommodate a missile whose dimensions were ill-defined at best. Moreover, both navies expected to replace their existing weapons with more advanced ones, hopefully at minimum cost in ship modification. The US *Cleveland* class missile cruiser conversions were designed with replacement of Terrier by Talos in mind. The abortive British Seaslug cruiser was designed to accept one of a variety of proposed long-range guided weapons or Phase 2 weapons. The British favored horizontal stowage almost from the start, reportedly because it reduced shock loads. Although the earliest American installation, on the *Boston* and *Canberra*, was vertical, it was unique, and all later missile cruisers employed horizontal stowage for their long boosted weapons. The British DNC argued at the time that vertical stowage led to undesirably large spaces in the ship; in the case of Seaslug such spaces would be three whole decks deep and this he considered highly undesirable – particularly near one end of the ship – for damage control reasons. In addition, the US handling system left no room for a 'lock' between magazine and launcher. Consequently, during loading the magazine was wide open to the weather. He argued that the US decision to go to horizontal stowage for later cruisers proved these points.

However, the two navies differed on missile configuration, which was chosen with stowage

arrangements in mind. Seaslug was to be stowed complete to achieve the required rate of fire. A 1948 DNC study showed that in this case it was best to stow the missiles horizontally, wrapping the boosters around them to minimize their length. This would not affect their other dimensions, since their fins would still protrude. It was assumed that assembly of missiles broken down in any way would greatly reduce the rate of fire. DNC did note that, were the missiles to be broken down (eg, with their fins removed) for stowage, tandem-boosted missiles (like the US Terrier and Talos) stowed horizontally would be most economical of space. The US Navy came to the opposite conclusion, that it would be extremely easy for crewmen to fit fins in the few seconds before a missile was rammed onto its launcher.

It is difficult to compare magazine volumes in terms of missile numbers, since so much depended on just how the volume was used. At one point, for example, it was argued that a magazine for 48 Seaslugs could accommodate no more than 20 or 30 Talos, since the US missile was much longer than the British one. On the other hand, in 1956, when the British missile cruiser magazine held 64 Seaslugs, that figure was equated to 124 Terrier, 64 Talos, or to 22 of a new long-range guided weapon, Blue Envoy (the Bristol Bloodhound 3, also described as the Stage 1¾ missile), with its wing tips detached and boost fins hinged down; or to ten Blue Envoy complete with wing tips but with boost fins hinged down. The Blue Envoy figure was particularly important because, given the expected life of the missile cruiser, it would have to be able to accept

In the Royal Navy, the helicopter-delivered torpedo replaced the abortive long-range ship-launched homing weapon. The MATCH (Medium-Range Anti-Submarine Torpedo Carrying Helicopter) helicopter was coached into position by the ship which launched it, and carried no anti-submarine sensor of its own. However, unlike the unmanned drone (DASH) developed for the same role by the US Navy, it can also direct gunfire, identify other ships, and carry a light anti-ship missile (AS-12, which was fired by Wasps at the Argentine submarine *Santa Fe* in the South Atlantic in 1982). Here, the first such helicopter, a Westland Wasp, is tested on a special rolling platform (designed to simulate ship motion) at RAE Bedford, February 1963. The current Lynx adds a Seaspray sea-search radar (to assist in making anti-ship missile attacks), but no ASW sensor. Like the Wasp, it can carry two torpedoes. [*CPL*]

modification to fire the follow-on weapon. However, by late 1956 it was no longer clear just what that follow-on would be.

At that time the Royal Navy was considering adopting a large land-based surface-to-air missile, Red Shoes/Green Flax (Thunderbird, the Stage 1½ missile). The space allowed for 64 Seaslug would take 25 assembled Green Flax plus 70 broken down, as against 10 to 20 Blue Envoy. Green Flax was attractive because it could be assembled in a matter of minutes, and therefore could be stowed in the broken-down condition. Although only 48 fully-assembled weapons could be carried, 64 could be carried if they were assembled except for their boost fins. Note that, unlike Seaslug, Blue Envoy and Thunderbird (Green Flax) were semi-actively guided. They would thus have qualified for longer-range status, since the accuracy of semi-active guidance increases as the missile nears the target. Beam-riding has the opposite performance.

The other alternative was a much-improved Seaslug, which might use existing shipboard equipment, and which was ultimately built as Mark 2. The missile handling gear had been designed to allow, from the first, for an increase in missile size. Of the two new weapons, Controller preferred Green Flax to Blue Envoy, but there was some question as to how much of an improvement it would represent. It was, after all, a land-based weapon which would have to be navalized. Since it was most unlikely that the Navy would find

sufficient funds for all three, the Director of Naval Ordnance proposed that effort be concentrated on only two, an improved Seaslug and a long-range weapon such as Blue Envoy. Blue Envoy offered much better long-range performance than Green Flax. It was, however, only in the research stage, and might not materialize until 1963. In the end it was cancelled in 1961.

Green Flax was expected to exceed Seaslug performance in some ways, but to be inferior in others. Like Seaslug, it had wrap-around boosters. By 1956, the Navy was already pressing for an American-type tandem-boosted missile as its next-generation weapon. Moreover, if Seaslug were to be retained for the missile destroyer, then Green Flax would be an undesirable complication. It would not be the long-awaited long-range guided weapon.

Then there was the launcher itself. Both the British and the early American missiles were beam-riders; the weapon had to be fired into the beam, which would 'capture' it and then guide it. At first the British expected to fire their weapons vertically from fixed launchers, but beam-riding actually required that the launcher be capable of train and elevation.

The British initially opted for a triple launcher, which was actually fitted to the experimental *Girdle Ness*. It was assumed that the three barrels of a triple launcher would elevate independently. Loading space would be either trainable or fixed. If trainable, it would carry six missiles for vertical ramming to the launcher. If fixed, the launcher would train to a fixed bearing for loading. There would be a magazine in which unfuelled missiles would be stowed; a testing space; a lay apart space for unserviceable missiles; and a ready use space where missiles would be filled and held ready for firing.

As the design developed, this elaborate system was drastically simplified. British observers of US practice noted that US weapons were maintained as ready-use rounds, and that the testing space was abandoned: dud missiles on the launcher arms were simply disposed of. The shifts to stowable liquid fuel, and then to solid fuel, eliminated some magazine stowage. In addition, the operational launcher was a twin-arm device in which both arms elevated together.

One issue here was the appropriate match between rate of fire and the number of guidance channels. A director would have to track the target throughout each missile engagement. Top weight in turn limited the number of directors, probably to two per launcher (and in many studies to only one). Loading would be fast enough to cope with the resulting rate of fire. That is, at Mach 2 an anti-aircraft missile would travel about 20,000 yards (ie, to approximately full range) in 30 seconds, which would be a reasonable approximation of reloading time. There was no point in firing faster than the system as a whole

could operate. Note that in the case of the US Talos, which had a much longer range (65nm and ultimately 125nm), multiple directors had to be provided, as otherwise the effective rate of fire would be far too slow.

On a subtler level, the missiles and their radar systems required much more electric power, and many more technicians. The electric problem was particularly severe for the Royal Navy, which in the past had relied on hydraulic power in its turrets. Thus the removal of, say, a battleship's 14in turret provided weight and space but no great increase in available electrical power. By way of contrast, the US Navy used electrical power almost exclusively in its gun mounts, and therefore had greater margins of available power in its existing ships.

Power requirements were so severe that in some cases lightweight gas turbines were used. For example, the British missile cruiser of 1956 was to have had four 1500kW steam turb-generators, as well as one 1250kW and one 500kW gas turbine. The action load requirement was to maintain the power-hungry missile system even when one of the two steam units was disabled. That would cost 5100kW, but only 4750kW would be available. The obvious solution, 2000kW steam turbo-generators, had to be rejected because it would require more boiler capacity, hence larger boiler spaces and a larger ship. Even gas turbines presented

Plymouth, a *Rothesay* (modified *Whitby*) type frigate, illustrates the effect of the helicopter torpedo delivery system. She was rebuilt in 1966-68, followed by the rest of the class. The small hangar and helipad have cost one of the two medium-range Limbos. Note, too, the elimination of the heavy 4.5in director of the earlier ship in favor of MRS3, and the elimination of the big 277Q surface search/height finding set. The quadruple Seacat short-range missile launcher, to replace the earlier twin (STAAG) 40mm gun, was included in the design from the beginning. However, due to delays in the Seacat program, all the ships of this class carried single 40mm guns aft for some years. [*USNI*]

TABLE 3-1: ASW SENSORS AND WEAPONS

NOMINAL RANGE	US	British	
2500 YARDS	QHB/ALFA	170/LIMBO	
5000 YARDS	SQS-4/MK 37	177/BIDDER	TORPEDO
	/DASH	/MATCH	HELICOPTER
	/RAT		MISSILE
10,000 YARDS	SQS-23/ASROC	184/IKARA	MISSILE

NOTES: Bidder was an unsuccessful British ship-launched long-range homing torpedo. Its failure left ships with a long-range sonar (177) but no weapon of sufficient range to exploit it. Hence the importance of MATCH, which first appeared in the Tribal class frigates. It is also the primary long-range attack weapon of *Leanders* and modified *Rothesays*. DASH and MATCH are often associated with the longer-range sonars, and the US Navy planned at one time to provide Mark 48 torpedoes for surface ships equipped with the even longer-range SQS-26.

In the cases both of MATCH and of DASH, the hull sonar was often supplemented by a variable-depth sonar, an independent Type 199 in the British case and a separate unit operating from the same stack (transmitter) in the US case.

The mortars generally required three-dimensional information. In the British case, Type 170 was used in early postwar ships both for search and for fire control. The US Navy preferred separate sets (QHB and SQG-1). Later British installations combined the long-range 177 (and later the 184) with the 170 acting as an attack set at short range.

problems, with their voluminous uptakes for both air intake and gas exhaust. Had the ship been built, she would have had a 750kW gas turbine aft and a 1500 or even a 1750kW unit forward.

Accommodation was a problem in both navies. However, the Royal Navy suffered particularly badly, because it suddenly had to increase not merely the numbers aboard but also the standard of accommodation. Towards the end of the war, messing arrangements had been changed to American-style centralized messing, at a cost in sleeping space, and postwar there were additional improvements in comfort, which were reflected in demands for space. These demands collided with the increased space demands of the new radars and weapons, to force up the prospective size of any British missile ship. Thus the history of the ultimately abortive British missile cruiser design shows, again and again, substantial increases in displacement due largely to the need to accommodate the full complement of the ship.

Perhaps the greatest surprise of the missile era was how few weapons could be carried. All of the early anti-aircraft missiles were much larger than the shells they replaced. Where a ship might carry 400-600 rounds for each of six guns (at one end), for a total of 2400-3600, an even larger physical area of ship might support no more than 50 or 100 anti-aircraft missiles.

Limited missile numbers made replenishment at sea even more important than it had been in the past. Yet sheer missile size made it extremely difficult, and increased the pressure to have more weapons. Moreover, around about 1954 the Royal Navy began to emphasize the new strategic concept of 'broken backed war', in which ships would have to operate at sea for an extended period (generally about 30 days) after the destruction of their bases, relying on underway replenishment alone. Ammunition endurance had never previously been studied, probably because

gun ammunition had generally not been a limiting factor in endurance. It would be virtually impossible to replenish four ton missiles at sea; the British concluded that the number of missiles, rather than fuel, would define endurance. They therefore decided, despite serious consequences in terms of ship cost, to increase the magazine capacity of their new missile cruiser by a third, from 48-64 weapons, in 1955. The US Navy did try to allow for replenishment, in the form of massive king posts and special ammunition-handling rigs.

Underwater Sensors and Weapons

World War II sonars, such as the US QC series and the British Asdic Type 128, were 'searchlights', projecting a focused beam of sound in one direction. The operator typically waited long enough for an echo to return before searching on another bearing. A fast-moving ship would enjoy only very incomplete coverage, because of the time lag between returns to the same bearing. Typically, then, sonars did not detect submarines before they attacked. Rather, they were a means of maintaining contact once the general location of a submarine had been revealed by, for example, a torpedo track. Sonar data, moreover, could be used for what amounted to fire control, either for depth charges or for ahead-thrown weapons such as Hedgehog or Squid.

The principal wartime developments were means of assuring that contact could be maintained or devices to improve the precision of fire control data. For example, the sonar beam could be split, and the echoes in the two beams compared. When they matched, the sonar searchlight was pointed directly at the target. The returns of the two beams could be compared continuously to generate tracking commands. Postwar, the Royal Navy introduced Four-Square, an attack (fire control) sonar which used this

The French E-50 class ocean escort *Le Bordelais* originally had an ASW battery limited to torpedoes, with a reload magazine between the sets of tubes, firing K2 and L3 torpedoes, on either side of the ship. The turbine-propelled K2 had a range of about 1000 meters at 50 knots; it was intended to be fired in salvoes of three (hence the triple tubes) against diesel-electric submarines at depths as great as 300 meters (about 1000ft). The warhead weighed 280 kilograms. From its introduction in 1956 to 1961 it was the principal French surface-fired ASW weapon. It was not retired until 1976. The L3, work on which had begun about a dozen years earlier, entered service in 1961. It had a 200 kilogram warhead, and a range of 5000 meters at 25.5 knots. Note the 375mm Bofors ASW mortar aft, just forward of the after director. It was added in the late 'fifties, replacing two K-guns. Note that the French E50, E52A and E52B class escorts all shared common hull and machinery plants. *Le Bordelais* was stricken in 1975. [*CPL*]

technique to track both in bearing and in elevation (ie, depth). Most sonars generated beams pointing down at a shallow angle, leaving a blind cone ('shadow zone') under a ship. The deeper the submarine, the greater the range at which it would pass into this cone. The solution was to tilt the sonar transducer, a device known as Maintenance of Close Contact (MCC) in the US Navy. The earliest example was the late-war QGB installed in *Sumner* and *Gearing* class destroyers.

A tilting transducer could also be used to determine target depth (actually target angle of depression). Such data became more important as ballistic underwater weapons gained range, ie, as the precision of fire control became more important. Postwar, for example, US ships equipped with Weapon Alfa typically had two sonars in separate domes: a search sonar such as QHB and a tilting fire control or attack sonar such as SQG-1.

The ultimate goal was always a sonar combining long range with a very high probability of detecting any submarine passing within that range. The US approach was *scanning*. The QHB sonar consisted of a ring of transducers. Its ping travelled outward in all directions, while a receiver revolved rapidly, scanning through all directions during a period of time shorter than each ping. As a result, any returning echo would be detected. In effect, QHB stared out in all directions simultaneously. It was the direct predecessor of all modern US sonars.

The other major issue was range itself. Many wartime sonars were calibrated for ranges of 5000 yards or more, but in fact they rarely detected targets beyond about 2500. That was particularly

unfortunate when submarines could fire their guided or pattern-running torpedoes from as much as 10,000 yards. In October 1948, the British First Sea Lord argued that this disparity made some means of destroying incoming torpedoes essential. He hoped for a weapon with a range of about 700 yards, automatically discharged. Fortunately, sonar range could increase dramatically at lower frequencies (which in turn demanded larger transducers for their correspondingly longer wave length and larger domes). The other major countermeasure was to silence ships so that submarines could not fire from such great ranges. British analysis suggested that silencing could halve submarine passive detection range – which still left the submarine beyond destroyer sonar range. It was still essential, then, to develop some means of destroying incoming torpedoes.

The US view was that fixed scanning transducers were particularly easy to enlarge, since there was no need to train them. QHB operated at about 25kc (kilocycles per second, now often denoted Kilo Hertz, or KHz), with a nominal range of about 2500 yards or less. The next US set, SQS-4, operated at about 10kc, and was credited with a nominal range of 5000 yards. This was sufficient to make stand-off attacks worthwhile. For a time SQS-4 was associated with a rocket-assisted torpedo called RAT.

SQS-4 was also associate with two other weapons: the ship-launched Mark 37 homing torpedo and a lightweight homing torpedo delivered by a drone helicopter, DASH. The long-range Mark 37 might, then, be considered an all-weather (albeit much slower) alternative to the

F 764

relatively fast DASH. It also proved considerably more reliable, since DASH had very little in the way of feedback. In each case, effective range was limited by the speed of delivery, since contact with a fast, violently evasive nuclear submarine might be expected to be intermittent at best.* More generally, weapon range can be associated with sensor development. Table 3-1 shows parallel US and British sensors and their associated weapons. MATCH (Medium-range Anti-submarine Torpedo Carrying Helicopter), the British lightweight helicopter (a Fairey Wasp), was, in effect, a manned DASH. It was by no means equivalent to a helicopter carrying its own sensor (either a dipping sonar or sonobuoys), and therefore able to re-acquire a target located only approximately by the host ship. Such re-location, as in the case of the US LAMPS, corresponds to a much longer effective range.**

Note that the helicopter imposes a relatively small load on the ship carrying it; DASH was invented by an (US) Atlantic destroyer force fearful that its ships would become impotent if only more modern ones could carry missile stand-off weapons. A manned helicopter such as MATCH, moreover, could be attractive in other roles, such as gunfire spotting.

*   *   *

By 1955, the US Navy was developing ships equipped with a 10,000-yard sonar, the 5kc SQS-23, and with its associated stand-off weapon,

* Thus, the classic characterization of a real, as opposed to a false contact: it vanishes.
** The sonar-equipped helicopter of the British County class has a different significance (see Chapter 4).

ASROC, which had alternative nuclear and torpedo payloads. An even lower-frequency sonar, SQS-26, with about twice that nominal range, was under development. Each drop in frequency had to be paid for by an increase in size; SQS-4 fit in a 100in dome, but SQS-26 domes were generally compared to 60-foot boats. These big transducers could not tilt, but it was possible to tilt their beams electrically, gaining the equivalent of MCC or depth-finding performance, and, in the largest units, bottom-bounce or convergence zone range (by projecting the beam downwards at a sufficiently steep angle).

These techniques pushed sonar range well beyond that possible with direct path signal propagation. Ray path spreading and attenuation limit direct path sonars to to 20,000 yards (and usually much less); convergence zone ranges (depending on sea conditions) may be 70,000 yards.

The other great sonar development was the rise of passive systems, particularly for submarines. The US Navy, for example, discovered the efficacy of German-designed low-frequency arrays when it tested the cruiser *Prinz Eugen*. The SSK program (see Chapter 8) was a direct consequence. The lower the frequency, the greater the range, so that ultimately a very low frequency system, SOSUS, could achieve oceanic ranges.

British destroyers were typically equipped with Type 128 in wartime. The first set to incorporate war experience was Type 144, developed from 1941 onwards. It was designed specifically to work with ahead-thrown weapons, such as Hedgehog. Type 144 stepped automatically over its 80-degree arc on either side of the ship, and it had a sophisticated display.

Inboard profile of the French ocean escort *Le Corse*, the prototype E50, as in 1957.

SENSORS
1. SONAR (RETRACTED)
2. ANX 2 (IFF; RADAR NOT SHOWN, HIGHER ON MAST)
3. UHF RADIO
4. VHF RADIO
5. SRD 7 (HF/DF)
6. VHF RADIO

WEAPONS
7. TRIPLE TORPEDO TUBE
8. TORPEDO LOADING ARRANGEMENT
9. PASSAGE
10. ELEVATOR TO RAISE TORPEDOES FROM MAGAZINE (CREW MESS TO STARBOARD)
11. TORPEDO MAGAZINE
12. 57mm TWIN MOUNT

13. 57mm MAGAZINE
14. 57mm HANDLING ROOM
15. OPTICAL DIRECTOR FOR 57mm GUNS
15A. 57mm RADAR DIRECTOR
16. ASW CONTROL ROOM
17. CIC
18. 20mm GUN (SINGLE)
19. BOFORS 375mm ASW ROCKET LAUNCHER
20. 375mm ROCKET MAGAZINE
21. FORMER DEPTH CHARGE STOWAGE

OTHER
22. COLD ROOM
23. CHAIN LOCKER
24. WINE STOWAGE
25. PROVISIONS

26. NAVIGATING BRIDGE
27. OPEN BRIDGE (LOOKOUT SIGHTS PORT AND STARBOARD)
28. WARDROOM
29. DIESEL GENERATOR
30. COFFERDAM
31. BOILER ROOM
32. ENGINE ROOM
33. MAIN RADIO ROOM
34. OIL FUEL
35. STEERING GEAR
36. MACHINE SHOP
37. CAPTAIN'S CABIN
38. GYRO
39. CREW SPACE
40. GENERAL STORES

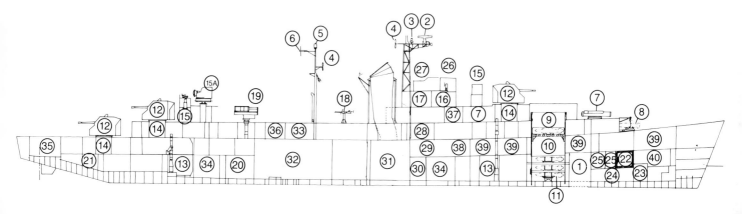

Squid required accurate three-dimensional information, supplied by a tilting sonar, Type 147. It had no operational US equivalent, and by the end of the war about 80 sets were in US service. The wartime US QDA was derived from Type 147.

In 1945, the Admiralty laid down its new sonar program on the assumption that the target of the next five years would be a fast diesel submarine, capable of 15 knots and a diving depth of 1000ft.

In 1948, the Royal Navy tested a new compound set, Type 160X, consisting of one 144 for listening, and another for search and attack, each training separately. An updated form entered service in 1950 as Type 164/165/166 in various forms. It appears in Chapter 6 as an interim set, but it was soon superseded by Type 170. Type 165 consisted of 164B plus a listening set, 174. Type 176, which is also to be found in Chapter 6, was an unsuccessful passive torpedo detector.

The Royal Navy found itself fighting U-boats in extremely shallow water in 1944-45. Often they were able to hide by lying on the bottom amid sunken ships and other debris. The solution was Type 162 (Cockchafer), which could trace a silhouette of a submarine on the sonar range recorder. It was the first side-scanning sonar.

The two principal postwar British lines of development were Four-Square (which became Type 170) and a scanning sonar, which became Type 177. Type 177 had a flat planar transducer, scanning electronically over a sector rather than over the entire circle. One consequence was that it could produce a more intense signal over that sector. It could also maintain contact more effectively, because scanning over the limited sector was faster. Type 177 operated at 7.5kc, slightly below the frequency of the contemporary US SQS-4. Range was probably somewhat greater, since the original requirement was for 8000 to 10,000 yards. The combination of 170 and 177 was generally associated with Limbo.

New sonar requirements were issued in 1950, on the basis of a future submarine speed of 25 knots and a diving depth of 1500ft. Existing equipment could not cope with such targets. The associated sonar was Type 184, the first British cylindrical scanner.

Sonar was not the only major ASW sensor. High-definition radars on aircraft and aboard ships could detect submarine periscopes and snorkel heads. For example, the US airborne early warning radar, APS-20, was installed aboard ASW aircraft such as the Lockhead P2V Neptune, not for fleet air defense but rather for submarine detection. Similarly, electronic countermeasures receivers (UHF/DF) could detect radar ranging signals from submarine attack periscopes: a submarine commander might use his passive sonar, but he would usually take a quick look (and a quick range) before exposing himself by firing torpedoes. Finally, whatever the Soviet attitude towards signalling, both navies continued to install the wartime-type HF/DF sets which had been so effective against the German U-boat fleet.

Four weapon categories were important:
— Torpedoes, guided, pattern-running, and unguided
   — Air-launched depth bombs
   — Ahead-thrown weapons
   — Anti-torpedo weapons.

Homing was probably the single most important wartime torpedo development. Applied to an anti-ship torpedo, it greatly increased the probability of a hit, with the important caveat that, the faster the torpedo (to reduce the target's chance of evading), the greater the noise level and the less the effective homing range. The US and German navies, for example, used submarine-launched homing torpedoes in wartime. From the point of view of ASW, homing allowed a submarine to fire from beyond the effective range of sonar and, therefore, of counter attack. It therefore inspired efforts to develop anti-torpedo weapons as well as the better known (and more successful) decoys, such as Fanfare (or T Mark 6, US), and Unifoxer and Type 182 (British).

Homing also made ASW much more effective, at least potentially, because for the first time an attacker could fire a weapon with more than a statistically small chance of hitting its maneuvering target. Aircraft, for example, generally attacked submarines they spotted on the surface. The submarine would dive at once, and rockets and depth charges had to be laid on the spot from which the boat had vanished. Moreover, they had to arrive within a few seconds of the crash-dive, as otherwise the submarine would be long gone. A homing torpedo could do much better. The first such weapon was the US Mark 24 (Fido), deployed in 1943. It remained the primary US air-launched homing torpedo for some years after the war, and was adapted as a wire-guided submarine weapon (Mark 27).

Most early ASW torpedoes homed passively. They were, therefore, limited in speed. Even so, they had very short acquisition ranges because the high-frequency sound on which they had to depend (for proper definition) were audible for only limited distances. On the other hand, it was often argued that an active-homing torpedo would tend to alert the intended victim. Like a passive homer, it would have to limit self-noise and thus might not be very fast.

Ship-launched homing torpedoes were attractive as a way of overcoming the poor statistics of depth charges fired at fast-moving, violently maneuvering targets. They ultimately replaced depth charges altogether at least in the West. Similarly, as submarines became faster and faster, even ahead-thrown depth charges became less effective. Rocket-launched or missile-carried stand-off homing torpedoes were the obvious next step, as once again the intelligence inherent in the torpedo could make up for the statistics of a pattern of depth charges, however laid. Current examples of this trend are the Australian-British Ikara, the French Malafon, the US ASROC, and the Soviet SS-N-14. This is not a new idea; the US

Navy tried to develop a weapon of this type, Grebe, between 1945 and 1955. Some of the British Z-weapons described briefly below were designed to fly through the air (on their own retractable wings), and then swim as torpedoes, using a common power plant. Often derided in print, they exemplify quite common current concepts, such as the underwater-air-underwater missile (SUBROC or the Soviet SS-N-15/16), which achieves high speed by spending most of its time in a less dense medium.

The path from ballistic weapon (depth charge or rocket depth charge) to homing torpedo has not been entirely smooth. Like a gun, a depth charge enjoys simplicity and certainty of operation, particularly in a noisy, shallow or countermeasure-filled environment. Early homing torpedoes were not always reliable, nor were they always fast enough (a 50 per cent margin is generally desired) to catch fast submarines. For example, the postwar British frigates were all designed to carry homing torpedoes in addition to their Limbo depth charge mortars. A few (and a Dutch destroyer) actually did. However, the British 21in homing weapon was rejected and the tubes removed around about 1960. Even now, homing torpedoes perform poorly under some conditions (as in the shallow water off the Falklands), and non-homing depth-charges may do better.

Lightweight triple tubes are currently very widely installed perhaps in part because they impose so low a cost on the ship carrying them. Moreover, at least in the US Navy, the same torpedo is also the missile and helicopter payload, so considerable numbers are generally available aboard ship. That would not be the case with a massive 21in weapon, probably stowed one to a tube.

Pattern-running developed as a simpler alternative to homing. A pattern-runner covers a relatively large area (or even volume) of water. If it moves fast enough, it can achieve a good probability of hitting one of several dispersed targets. Perhaps the most striking example was FANCY, the first British submarine-launched anti-submarine weapon. It was a very fast (hydrogen peroxide) pattern-running torpedo, intended to be fired at a set depth. A straight-runner would have had far too little chance of hitting a target in three-dimensional space, but the pattern-runner could try different bearings and depths around its original course. It used a proximity fuse to add to its hit probability. The results cannot have been altogether encouraging, but they were much better than nothing.

The other major wartime developments in torpedo technology were hydrogen peroxide (HTP) propulsion for longer range at higher speed; and electric propulsion (for quieter wakeless operation); and homing (against both ships and submarines).

Although the Royal Navy developed many postwar experimental torpedoes, the principal types were:

— Dealer B, Mark 30, an 18in passive electric air-launched ASW weapon, approved for service in 1954 but replaced by the lighter US Mark 43. It circled at 12 knots, acquired its target, homed, and then attacked at 19.5 knots. Dealer B was cancelled in favor of Pentane.* The standard British lightweight torpedo of the 'sixties (needed for helicopter delivery) was an anglicised version of the US Mark 44.

— Bidder, or Mark 20, a passive torpedo launched either by Escorts (Mark 20E) or by Submarines (Mark 20S). Mark 20E had two speeds: 24 knots for a fast fore-run, then a quieter 15 knots to acquire its target. Mark 20S had only a single speed: 20 knots. Bidder shared a common ancestry with Dealer. Mark 22, a cable-set version, was cancelled in favor of Mark 23.

— Pentane, Mark 21, a heavy 30-knot active-homing ASW torpedo which might be fired either from aircraft or from ships. It was cancelled in 1958, as the large aircraft (Gannet) capable of delivering a 21in torpedo were withdrawn from service.

— Fancy, Mark 12, the submarine-launched hydrogen peroxide pattern-running torpedo. It was withdrawn after one exploded and sank the submarine *Sidon* in Portsmouth Harbor on 16 June 1955. Fancy was a modified Mark 8 steam torpedo, and it was later argued that leakage inherent in the design made some such explosion inevitable. The requirement for Mark 12 was cancelled in January 1959.

— Mackle, a long-range wire-guided torpedo for submarines. The development contract with Vickers-Armstrong was terminated in 1956 and the weapon simplified as GROG. It was a lengthened Mark 20, the extra length carrying a drum of guidance wire. Grog (Mark 23) began trials in 1959 and entered service in 1966.

— Ongar, a long-range, electric, wire-guided, submarine-launched torpedo which entered service as Tigerfish (Mark 24). The staff requirement for this weapon was written in 1959.

The Royal Navy also plannned to use several American torpedoes: the short 19in Mark 37 as a submarine anti-escort (escape) weapon, and the 21in Mark 35 from surface ships.

In 1945, the chief limitations of ahead-throwing weapons were their lack of flexibility: none of them was really adjustable in range, nor could any of them train. A successful engagement, then, required that the attacking ship be aimed precisely at the submarine, and also that the weapon be fired at a fixed, precise, moment. The faster the submarine, the more constricting were those

* In 1957, British work on lightweight (air-deliverable) torpedoes was stopped in favor of concentration on ship- and submarine-launched weapons. At that time preliminary work was being done on a 14in, 25-knot, active/passive homer for helicopter delivery, using the motor of the Mark 30. In the mid 'sixties the Royal Navy began work on a Mark 31 alternative to the US Mark 44, but it was cancelled in 1971 in favor of purchasing the US Mark 46.

The French E52A type frigate *Le Gascon* is shown at the Jamestown Naval Review, 1957. Like *Le Corse,* she has 12 ASW torpedo tubes, although in this case each bank of three is served by a small three-torpedo magazine abaft it, so that she carries a total of 24 torpedoes. She also carried 25 depth charges and 48 rockets for her sextuple launcher (forward). Compared to *Le Corse,* she had her torpedo tubes moved down to the main deck for better stability. The last four ships of the class (E52B type) had a new 305mm mortar (as in *Commandante Rivière* class) mounted in X position aft, replacing one of the two twin 57mm mounts aft. *Le Gascon* was stricken in 1977. [*USN*]

Le Provencal, an E52B class escort, is shown on trial, 29 May 1959. The big 305mm ASW mortar has not yet been mounted aft. Note that, unlike an E52A, she has no reloads for her ASW torpedoes. The E52 class was to have been followed by an E54 class specialist ASW escort, in effect a French equivalent of the British Type 14. Comparative characteristics were (E52 in parentheses): 300ft (326ft) LOA, 292ft (311ft 8in) LWL, 30ft 1in (33ft 10in) in beam, 9ft 8in (std)(10ft 10in full load draft), 1320 (1673) tons fully loaded (E54, 1180 tons standard); 15,000 (20,000shp), 25 (26) knots; endurance 4500nm at 12 knots (4200/15). E54 weapons: two twin 40mm (both controlled by Mark 63 fire control system; both aft, one on the main deck and one superfiring over it); one sextuple Bofors rocket launcher forward (60 rockets), and 12 torpedo tubes. A proposed NATO version for Portugal would have had two fixed torpedo tubes on each side, 20 degrees off the bow (4 torpedoes in all). [*USN*]

Like the British *Rothesays,* the US *Dealeys* were modified to deliver helicopter-borne torpedoes. The difference was that in their case the helicopter was a drone, DASH. Note the small hangar and helipad aft, and the standard triple torpedo tubes just forward of it. This FRAM-like conversion also included installation of a new long-range sonar, SQS-23. USS *Lester* is shown. As early as 1954, a US Navy comparison of existing modern escort designs emphasized the long uncluttered *Dealey* deck as a resource for later growth, as here. [*USN*]

None of the big surface to air missile programs envisaged a short-range point defense weapon; note that the British missile cruisers of Chapter 5 were armed, not with a small missile, but with twin L70 Bofors guns. the Short Seacat was a very successful simple weapon, actually developed after the period of this book. It began as a research missile (SX-A5) derived from the Malkara *anti-tank* weapon (1956), and the first Seacat contract was let in April 1958. It flew in 1960, the first sea trials aboard *Decoy* following in 1961. Seacat was soon adopted as a replacement for the planned twin L70 Bofors. Here it is shown aboard the Swedish destroyer *Södermanland*, 20 September 1963. [*CPL*]

Petrel was the US Navy's major postwar anti-ship missile project. Here it is being carried by a P2V-6B Neptune patrol bomber, one of 16 built for the purpose. P2V-6 was designed primarily for mining and surface attack, and it had a smaller radar (APS-33) than the APS-20 of the ASW versions of the Neptune. The Navy view of surface attack is shown by the fact that the single squadron of Petrel aircraft was given to the Naval Reserve as an emergency naval capability. [*USN*]

conditions. Postwar weapons were attempts to overcome these limits

The United States developed an automatic rapid-firing trainable rocket launcher, Weapon Alfa. It was extremely complex, and development was protracted. The interim alternative was a trainable Hedgehog, with about a third the range. Like Weapon Alfa, it filled a destroyer gun position. Remarkably, the US Operational Development Force discovered that the spread of projectiles from two fixed, properly oriented, Hedgehogs was nearly as effective as the movable pattern of the more complex trainable unit. In the early 'fifties many US destroyers were, therefore, fitted with pairs of conventional Hedgehogs on their 01 (superstructure) decks.

By 1946 the Royal Navy had concluded that Squid was the only existing weapon which could

deal with existing fast submarines. They considered it twice as effective as Hedgehog, and nearly ten times as effective as depth charges. It was, however, limited because it was fixed both in train and in range. Just before firing, a ship armed with it (or, for that matter, armed with the wartime Hedgehog) had to maneuver so that the target submarine lay within the lethal area defined by the weapon. It seemed unlikely that an attacking surface ship could maneuver fast enough or precisely enough to deal with a submarine moving faster than 15 knots.

Limbo was designed to remove this limitation. Unlike Squid, it was trainable and its range could be varied between 380 and 1000 yards. A longer range would have been preferable, but it would have required an entirely different type of weapon, using rocket projectiles. It was argued that, because it was impossible to control the temperature of their propellant, rockets could not be fired accurately enough.

The US Navy also concluded that a trainable weapon was needed to deal with fast submarines, but it chose an automatic rocket-launcher, Weapon Alfa (Mark 108).

As for the two anti-weapon options, attempts were made both in Britain and in the United States to develop systems capable of killing oncoming torpedoes, generally by exploding powerful charges in their path. As in the case of anti-missile weapons, there was always a fear that the torpedo would not be damaged badly enough, that it would still keep coming.

Finally, there were towed decoys such as the British Foxer and the US Fanfare (T Mark 6). The US Navy also experimented briefly with rocket-projected noise-makers (NAE Beacons).

Anti-Ship Missiles

In 1945, the great question of strike warfare was how to sink a well-defended warship. Dive bombing, which was the most accurate means of delivery, was clearly extremely dangerous. But it was not lethal enough: better to deliver an underwater blow. However, existing torpedoes, required very dangerous close approaches by large numbers of aircraft.

Neither of the major Western navies pursued these questions very actively beyond about 1950, since each had to concentrate limited resources on much more pressing problems: ASW in both cases, and nuclear attack in the case of the US Navy. The wartime problem of attacking large surface warships surely seemed somewhat remote, although it was never entirely disregarded.

Even so, the projects pursued immediately after World War II give some idea of the offensive capabilities inherent in the new technology.

The two major US projects were a homing bomb (Dove) and a series of radar-guided winged missiles, carrying homing torpedoes and plunge (underwater explosion) bombs. The existing air-launched anti-ship missile, the radar-guided Bat, had to be discarded in 1948 when it was found to be susceptible to a simple countermeasure.

Dove was a 1000-pound general purpose bomb, fitted with an infra-red homing device. In a striking parallel to later modular 'smart bomb' projects, its proponents hoped to manufacture components for field modification of the large number of existing weapons. Development began in 1943. Dove came close to operational evaluation several times, but work on infra-red homing was directed instead toward the more urgent problem of air-to-air missiles.

The other major US missile project, code-named Kingfisher, was conceived as a torpedo-carring glider or jet using Bat (active radar) guidance. Kingfisher A and B were interim test devices. Kingfisher C was redesignated AUM-N-2, and ultimately entered limited service as Petrel, carried

by Neptune land-based patrol bombers. Kingfisher D, Diver, AUM-N-4, was an equivalent weapon intended to carry a torpedo which would provide propulsion in the air as well as in the water. It never materialized because no suitable torpedo was developed. Kingfisher E, Grebe (SUM-N-2), was a ship-launched ASW stand-off missile carrying a Mark 35 (later Mark 41) heavy torpedo. It never entered service, but the modern French Malafon and the Australian Ikara embody much the same concept. Kingfisher F, Puffin (AUM-N-6) was never fully developed. It was to have been an air-launched, high-altitude powered missile carrying an unpowered plunge bomb. Development was stopped on 1 October 1949, due to the severe budget pinch.

Petrel carried a Mark 21 anti-ship homing torpedo. It had a range of about 20nm, flying straight and level (at about 200ft) until it was 1500 yards from the target, at which point the engine shut down and the missile dove into the water, entering at the range of about 800 yards. Its X-band radar could distinguish targets 200 yards apart (in range), but the missile could be defeated either by jamming or by increasing speed above 33 knots – which reflected limitations inherent in its torpedo.

Like Petrel, Puffin was to have approached its target at low altitude, beginning its climb at a range of 10,000 yards, and reaching 3000ft at about 3000 yards. It would then power-dive into the water, hitting about 100ft from the target, to explode its 250-pound warhead underwater. It would have been smaller than Petrel (1250 *vs* 3300 pounds) and faster (500 *vs* 350 knots), hence much more difficult to hit.

The Royal Navy ended World War II with a greater variety of anti-ship weapon projects. In 1945, the Admiralty contemplated a long-term guided weapons program:-

— Weapon X (ship *vs* ship): a high-speed flat-trajectory weapon with final underwater attack at 30,000 yards.

— Weapon Y (ship *vs* ship): a guided projectile for steep attack on capital ships (complementary X in that it is much more difficult to counter) for 10,000 to 30,000 yards.

— Weapon Z (ship *vs* ship): an airborne, ship-launched homing torpedo, air range 16,000 yards, total range 20,000 yards.

— Ship-launched, air-controlled weapons for longer ranges were also envisaged, as were a variety of air weapons.

All were considered important, but the contemporary surface-to-air weapon (GAP) was to be emphasized 'because it is vital to the continued existence of the Navy'. Apparently, only the Z series was pursued postwar. It included at least the following:

— Zonal: Ship-launched winged torpedo propelled at low altitude by ducted propeller (500 knots). Entered water beyond anti-aircraft range, homed actively at 60 knots.

— Zoster: Air-launched version of Zonal.

— Zombi: Submarine-launched 30in weapon to home at up to 1000ft depth.

— Zeta: ASW air-launched weapon

The entire Z-weapon program was cancelled in 1949, and modern commentators have suggested that the weapons were impractical with existing – in some cases, with much later – technology. Homing ranges probably would not have exceeded 150 yards, far too little to be useful.

The two major postwar air-launched, anti-ship development projects were a heavy air-launched rocket (Uncle Tom) designed to hit underwater, and a toss-bombed torpedo, Bootleg. Uncle Tom was renamed Red Angel postwar, development continuing into the 'fifties.

Red Angel was an 11.25in rocket, 129in long, weighing 1055 pounds (of which 88 was high explosive). It could be launched from 5000 to 6000 yards. For example, an airplane at 400 knots and 2000ft could achieve a range of 5250 yards, and the rocket would have a velocity of 1500ft/sec when it hit the water. The new Wyvern strike bomber was its most likely platform, carrying two.

Bootleg was a 20in jet-propelled torpedo (150in long, 1730 pound including 575 pounds of explosive), toss-bombed at 300 to 500 knots at a range of 5000 yards. Once it hit the water, it would cover 750 to 1000 yards at 70 knots. It ran at a depth of 30ft, using a proximity pistol to explode. In theory, it should have had a much higher hitting probability than Red Angel (which was susceptible to errors in elevation angle), but its basic fire control problem was more complex, and Red Angel would be easier to produce.

The operational air-launched weapons were the wartime 18in torpedo (range 2500 yards), the 3in rocket, and bombs, principally a 2000-pound AP, a 1000-pound MC, and a 500-pound SAP. The ongoing hydrogen peroxide torpedo work was expected to lead to a 7000-yard weapon.

Radar directed anti-aircraft fire would probably be effective inside 3000 yards, and the Fleet Air Arm wanted to attack at the lowest possible altitude, where fire control would be ineffective. That greatly complicated any attack on an armored ship, such as a Soviet cruiser. The MC bomb, for example, was unlikely to penetrate at low altitude, and it was unlikely to hit if dropped from high altitude, where the airplane carrying it would be vulnerable. The AP bomb could penetrate any armor, but it was unlikely to hit. Small rockets would do no more than superficial damage.

Given these weapons, the Fleet Air Arm considered Soviet cruisers extremely difficult targets. In 1948, for example, an official handbook on the Fleet Air Arm suggested that a mixed force of two to three squadrons of Fireflies and Sea Furies with an adequate anti-flak escort 'has a fair chance of crippling if not sinking a single cruiser'.

The classic sinking weapon, the torpedo, could be carried only by a single squadron of Firebrands, which most likely would not be present in any particular emergency. In any case, the existing aerial torpedo was too slow to be sure of hitting a fast, violently maneuvering target.

Red Angel was expected to kill with a few hits, but it had only a very low development priority (1952). Bootleg was described as a 'doubtful starter'.

Revived interest in the Soviet cruiser threat (about 1952) made the absence of modern anti-ship stand-off weapons particularly uncomfortable, since carrier air groups were too small to support specialized strike aircraft. Specialist ASW aircraft such as the new Gannet cleary lacked the performance to evade heavy anti-aircraft fire. Yet a review of existing projects showed that none had been particularly successful: the Navy still relied on a combination of air-launched 3in rockets and the 18in air-launched torpedo. The only near-term solution was a tactical nuclear weapon; for the long-term, the Royal Navy sought a new 3300-pound anti-ship missile, code-named Green Cheese.

It appeared, then, that Green Cheese, carried by Gannets, would finally solve the problem of defending trade routes from marauding Soviet cruisers. Unfortunately, the weapon was too large to be carried by an un-modified Gannet. The alternative, a tactical nuclear weapon, was rejected on grounds of scarcity: surely it would not be allocated for this purpose. For a time, then, it appeared that trade protection carriers would have to accommodate small detachments of strike aircraft (in future, Buccaneers) specifically to carry Green Cheese. The Gannet alternative became moot in any case as these aircraft were withdrawn in favor of ASW helicopters (see Chapter 4).

Green Cheese was cancelled in 1957, along with Blue Slug (the ship-to-ship weapon) and Red Dean, an air-to-air weapon. That left only Blue Jay (an air-to-air, infra-red missile, which became Firestreak), and Seaslug. At this time, however, several projects were still under consideration: Advanced Seaslug (Mk II, which had some anti-ship capability and thus made up for the loss of Blue Slug), Green Light (a line-of-sight, command guidance, small ship SAM, which became Seacat), Blue Envoy (an ultimately abortive 250nm ramjet surface-to-air missile), and Orange Nell (an abortive anti-missile weapon).

Of the cancelled missiles, then, only Green Cheese left a real gap. Without it, the Royal Navy had no non-nuclear, all-weather, stand-off, anti-ship weapon other than a tactical nuclear bomb. Bullpup was purchased from the United States as an alternative.

4
CARRIERS AND NAVAL AVIATION

The great question in naval aviation has always been the extent to which aircraft designers must compromise in order to adapt their products to ships of reasonable size and cost. Before 1939, compromise seemed minimal. Prewar British aircraft could land without resort to arresting gear, a case in point being the Hurricanes which came aboard *Glorious* in April 1940, during the evacuation from Norway. Aircraft could also generally make rolling take-offs, at least under favourable wind conditions. Thus there was no question of limitation by catapult power. The only real limits imposed by carrier design were aircraft weight (deck and elevator stressing) and dimensions (of elevators or hangers). Most wartime naval aircraft were both competitive with the best land-based types and suitable for operation from the full range of carriers, from the least expensive converted merchant ships on up. Aircraft, then, did not in themselves enforce a high minimum carrier size – or cost. The British *Colossus* class, designed in 1942, was the great demonstration of just how unsophisticated a successful carrier could be.

However, as aircraft performance grew, and as aircraft grew substantially heavier, arrested landings became mandatory, and more and more

take-offs required catapulting. Thus, by 1945, the theoretical limits built into arresting gear and catapults defined actual aircraft design limits, which applied to such existing fighters as the Seafire, Hellcat, and Corsair. These aircraft in turn would soon be outclassed by new land-based fighters. Moreover, both the US and Royal Navies planned new heavy carrier-borne strike aircraft well beyond the weight, size, and speed limits imposed by existing ships. Propeller-driven fighters were not as serious a problem, but jets would add new difficulties.

The question in 1945, then, was whether naval aircraft could continue to compete with land-based craft on equal terms. Clearly, some roles, most notably strike and fleet air defense, would demand high performance. For others, such as ASW, lower-performance aircraft might suffice. The high-performance approach led to steam catapults, angled flight decks, and much larger carriers. The other approach led, first, to new generations of aircraft suited for operation from second-line carriers, such as the British Seamew and the US S2F (later S-2) Tracker. There was also a third approach, a radical change in aircraft design which might make operation from very small carriers practical. Ramp or 'zero-length'

The Royal Navy ended World War II with six large armored carriers, suddenly too small for the new generation of aircraft. Moreover, the same protection which had so benefited them in wartime also greatly complicated any attempt to modernize them. *Implacable* is shown at Pearl Harbor in June 1945. Refitted in 1948-49, she served as flagship of the Home Fleet in 1949-50, then in the training squadron. She was reduced to reserve in 1954, plans to rebuild her having been dropped. [USN]

take-off was an early version tried by both the US and British navies. There were also helicopters, which presented entirely new possibilities. Finally, this line led to current VSTOLs such as the Sea Harrier.

These issues raise a further question. One way to characterize the relationship between carrier and airplane is to define the maximum airplane which can fly from a given carrier, which is determined by catapult, arresting gear, and (to a limited extent) by deck size. Alternatively, however, the relationship can be defined in operational terms. The carrier should be able to support a tactically useful air group, sufficient in size to provide both self-defense and some surplus of air power. That implies an air group of a certain minimum size. Moreover, the air group must be sustained in operation for some useful length of time, before the carrier must retire to replenish fuel and weapons.

The meaning of these terms depends on the carrier role. In the US Navy, that was often strike warfare. The carrier had to be able to help defend herself, but her main justification was her striking power. Defensive aircraft constituted a more or less fixed 'overhead'. The larger the carrier, the greater the excess air power available for projection. The contemporary Royal Navy needed fighter carriers to defend fleets and convoys from air attack and also to deal with 'snooping' aircraft directing submarine attacks. The fighters themselves would not have to carry much fuel or many weapons, but they would need high performance. That, as reflected in catapults and arresting gear, set minimum carrier size, at or beyond British means. Vertical take-off (VTOL) seemed to make effective carriers affordable, since studies showed that even a 20,000-ton hull might suffice. For a time, around about 1956, the Admiralty Board favoured a 30,000-ton trade protection carrier, which would have been designed for ultimate conversion to VTOL operation. However, it was delayed, and by 1957 the Royal Navy was shifting back towards strike carriers. Such ships would have to mount intensive attacks, by many aircraft, which in turn would require substantial amounts of fuel and weapons, in a large hull. Moreover, vertical take-off limited weapon and fuel loads, so it, too, became less attractive.

For its part, the US Navy sought to develop a VTOL fighter usable from the many surviving escort carriers. Grumman, for example, received a 1947 contract to design a small jet which could take off from a zero-length launcher. It was not built, but both Convair and Lockheed constructed prototypes of turboprop-powered tail-siters, referred to in official correspondence as 'convoy fighters'. The Navy also financed the jet-powered Ryan X-13 tail-sitter.

Ironically, current US doctrine emphasizes long-range fleet air defense as one of several ways of destroying the threat of the Soviet naval air arm. Thus, what might in the past have seemed

'overhead' is now viewed as an offensive element of the carrier air group. Moreover, there has always been tension between single- and multi-purpose approaches to naval aircraft design. The single-purpose airplane can be smaller and more efficient. However, a multi-purpose airplane is not so much more difficult to support, and it allows an air group to shift roles back and forth. For example, in 1952 the US Navy held a design competition for a single purpose supersonic interceptor, which became the Vought Crusader (F-8). At this time nuclear weapons delivery was an important, and quite separate, carrier aircraft role. A few years later, an internal Navy study showed that the emerging missile-armed 'fleet air defense' role was compatible with high-speed nuclear attack. The Navy-issued specification resulted in an abortive design, the Grumman F12F. The Navy actually bought the McDonnell Phantom, which evolved from a strike airplane, and became the standard carrier interceptor. At the time of writing, the Navy is shifting back towards multi-purpose aircraft with the McDonnell-Douglas F/A-18 Hornet, and with modifications which may make the Grumman A-6 Intruder attack bomber a part-time long-range air defense picket (A6F version).

ASW aircraft presented much the same issue. For most of World War II, aircraft detected surfaced submarines either visually or by radar, and attacked them as they dove. They could use sonobuoys to confirm contacts, and from 1943 onwards they had homing torpedoes with which to attack fully submerged submarines. As the Germans introduced snorkels, existing radars

Off Spithead in March 1952, *Eagle* operates a transitional air group. The Supermarine Attacker jet fighters had been developed (as an interim type) from the piston-engined Spiteful. They shared the same wing, which was considered the most difficult element of an airplane to design. Further aft are Sea Fury piston-engine fighters, developed during World War II, and, to starboard, a solitary Firebrand single-seat attack bomber, one of fewer than 20 in first-line Fleet Air Arm service at the time. [CPL]

From a carrier design point of view, perhaps the most unsettling feature of the new jets was the rate at which they drank fuel. The twin-engine McDonnell Banshee was prized because it could shut down one engine to conserve fuel. However, it was considerably more expensive than the contemporary single-engine Grumman Panther, which was built in greater numbers. These are F2H-2Ps of VC-61, the fleet composite photo reconnaissance squadron. It supplied detachments to the carriers. The tail code was PP. [McDonnell Douglas]

became much less effective. However, late in the war, several U-boats were detected by visual observation of the exhaust plumes of their snorkels, localized by sonobuoy, and sunk by torpedo. In 1945, it appeared that it would require a large airborne radar (otherwise used only for airborne early warning) to detect a snorkel or a periscope at a useful range. The US Navy, therefore, developed team tactics. A radar search plane, such as a Grumman AF-2W, would locate the snorkel at a distance. At shorter range or at low altitude, sea clutter would obscure that target. Moreover, the big APS-20 radar was much too heavy to allow for weapons or sonobuoys. Thus the AF-2W was accompanied by an AF-2S, carrying a shorter-range attack radar, and weapons such as homing torpedoes, depth charges, and 5in rockets.

The combination was less than satisfactory, since a carrier of a given size could carry far fewer teams than (somewhat larger) single aircraft. Hence the development of the 'single package' concept, exemplified by the Grumman S-2 Tracker. The Royal Navy, enjoying more modest carrier resources, had reached the same conclusion somewhat earlier, in the form of Specification GR 17/45, which produced the Fairey Gannet.

ASW helicopters raised essentially the same question. In their case the primary search sensor was a dipping sonar (sonobuoys in some later cases), and by the late 'fifties both the Royal and US Navies had operational single-package

helicopters (the US Sikorsky SH-34 and its Westland-built derivative, the Wessex).

ASW helicopters raised some new questions, however. By the mid 'fifties the Royal Navy was being driven to a choice between fixed- and rotary-wing ASW aircraft. The major ASW roles were defined as:
— Deterrence (force down), which was useful only against conventional submarines.
— General search (ahead of a force or convoy) primarily to locate a surfaced submarine or snorkeller, using visual and/or radar detection.
— Limited area search, using a dipping sonar or sonobuoys to locate a submarine in an area defined by a sinking, a sighting or a radio intercept.
— Close escort.
— Fix and hold (for surface ship or aircraft).
— Attack.

In a general search, fixed-wing aircraft could cover a greater area, and had the advantage of radar, which might not be fitted to helicopters for some time. However, AEW aircraft could do this job more effectively, using their superior radar.

Dipping sonar was credited with an overwhelming advantage in a limited-area search. A fixed wing airplane would be limited in search area by its buoy load; at this time the search area defined by a buoy was considered approximately that of a single dip. Buoys might improve very considerably, but in that case they could certainly also be carried by helicopters. Note that the one factor not taken into account was the time it would take a helicopter to reach a relatively distant local area defined, for example, by a sinking or by a radio direction-finder.

For close escort, the helicopter was accorded an enormous advantage; it could already sometimes replace a ship to fill a temporary gap in a screen. At this time, new US dipping sonars were expected to allow helicopters to sweep effectively at fleet speed, up to about 30 knots (existing equipment permitted only about a 17-knot speed of advance for a fully effective search).

It was clearly easier for helicopters to fix the target, and they were better able to hold it.

With their greater load-carrying capacity, fixed wing aircraft could carry a killing weapon, but it seemed certain that by 1960 the helicopter would be able to carry an effective weapon of its own. Certainly it would be able to place its weapon more effectively.

Finally, given all-weather capability (which was then under development), the helicopter could operate when aircraft could not.

The conclusion, then, was that effort should be concentrated on developing an all-weather helicopter to replace the existing Gannet. The only role left to the fixed-wing ASW airplane seemed to be distant search, and that might well be left to airborne early warning aircraft. This implied that distant search was for the purpose of evading, rather than attacking, submarines.

There was, to be sure, one problem. Flag Officer Aircraft Carriers pointed out that helicopter

operation from a flight deck would conflict with the fighter launch-and-recovery cycle. The ideal solution was to remove the helicopters from the flight deck. The Royal Navy tried several approaches. The first was to place large (carrier-type) helicopters aboard the carrier escorts, the County class missiles destroyers. Unfortunately, a single destroyer would find it difficult to maintain a single large helicopter, and handling and launching arrangements (which had been introduced late in the design) were awkward at best.

The next alternative was to provide a separate helicopter carrier, the escort cruiser, within the fleet. Between about 1960 and 1962 this concept evolved from a cruiser with a centerline superstructure toward a small aircraft carrier

The angled deck helped solve the problem of jet operation from carriers. Here a Sea Vixen lands aboard *Ark Royal*. Because it does not fly directly up the carrier's flight deck, it cannot hit aircraft parked forward of the landing zone, should it miss the arresting wires. On the other hand, the angled deck complicates the pilot's job, since he cannot follow the most obvious visual clue, the ship's wake. In the abortive CVA01 design of the 'sixties, the British tried to solve this problem by providing two virtually parallel decks, one for landing and one for parking and take-off. Thus a pilot would land very nearly parallel to the ship's axis, without threatening the aircraft park or aircraft on the catapults. [MoD]

The mirror landing sight was another key to successful jet carrier operation, because it allowed the pilot to sense the need for glide slope corrections much more quickly. This one, on the starboard side of *Albion*, was photographed aboard her in the Mediterranean, November 1954. A similar unit was mounted to port. [CPL]

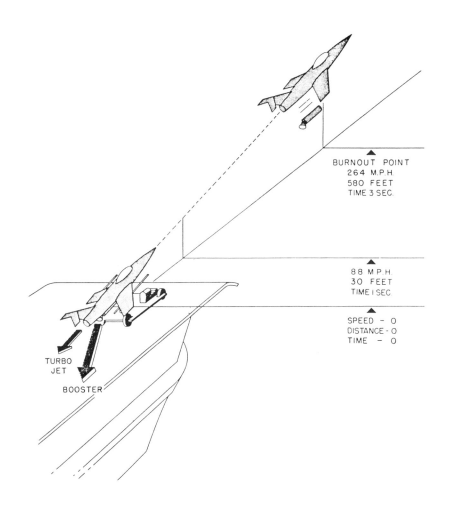

BURNOUT POINT
264 M.P.H.
580 FEET
TIME 3 SEC.

88 M.P.H.
30 FEET
TIME I SEC.

SPEED — 0
DISTANCE — 0
TIME — 0

TURBO
JET

BOOSTER

group requirements are sheer numbers (for tactics), with their accompanying fuel and weapons. All force up the minimum acceptable size of a carrier. Thus the advent of (say) efficient supersonic VSTOL aircraft will not in itself drive down the size of carriers. If the Soviet ship now under construction should emerge as a 65,000-ton VSTOL carrier, it will prove this point particularly well. In the Falklands, the small size of the British carrier air groups seems to have been a matter of some concern, With fewer than twenty Sea Harriers present, for example, the loss of two (by mid-air collision) prior to the landings was particularly serious.

This was by no means universally accepted, particularly soon after World War II. In the US case, if the role of the carrier was primarily to deliver a small number of nuclear weapons, even a small number of long-range bombers would suffice. The design of the abortive postwar super-carrier *United States*, then, was fixed by the minimum requirements of a notional 100,000 pound bomber.*

The other alternative was to accept much reduced aircraft performance as the price of retaining affordable carriers. Carrier aviation flowered on a world scale after 1945 because the minimum, in the form of a *Colossus* class carrier, was within the means of many navies. In 1945, it was already obvious that a *Colossus* was far too small and far too slow to be an efficient carrier. That was not the point. It was *a* carrier. As jet aircraft developed through the 'fifties, the price of a minimum modern capability rose; navies had to choose between retaining obsolete aircraft and abandoning carrier airpower altogether. India, for example, chose to retain the Sea Hawk fighter, designed to a 1946 British specification. Australia, Canada, and the Netherlands ultimately gave up on carrier aviation.

The alternative, high minimum carrier cost, had an important consequence. No navy could have very many of them, and these few ships inevitably consumed a large fraction of any naval budget, both for construction and for operation. All other elements of sea power were made up of relatively numerous units. A few destroyers, a few aircraft, a few hundred seamen, all were relatively inexpensive. With carriers, the choice to build was inevitably expensive – and therefore politically contentious. Similarly, any attempt to cut naval expenses inevitably fastened on the most expensive single items. That was why US active carrier strength declined so radically under the impact of tighter budgets in 1948-50.

In 1945-50 the great questions were how to keep

The new technology seemed bound to make existing small carriers obsolete, yet it would be increasingly important to protect convoys at sea against snooping long-range aircraft, which might coach submarines into position — not to mention the new jet bombers. Both the US and the Royal Navy therefore sought some means of achieving sufficient fighter performance in an airplane which could fly from existing small carriers. Grumman's Design 84 responded to a Bureau of Aeronautics requirement issued in 1947. Grumman found that the characteristics of existing escort carriers ruled out anything but the simplest and lightest fighter. It proposed a single-engine airplane weighing 12,800 pounds and boosted from a ramp by disposable rockets. Maximum speed would be about 650mph, and the airplane would fight at about 40,000ft. Indeed, Grumman argued that the key to the problem was rocket-boosted take-off, a solution later tried on land.

similar in outline to the later *Invincible* class VSTOL carrier. When the escort cruiser (and the CVA 01 which it was to have escorted) were cancelled, two *Tiger* class cruisers were converted as rudimentary helicopter carriers.

The final stage was quite ironic. From a defensive point of view, the carrier provided high-performance fighters for air defense, while the escort cruiser provided helicopters for local ASW defense. When the last British fixed-wing carrier, CVA 01, was cancelled, it was argued that new high-performance missiles (Sea Dart) could replace the fighters, at least for local air defense. It was still true, however, that small ships could not themselves support helicopters capable of all the roles envisaged in 1955. Therefore, the helicopter carrier was still necessary. It became HMS *Invincible*. Perhaps the greatest irony was the discovery that the high-performance missiles were not nearly so effective as expected, so that carrier fighters were still the primary means of fleet air defense in the Falklands – not to mention being the main fleet striking arm.

The current US view is that no matter how modest the demands her aircraft may make on catapults and arresting gear, the most critical air

* In 1948-49 the Royal Navy briefly considered a modification of existing carriers to launch a notional heavy bomber with a 10,000-pound bomb, presumably on a one-way mission with submarine recovery. This roughly paralleled the US interim project to launch Neptune (P2V) bombers from carriers, using rocket-assisted take-off. The Neptunes, too, would have ditched on their return.

For both the Royal Navy and the US Navy, the development of a single-package or hunter-killer ASW airplane was a primary postwar goal. The alternative was to operate separate hunters with high-powered snorkel-detection radars and killers equipped with smaller attack radars and also with searchlights which could be used to illuminate and thus to identify surface contacts at night. The first US combination was a pair of conversions of war-built Avenger torpedo-bombers: TBM-3W (foreground, hunter) and TBM-3S (killer) of VS-26 are shown over Norfolk, February 1953. A searchlight pod is visible under the wing of the TBM-3S. Many aircraft of these types were distributed to foreign navies under MDAP. Note that the TBM-3W had originally been developed as an airborne early warning aircraft, under Project Cadillac.[*Grumman*]

up with the new technology of jet aircraft and whether to seek the ability to deliver the new heavy weapons, especially atomic bombs, ie, whether greatly to increase the unit size and weight of carrier-based aircraft. The threat of attack by enemy jet bombers caused the development of new types of aircraft (AEW), air weapons (missiles), and the earliest automated combat systems. Each influences carrier design and operation.

Perhaps most important of all, neither the US nor the British Navy could afford to build very many new aircraft carriers. For quite some time after 1945, then, they would have to make do with existing ships, more or less radically modified. The extent to which these ships could deal with rapidly changing aircraft would determine the extent to which the navies owning them could continue to operate freely at sea, particularly near the land. This was, of course, a function of aircraft as well as of ship design, so that, over time, the demands which an aircraft of a given fixed performance placed on a ship actually decreased. The current Sea Harrier is the ultimate example of this trend.

Postwar aircraft development was extremely fast, pushed by a combination of advances in engine design and in aerodynamics. For example, 600 knots seemed quite fast in 1945, but in 1952 the US Navy requested proposals for a supersonic fighter capable of about twice that speed, and the contest winner, the LTV Crusader (F-8) flew in March 1955, deliveries beginning in 1957. This change compounded accelerated wartime naval aircraft development, which had approximately doubled the weight of the average naval airplane

in five years. The rapid flow of new generations of aircraft (and, for that matter, of air weapons) had to complicate the operation of all carriers, particularly the smaller ones.

More highly streamlined than their propeller-driven predecessors, jets took off and landed at higher speeds. Their engines produced less effective power at very low speeds, so, unlike earlier naval aircraft, they could not make rolling take-offs. They had, therefore, to depend entirely on catapults, but in 1945 existing types were only marginally suitable, requiring considerable assistance from wind over the flight deck. Jets also used much more fuel per hour, so that sustained air operations required much more fuel capacity – a particular problem. Finally, they continued a wartime trend towards heavier aircraft.

Taking off or landing, pilot and airplane could be subjected only to so much acceleration or deceleration; that in turn set a lower limit on the length in which it could gain or lose a given amount of speed. No matter how powerful the catapult, the carrier flight deck had to allow for that length. Similarly, it had to allow for sufficient length for landing deceleration (ie, for arrester wire pull-out). Jets, moreover, tended to snag a wire well forward of the stern, due to their steeper glide slope. Thus the area of carrier flight decks were zoned, with a landing area aft, a parking area amidships (protected by crash barriers), and a take-off area forward, with or without catapults.

Higher speed also meant higher energy, hence heavier catapults and arresting gear. Existing US and British catapults were almost all hydraulic, transferring power from hydraulic ram to catapult

The Grumman AF-2W Guardian was the hunter developed for US postwar carrier ASW squadrons. The largest US single-engine carrier airplane, at a combat weight of almost 20,000 pounds, it stretched the capabilities of existing escort carriers to the point where fleet carriers had to be converted. They were designated CVS, and served through until the early 'seventies. Note that the AF-2W was never described as an airborne early warning airplane, even though it shared the standard AEW APS-20 radar. This air-to-air view shows an airplane of VS-37 off the Japanese coast in 1955. The accompanying killer was an AF-2S, using the same airframe, and typically carrying a Mark 41 torpedo and six 5in HVAR rockets (or a Mark 34, three depth bombs, and four 3.5in ASW rockets). It used sonobuoys to localize its target. The AF-2S had a crew of three, the AF-2W a crew of four. The twin-engine S-2 which replaced both had a crew of four, and weighed about 23,000 pounds. [*Grumman*]

shuttle by a series of cables and pulleys. They in turn limited the energy such a device could deliver, and from 1946 onwards both navies sought some alternative. The favored US concept was a powder or explosively-driven catapult. The Royal Navy developed instead the much more successful steam catapult, which drew its energies from a ship's boilers.

British BH3 catapults in service in 1945 could launch a 20,000-pound aircraft at 66 knots. With wind over deck (about 22 knots in a light carrier), this was expected to launch the new single-package ASW aircraft (GR 17/45, later the Fairey Gannet), but not planned high-performance aircraft (Attacker, Wyvern, Scimitar, or Sea Hawk) which took off at 100 to 123 knots. HMS *Eagle* introduced its successor, BH5, a hydro-pneumatic catapult capable of 30,000 pound at 75 knots. As of 1952, it could launch all aircraft projected within the next few years, but some wind over the deck was required, entailing alteration of carrier course. The parallel US units were the H4 in wartime carriers, and the H8 in the first rebuilt *Essexes*. An H9 was projected for the *United States*, but it was superseded in subsequent ships by steam catapults.

The first British steam catapult, BS4, could launch 30,000 pounds at 105 knots in its least powerful version. It had actually been proposed as early as 1936, but money was not available. The Germans used a similar device to launch their flying bombs, and the British inventor of the steam catapult, Mr C C Mitchell, built one from parts

recovered in France in 1944. After very successful trials, the Admiralty decided to begin development in 1946. Trials in *Perseus* from 1951 onwards were successful, including demonstrations in the United States. The Americans were at first skeptical, one of their chief criticisms being that as it was driven by the ship's steam supply, power would be lost by the ship during launching operations. Experience during trials showed, however, that this was not so. *Ark Royal* had the first two operational British units.

Existing arresting gear was similarly limited: 20,000 pounds/56 knots on light fleets, 20,000 pounds/63 knots on fleet carriers, and 20,000 pound/92 knots in *Eagle*. Even the latter could not accept the Scimitar fighter then expected in 1955-56, and later new and modernized ships would be fitted with 25,000 pounds/103-knot or 30,000 pounds/95-knot gear.

Fuel was another problem. Aviation gasoline (avgas) can create an explosive vapor. It was, therefore, generally stowed under armor, sharing a carrier's limited protected volume (armored box) with machinery and magazines. Jets required much more fuel, which meant more volume. On the other hand, they could burn much less dangerous substances, such as kerosene, more akin to boiler fuel than to gasoline. It took some time for the potential benefit, that aviation fuel could be stowed in unarmored tanks, to be realized, because for some years, well into the 'fifties, such jet fuels were relatively scarce. This was a particular problem for the Royal Navy. In wartime, Britain would import most of her petroleum products from the United States, or at least from US-controlled refineries. Moreover, the Royal Navy would represent only a very small fraction of total British aviation fuel imports. Therefore, US decisions might well determine British fuel policy, hence the impact of jet fuel on carrier design and operation.

Unfortunately, the yield of kerosene per barrel of oil was much lower than the yield of more volatile products such as gasoline, to the point where it appeared in 1952, that there would never be enough kerosene to serve as jet fuel on a world-wide basis. The NATO countries therefore agreed to standardize on a 'wide-cut' gasoline, AVTAG, which had to be stowed under armor, like avgas before it. That in turn brought a carrier's aviation fuel stowage back to that of pre-jet days, greatly reducing her effective endurance. The US Navy adopted a compromise system, stowing kerosene in unarmored tanks and mixing it with avgas to form an equivalent to AVTAG. Typically, that increased air group endurance from three and a half to seven and a half days.

This system had several disadvantages. It required special pump rooms within the armored box, which themselves consumed that valuable volume. In addition, once fuel had been mixed, it could not be pumped back into the original tanks. If aircraft had to be de-fuelled, then, their fuel would have to be directed into additional (protected) tanks. The Royal Navy initially adopted the American system, then abandoned it for a time in favor of AVTAG, a decision reflected in the development of the *Victorious* design (see below). Ultimately, it (and the US Navy) was saved by the proliferation of jet aircraft and then by increasing production of just the type of fuel which had seemed so scarce in the early 'fifties. Thus, the US Navy would eventually convert its boilers to burn distillate fuel, which amounted to JP-5. In carriers, that meant that the same tanks could be used either to fuel the ship or to fuel her air group, and thus that a captain could trade off ship endurance against air group endurance.

New generations of weapons also needed more space. For example, streamlined (low-drag) bombs took up more space per unit weight. Jets could carry heavier bomb loads, so a given air group required either more weapons or more frequent underway replenishment.

The ideal solution was a new, much larger, carrier, such as the USS *United States*, laid down and then cancelled in 1949. Reconstruction was, however, much more common. Britain faced a special problem, in that in 1945 she had six new carriers (the two *Ark Royals* and the four *Hermes*) under construction. They could be redesigned (modernized), but only to an extent limited by their basic designs. The much larger *Maltas*, which would have allowed more room for maneuver, were cancelled in 1945, without ever having been laid down. Unlike in 1945 destroyers and frigates, they seemed to have had little impact on postwar

Cold-weather operations were a major postwar theme of US naval development. Although cold weather was usually associated with strategies calling for air strikes against the Soviet Union, carriers off Korea, as illustrated here, encountered snow and ice. The propeller-driven airplane is an AD-4Q ECM-equipped attack bomber of composite squadron VA(AW)-35. Behind it are night-fighing Corsair fighters, and a Banshee jet fighter is visible to the right, with others further aft. [*McDonnell Douglas*]

The Douglas Skyraider was the symbol of postwar US naval tactical strike warfare. An AD-4 attack bomber of Carrier Air Group 2 (CVG-2) and an AD-4W AEW of one of the two carrier composite airborne early warning squadrons, VC-11, are shown. Note that the AEW airplane has been repaired with the rudder of an attack Skyraider (probably tail letter D), and therefore shows only the D of its ND tail code. [*McDonnell Douglas*]

'Heinemann's Hot Rod', the small Douglas A4D (A-4) Skyhawk, was designed specifically to deliver nuclear weapons. This A-4 carries a dummy atomic weapon on her centerline. Note that she shows no wing-root 20mm cannon. [*McDonnell Douglas*]

British carrier thinking. It appears in retrospect that the very strict limitations under which the Royal Navy labored drove it to innovations which overcame those limits: for example, the steam catapult and the angled deck. The third great British carrier invention, the mirror landing sight, was valuable but not fundamental. Another major British innovation, the flexible deck, proved less useful.

This latter had been inspired by the perception that naval aircraft, with their 'controlled crash' landings, needed heavier undercarriages than their land-based counterparts. These in turn exacted a weight and space (hence performance) penalty. It was also becoming more difficult to find room for a retracted undercarriage in the thinner wings required at higher speeds. Given a properly

The Supermarine Scimitar was developed as a day fighter-bomber. By 1954, it was also a potential alternative for the new Sea Vixen two-seat night fighter. Development ceased because an even better alternative, the Blackburn Buccaneer, was in prospect. As a result, the two 1954 alternatives, the Scimitar and the Sea Vixen, served together until the one with greater potential, the Scimitar, was retired while the less flexible one, the Sea Vixen, remained. Scimitars are shown aboard *Ark Royal,* off Scotland, in September 1966. [*CPL*]

designed flexible deck, a jet entirely without wheels could be landed. The next problem was to move it to a separate flying-off deck in minimum time.

The original concept was to have a carrier with a flexible deck, capable of operating only aircraft without undercarriages. However, it was impractical to design an undercarriageless ASW airplane*. Moreover, it would be some years before the change-over from conventional to new

types of aircraft could be completed. The Admiralty Staff therefore developed a tentative requirement for a 'hybrid' carrier with a deck covering, inflatable and deflatable in three minutes. However, the project died. The prospective short-term gains were too small. Moreover, it appeared, by the early 'fifties, that the next generation of naval aircraft would be VTOLs, using jet blast to launch themselves. Such operation was clearly not compatible with a rubberized deck covering. Thus, the 1952 British carrier design specified a steel deck without flexible covering.

Angling the land-on portion of the flight deck had two primary virtues. First, it was now possible to accept both long catapults *and* long arrester gear run-outs on a relatively short hull, since the arrester gear could pull-out beyond (to one side of) the beginning of the catapult. Second, a jet no longer had to land into the area immediately abaft the catapult. The higher its performance, the greater the risk that it would 'bolt', or miss the arresting wires, altogether. Now a 'bolter' could simply fly off for another try.

The other major carrier innovation, for the Royal Navy, was the deck-edge or side elevator, which had been introduced by the US Navy in 1941.

* ASW required long endurance, which in turn implied turboprop power. It was difficult to design an efficient turboprop airframe in which the propeller tips were sufficiently far from the deck to tolerate an undercarriageless landing.

Sea Vixens (at the bow), Scimitars, and two Gannet airborne early warning aircraft share the flight deck of the modernized light fleet carrier *Hermes*, February 1961. The big radar atop the bridge is Type 984. Through the 'fifties, the Royal Navy considered it the only possible solution to the problem of mass jet raids, as it could follow multiple targets nearly simultaneously in three dimensions. Unfortunately, it was extremely difficult to maintain, and it was discarded in favor of much simpler sets such as the two-dimensional Type 965. Type 984 was associated with an automated plotting system called the Comprehensive Display System (CDS), which could track up to 48 aircraft simultaneously. [*CPL*]

Carriers generally had their forward elevators in their aircraft parking areas forward. If an airplane could not be folded, it would block that area, and it could not be struck below. Moreover, without a deck-edge elevator to carry landing aircraft below, they would have to be parked over the catapults, blocking them, while awaiting the forward elevator. The Pacific War experience emphasized the former problem; jet operations (with their short endurance and hence fast operating cycles) the latter. A deck-edge elevator amidships could clear aircraft from the parking area forward of the bridge; it could move them from the hanger to the port catapult during landing-on operations; while lowered, it allowed engines to be run-up without interfering with the flight deck; it was a convenient ditching point for damaged aircraft in wartime; and it allowed transportation of aircraft between hangar and flight decks during flight operations.

British observers in the Pacific were so impressed with the deck-edge elevator that it was included in the *Malta* design. However, it was difficult to fit into a British-type armored carrier, in which the flight deck was integral with the hull structure. Only the much-modified *Ark Royal* and *Hermes* were completed with it. In the former, it served the upper hangar only, was not considered a great success, and was later removed. A deck-edge elevator created particular problems in British carriers, in which the flight deck was the strength deck and the hull sides contributed to overall strength. Much the same might be said of the larger postwar American carriers; the solution to this shear strain problem was a major accomplishment. Some British officers, moreover, considered deck-edge elevators vulnerable to sea damage in the rough waters of the north. However, postwar US carriers were designed without any centerline elevators, depending exclusively on deck-edge units.

*   *   *

The new jet bombers and guided missiles also radically changed carrier equipment and operation. They cut available reaction time (since the bomber approached much more rapidly). Since missiles (and nuclear weapons) had much higher hit and kill probabilities than torpedoes, aircraft no longer had to approach in waves. They could approach singly, from all directions, to saturate fleet defenses. Finally, air attack could increasingly be expected in all weather, making the largely day-fighter forces of World War II obsolescent. Whatever the long-range effects of anti-aircraft missile development, moreover, between 1945 and 1955 the burden of fleet air defense clearly fell on carrier fighters. After all, the guns were useless beyond about 10,000 yards.

Fighter control was analogous to gun control. Targets were generally detected by long-range radars. Fighter controllers in the Action Information Center (British) or Combat

Information Center (US) assigned individual fighters or groups of fighters to targets, vectoring them into position, generally on the basis of manual plots of target and fighter positions. Individual pilots provided fire control, sometimes (in night fighters) assisted by airborne radars.

Like the gun system, the carrier fighter system had a finite target-handling capacity. This capacity was not nearly so well defined as in the gun case, because it depended on the way in which the fighters were used, as well as on the sheer numbers of fighters and fighter controllers. However, in 1945 there was increasing concern that enemy air attackers might be able to saturate fleet air defenses, presenting targets in such rapid succession that many would penetrate.

Classical air tactics had stressed mass attacks, which might overwhelm the gun defenses of the target ship. However, in order to reach that level of saturation, the attackers would have to approach together, and from the defending carrier's point of view they would constitute a single mass target, which could be tracked and attacked as a unit. However, if individual airplanes had a reasonable chance of success in the face of shipboard weapons, then there was little reason for them to approach together. They could present the carrier fighter controllers with so many widely separated targets that the carrier, the long-range element of fleet air defense, would itself be saturated. This was just what the Kamikazes had tried off Okinawa.

Automation was the solution to saturation. Experiments showed that existing techniques based on hand compilation of verbally relayed information from radar scopes was subject to saturation. The Royal Navy led in developing a wholly electronic Comprehensive Display System (CDS) to record, store, and classify all data observed by the radar, presenting selected data on a variety of electronic plots as required. Versions

The projected Saunders-Roe SR177 mixed-power (rocket/jet) fighter would have been the ultimate deck-launched interceptor. Armament would have consisted of a pair of wingtip-mounted Firestreak air-to-air missiles. Radius of action, against Mach 0.9 - Mach 1.3 bombers at 40,000 - 80,000ft, was estimated as 160nm; the fighter was expected to intercept bombers at 60,000ft, at a range of 55nm. Take-off weight would have been 27,348 pounds, and landing weight 16,200 pounds. Design work began in February 1954, and the aircraft was to have been flown by both the Royal Navy and the RAF. The Royal Navy project was cancelled in August 1957. [BHC]

DESIGN 118   G-82961

By way of contrast, the US Navy sought a long-range fleet air defense fighter which would orbit on a Combat Air Patrol (CAP) station, using missiles to deal with bombers. Navy studies of the early 'fifties showed that such a fighter would also be effective in the nuclear strike role. The Grumman XF12F (Design 118), shown here, typifies contemporary US Navy thinking, because it was designed to a US Navy specification. The XF12F was actually ordered, but it was cancelled due to the much superior expected performance of the McDonnell-Douglas Phantom (F4H), essentially a heavy attack fighter modified to meet much the same requirement. A Grumman brochure, dated December 1955, described it as a 'task force defense fighter' protecting a hypothetical 1960s task force spread out over a circular area with a radius of about 100nm. Radar picket destroyers and AEW aircraft would provide warning out to about 250nm, and missiles would provide an inner defense out to about 80nm. The fighter, then, would be committed when targets approached within about 200nm, and would have to kill them before they reached the 100nm radius. It was assumed that the number of CAP stations would be minimized, since the fewer the defensive fighters, the greater the offensive firepower of the force. Grumman assumed that they would be equally spaced, and that the most

difficult targets would be those approaching between adjacent stations. The fighter would be armed with a combination of two semi-submerged Sparrow all-weather (radar) missiles and three Sidewinder (infra-red) missiles (in a small internal bay), so that it could attack each target at least twice, with different weapons corresponding to different kinds of possible enemy countermeasures. Power would be provided by two J79 turbojets (as in the F-4) boosted by a 5000 pound thrust rocket under the tail. On afterburning engines, it would reach Mach 2 at 35,000 to 58,000ft; the rocket would maintain this speed up to 75,700ft. The fighter would climb to 45,000ft in two and a half minutes. On full internal fuel, it could fly for about two and a half hours, including orbit time. It would take off at 46,516 pounds (126.7 knots, within the capabilities of the US C-11-1 steam catapult) and land at 94.2 knots at 30,466 pounds. Wing span was 44ft, and length 58.5ft. Alternatively, it could carry a 3300-pound nuclear weapon, taking off at 47,004 pounds. In that case fuel would replace the two Sparrows, and the airplane would also carry underwing tanks. [*Grumman*]

capable of storing 16,24 or 48 tracks were developed, as well as a Digital Plot Transmission (DPT) which permitted ships in a group to share their data. The US Naval Tactical Data System (NTDS) was a somewhat later parallel development using different technology. CDS in turn was tied to a new long-range three-dimensional radar, Type 984. Thus, the combination of 984 and CDS became an essential element in any future British task force, as understood about 1952-55. It could be aboard a carrier or a FADE or, later, a missile cruiser.

Type 984 was also expected to increase warning time. However, like any shipboard radar, it had a limited horizon. Radar range translated into warning time. For example, a radar located 100ft above water might detect raiders flying at 10,000ft at a range as great as 150nm, half an hour out. However, the same airplanes, flying at 100ft, might be detected only about 25nm away, only about five minutes away. Wartime carrier-based fighters had been effective largely because of radar fighter control, with the radar located aboard the carrier. Pickets (such as FADE) were an alternative, and did extend the fleet's horizon, but they complicated control arrangements. In 1945, however, the US Navy introduced radar pickets, to provide early warning of low fliers, and, incidentally, to control sections of fleet fighters. It also developed an airborne early warning radar, APS-20, which could also detect low fliers beyond the carrier's radar horizon. Control was simple because the airborne pickets (Cadillac I) transmitted *their* radar pictures directly to the carrier and therefore might be considered part of the carrier's radar suit. It was argued at the time that, since the AEW airplane had no height-finder, it could not effectively direct fighters in any case. The alternative, Cadillac II (a converted heavy bomber) combined radar and fighter controllers in a single land-based airplane. At first it, too, had no height-finder, but later US land-based AEW aircraft (EC-121s) had separate height-finding radars. Only much later could both roles be combined in a ship-based aircraft, the Grumman E-1B. The E-1B did have a combined search/height-finding radar, as has the current E-2C.

AEW had another function as well: sea (surface) search. It had originally been conceived as an alternative to shorter-range sea search (ASV in British parlance) radars. Well controlled fighters could generally expect to destroy an ASV-equipped search airplane before it ever detected the ships it sought. AEW would greatly extend radar search range. For example, an AEW-equipped snooper might be a particularly difficult target for a trade protection carrier. Similarly, British AEW aircraft might greatly simplify the problem of catching surface raiders, which had been so difficult in wartime. Similarly, an AEW airplane could operate as a strike leader, although individual strike aircraft would still need their own shorter-range radars. Otherwise the presence of the distinctive AEW signal would reveal the strike target.

Eagle displays her interim angled deck off Weymouth, April 1959. Physically, the main modification it required was a slight extension of the port forward side of the flight deck, so that two of the eight twin 4.5in guns had to be blanked off. A search and rescue helicopter sits between the two hydraulic catapults forward, with a Seahawk fighter on the starboard catapult. Further aft are more Seahawks, five Sea Venoms (three of them folded, on the port side), four dark-blue Skyraider early warning aircraft and four ASW Gannets. Note the great size of these twin-engine (both geared to one contraprop) single-package aircraft. The ship was rebuilt in 1959-64. [*CPL*]

Eagle emerged from reconstruction with a sharply angled deck and with the 984 three/dimensional radar. She is shown in March 1965. Note the landing spots painted on her flight deck for her complement of ASW helicopters, and the pri-fly built out from the port side of her island. This reconstruction also included installation of two powerful steam catapults, which were *not* located in the positions formerly occupied by the hydraulic catapults they replaced. Instead, one was placed on the new sponson. Note the jet blast deflectors (retracted) at the ends of the catapults. [*MoD*]

The Royal Navy decided not to buy Cadillac in 1945. Its technologists felt that they could do better, given sufficient funds, and that buying only one or two would do little good. The experimental aircraft would be too easy to write off in a trial, and would cost too many scarce dollars. This was perfectly reasonable in the context of the postwar strategic assumptions. Only late, when Britain began to rearm, did it become clear that she could not afford to develop an airborne early warning (AEW) system of her own. US Skyraiders were, therefore, obtained under MDAP. Later, a Gannet AEW version was developed, but it still used a version of the old US AEW radar, APS-20.

In 1945, the Naval Staff hoped to develop a demonstrator AEW in four years, a development version in six, and a production model in eight years. However, given the pressure of other

Ark Royal (foreground) and the first US postwar carrier, *Forrestal*, illustrate contrasting circumstances and ideas in this 1957 photograph. Modified from a wartime design, the British carrier had only a shallow angle to her deck, so that landing space forward of it was severely limited, as indicated by the lines on her flight deck. The big sponson of the US carrier allowed for much more parking space. Note, too, that all of the elevators of the US carrier extend out to the deck edge, whereas *Ark Royal* had only a single deck-edge elevator (which proved unsatisfactory, given her double-hangar design). Less visible is the contrast between the very long island of the British ship and the cramped island of the US carrier, which has been cut back severely to provide space for flight deck operations. The US air group is designed primarily for strike operations, with eight A3D (later designated A-3) strategic bombers visible. The piston-engine aircraft amidships are all medium bombers (Douglas AD, later A-1, Skyraiders). The fighters are Furies (day interceptors, modified North American Sabres) and all-weather Demons. The British carrier shows only a combination of day (Seahawk) and night (Sea Venom) fighters, with four airborne early warning aircraft on her fantail. Some of the difference is due to size, but note that modernized US *Essexes*, which were somewhat smaller than *Ark Royal,* also operated the big bombers. [*USNI*]

projects, there were never enough scientists to achieve this. The Staff target written at the time showed, in parenthesis, 'preliminary but conservative estimates of the extent to which Staff targets could be met':
— Detection of a small group of aircraft three to four at 170-200nm (the system could probably detect individual low fliers in calm seas at 70nm, three to four at 90nm; in moderate or rough seas clutter would make results less satisfactory).
— Height-finding (an actual system could probably obtain some indication of height zone).
— Detect a surface ship (destroyer) at 20 to 200nm (an actual system could probably detect at 150nm).
— Radio relay to ship at 100nm on line of sight (can be met).

Picket ships (FADE) were an attractive alternative against low fliers. However, experience at Okinawa showed that such ships were early and attractive targets for enemy roll-back attacks. The needed their own combat air patrols for cover. Later, it would be argued (in the United States) that picket destroyers generally could not match carrier speed in rough weather, but the AEW aircraft could still be flown off.

At this time a minimum range of 120nm against low-fliers (more against jets) was required for effective warning. Unfortunately, the aerial to detect low fliers at 170 to 200 miles was 20 by 10ft,

too large to be carried by 30,000-pound carrier aircraft. Carrier aircraft therefore would probably be able to detect aircraft flying at 500 to 3000ft out to 60 or 70nm; sea returns interfered inside 40nm. The British concluded that very large numbers would be needed, perhaps at least six AEW aircraft each 50nm from the main body and 50nm apart for all-round cover. Full 24-hour coverage would require a total of 54 aircraft, on the basis of a ratio of one airplane in the air to a total of nine. These figures are interesting as in indication of the very high cost of continuous air operations, as envisaged in 1946. At this time the Director of Navigation, who was responsible for air control, suggested an alternative which gives some idea of naval operation as it was understood just after World War II.

Six FADE with current air control radars (Types 980 and 981, soon replaced by 982/983) could steam 50nm apart. The main body itself would be equipped with powerful radars. If the fleet contained a total of nine AEW aircraft, one could be maintained in the air full-time, circling the fleet once every hour 40nm from task force center.

Main body would provide high cover (25,000ft) to about 160nm (Type 960) and medium cover (5000ft) to about 100nm (Type 960). It would also enjoy low cover (100ft) to about 25nm (Type 980 or Type 277). In turn, the pickets would provide high or medium gapless coverage out to an average of 100nm from fleet center, and low cover to a range varying from 50 to 75 nm from fleet center (50nm

Victorious was the only British World War II-built fleet carrier to be completely rebuilt. She was approximately equivalent to the large rebuilt light carrier *Hermes*. She, *Eagle*, and *Hermes* were the only British warships to carry the large 984 air control radar, which the British considered essential to task force air defense. [*MoD*]

at each mid-point between pickets).

The AEW airplane would detect destroyers and large ships out to 190nm (150nm radar range plus 40nm range from fleet center). It would also detect single aircraft on each bearing from the Fleet once every hour to a maximum of 110nm. Such detection, however, would be of little value since the chances of the aircraft being on the right bearing to detect an incoming raid at this range were estimated at about four or five to one against. The alternative, having the AEW orbit over the main body, would detect surface targets out to 150 nm, and air targets (if they were high enough) out to 60-70nm.

This combination would give five to eight minutes warning against low fliers. This was 65nm short of the stated requirement. However, AEW range could not be increased, and it would be extremely expensive to increase either AEW or FADE numbers. A total of 16 FADE would be required to achieve 120nm warning, and then a wide gap (75nm) would be left between the area covered by the pickets and that covered by the main body, although some of the gap would be covered by the orbiting AEW airplane.

From the carrier point of view, AEW added to the essential 'overhead', both in numbers of aircraft and in maintenance load. AEW requirements were increased, moreover, because the APS-20 AEW radar was also the best available early postwar snorkel and periscope detector, hence an essential ASW sensor. Long detection

range was also presumably attractive in the anti-snooper role.

Wartime carrier operations showed the need for another new element: improved underway replenishment. In the Pacific, in 1945, carriers engaged for the first time in really intensive strike operations, far from their bases. One British Admiral compared the final US operation against Japan to attacks on Newfoundland, in Canada, carried out by a fleet based at Alexandria, with its forward base in the Azores. The fleet's appetite for aircraft fuel would inevitably grow, since jets consumed far more per hour than their propeller-driven forebears. Although the carriers themselves were able to accommodate more, replenishment would also have to be more frequent. The US Navy, contemplating intensive operations in the north, had an additional problem. In the Pacific, it had been able to schedule lengthy replenishments with a reasonable certainty that the weather would not interfere. In rougher seas, on the other hand, suitable weather would not be so easily predictable, and intervals of sufficiently calm weather would be relatively brief. Moreover, submarines and long-range bombers would pose much greater threats to a fleet made vulnerable as it slowed to replenish.

The US Navy had spent much of the interwar period pondering the requirements of a future Pacific War, in which it would enjoy the services of few if any bases. It therefore built up a massive fleet train, consisting of mobile base forces (such as submarine tenders and repair ships) and a mobile replenishment force which ferried fuel, ammunition, and stores from the advanced bases (to which they had been brought by conventional tankers and freighters) to the carrier task forces. Replenishment at sea was a lengthy process because transfer rates were relatively slow, and because several ships (typically tankers, and ammunition and stores ships) had to come alongside in sequence.

For the Royal Navy, the Pacific experience had been traumatic. Ironically, the Royal Navy had become convinced of the need for special ships for forward basing during the Ethiopian crisis of 1935-36. A Mobile Naval Base Depot ship (MNBDO) was tentatively included in the 1936 program. This concept had been developed from 1919 onwards, and such a ship was considered essential for warfare in the Mediterranean or in the Far East. The Ethiopian crisis showed the need for a special tender to assist in advanced base defence, acting as base ship for the senior naval officer, depot ship for a controlled (defensive) mining unit, stores issue ship, temporary anti-aircraft defense (pending the establishment of a battery ashore), and base radio ship. It would not replace transports and freighters which would carry the gun defenses for the base, the wheeled transport, and the personnel. Nor could it provide amenities for a base in an entirely remote area. The idea was not new; the battleship *Agincourt* was recommissioned in 1921 specifically as a prototype MNBDO, but had to be broken up (under the Washington Treaty) before she could be modified.

However, in general the prewar Royal Navy had enjoyed well-stocked bases, and consequently had not had to develop a mobile logistic force, either for forward basing for for underway replenishment at sea. By 1943, when the decision to send a major fleet to the Pacific had been made, it was clear that this strategic decision would entail a major logistical program, a great hardship for a country dependent on, and badly short of, the merchant ships which would have to serve in the fleet train. The improvised fleet train did function, although a British historian, H P Wilmott, has suggested that it could not have functioned for many more months. As in the case of the carriers themselves, new carrier support ships seemed necessary.

The postwar British naval strategy also required effective underway replenishment. In a 'broken-backed' war, the fleet would have to function outside its peacetime base structure, relying on a combination of hasty mobile bases and, above all, on underway replenishment, for its continued viability.

The result of all of this experience was intense interest in 'one-stop' underway replenishment ships, which would combine fuel and ammunition in a single hull. Such vessels were actually operated during the war by the German Navy, which could provide only single supply ships to

replenish its raiding warships. Two of these fast resupply vessels, renamed USS *Conecuh* and HMS *Bulawayo,* were tested postwar. In the US case, a single-stop ship was proposed by the Atlantic Fleet as early as 1946, and tentatively included in the long-range shipbuilding plan (as the AOR) in 1950. The *Conecuh* was refitted and tested in the Mediterranean in 1953, and ultimately six AOR and four faster AOE were built, the latter specifically to support fast carrier strike operations. Similar but smaller AORs have since become standard in NATO navies, supporting escort (HUK) groups.

*   *   *

In 1945, the Fleet Air Arm was largely oriented toward fleet air defense, with fighter-heavy carrier air groups. However, it was also buying a series of long-range heavy strike aircraft, all weighing about 20,000 pounds at take-off: the single-engine Wyvern strike fighter, the Spearfish torpedo and dive bomber, the twin-engine Sea Mosquito torpedo bomber, the twin-engine Sea Hornet fighter-bomber, and the Short Sturgeon strike leader. Its standard fighters, the British Seafire and the US Corsair, were to be replaced by the single-engine Sea Fury. Many of the new aircraft were only marginally – if at all – operable from existing British carriers.

With the end of the war, the strategy most of these airplanes represented came into question, just as their production runs began. Only the Sea Hornet and Wyvern ever saw real service. A few Sea Mosquitoes were built, but they were never operational as strike aircraft. The big Sturgeon was cancelled, although a few saw service as target-towers. The only early postwar British strike aircraft was the Blackburn Firebrand, which had to be retained in service through the early 'fifties because of engine problems encountered by its intended successor, the Wyvern.

Moreover, all of these piston engine aircraft would soon be obsolete. The Fleet Air Arm was allowed to run down while a new generation of jet combat aircraft was developed. Existing RAF Meteors and Vampires were flown experimentally from carriers, but neither was really satisfactory. Sixty Supermarine Attacker jet fighters were ordered, the first in August 1948, to gain experience while a more satisfactory airplane was developed. With the outbreak of the Korean War, this decidedly interim fighter had to be produced in greater numbers, pending production of the more satisfactory Hawker Sea Hawk (N7/46) day fighter (ordered in November 1949 for delivery in May 1953). Ultimately, it equipped three of a total of nine fighter squadrons.

The Sea Hawk itself was outclassed by the MiG-15 before it could enter service. That made introduction of its swept-wing successor, the Scimitar (N113, or N9/47) particularly urgent. As insurance against slow development, twenty hooked versions of a new standard RAF fighter, the Supermarine Swift, were ordered for

evaluation. They would enter production if the Scimitar was not available in time.

This very rapid evolution strained the carrier force. The Sea Hawk could operate from new and modernized fleet and light fleet carriers. The Scimitar required the larger deck of a modernized fleet carrier or a new carrier (with the latest arrester gear).

Until the jets could enter service, the Royal Navy would have to rely on the Sea Fury, an advanced propeller-driven fighter. By 1952, the Sea Fury was no longer in production, but Sea Hawk deliveries were not scheduled for another year. The US Navy offered 100 Corsairs as a stopgap, free of charge (against cuts in the FY53 British MDAP request). They were not, in the end, supplied.

The only existing early postwar naval night fighter was the de Havilland Hornet, a twin-engine propeller type. A specification for a twin-jet replacement, N40/46, was drawn up, but it was not satisfactory, and was ultimately superseded by N14/49, which became the de Havilland Sea Vixen (DH 110). This pace of development was

satisfactory given the policy behind the Nine Year Plan. However, once war broke out in 1950, some interim aircraft was urgently needed. It became the de Havilland Sea Venom, ordered in January 1951. Less demanding than higher-performance fighters, the Sea Venom was to have armed 'trade protection' carriers after it was superseded aboard fleet units.

By about 1953, then, the Royal Navy could look forward to a future fighter force consisting of swept-wing Supermarine N113 (Scimitar) day fighters and de Havilland Sea Vixen night fighters. As an interim measure, it ordered twenty Supermarine Swifts, which were to have been equipped with arrester hooks. they were not delivered, due to problems with the basic Swift.

Meanwhile, the Navy's own doctrine was shifting away from the day/night distinction. Instead, future fighters would be classified as high- or low-level, the split being at about 45,000ft. A low-level fighter would have to be rugged, to maneuver at high speed. It would also have to loiter for long periods on Combat Air Patrol, since it would enjoy relatively little radar warning. A

Even the large war-designed light carriers seemed smaller and smaller as postwar aircraft grew in size. *Albion* is shown in February 1957. The light-colored helicopter is for search and rescue; the dark ones are ASW Wessexes, equipped with dipping sonars. Abaft them are Seahawk fighters, then Skyraider airborne early warning aircraft (still wearing their Suez identification stripes), and Gannet ASW aircraft-the helicopters have not yet taken over completely. Note how little space is (or might be) left over for strike operations. *Albion* was obsolescent, with only an interim angled deck and hydraulic catapults. She would soon become a helicopter assault carrier. [*USNI*]

high-altitude fighter would enjoy considerable warning, since the radar horizon at high altitude would be many miles away. Hence it could be deck-launched on warning, if it could climb fast enough. It appeared that no single airplane could really do both jobs, since the rugged structure of the low-altitude fighter would make for a wing loaded too heavily to fly effectively at very high altitudes. On the other hand, the ruggedness inherent in the low-altitude fighter would make it suitable for low-level attack.

Both types would need radar. Attacks might well be made in any weather, day or night, so there was little point in purely visual interception. At high altitude, moreover, targets might be difficult to detect against a featureless sky. Given these considerations, neither of the existing new fighters was entirely satisfactory. The Sea Vixen was lightly loaded, and so could fly well at very high altitudes. However, its light structure left little room for development. It was clearly poorly adapted to strike warfare. The existing Scimitar lacked a radar, and the Royal Navy wanted a dedicated radar operator in any all-weather fighter. Yet its rugged structure suggested considerable potential for development, both as a fighter and as an attack bomber.

In 1954, then, the Admiralty tentatively decided to develop a two-seat version of the Scimitar, using the new technologies of the 'area rule' and blown flaps to achieve both higher speed and an acceptable landing speed. New engines (after burners) might well boost it to supersonic speed. This was not really an alternative to the Sea Vixen,

but the Radical Review showed just how tight money was. If the Navy could only have one of the two, and if the two-seat Scimitar succeeded, the Sea Vixen was to have been cancelled. In fact, however, the two-seat Scimitar competed with a third airplane, the NA39 (Buccaneer) in the strike role. The effect of the Radical Review, then, was to allow production of the least advanced (day fighter) version of the Scimitar, but not of the two-seat or supersonic version. Work also began on a true high-altitude fighter, the mixed rocket-jet Saunders-Roe SR177. Both weather and shipboard radar performance would be better at very high altitudes, so a single-seater radar could be accepted. Deck-launched tactics required a very high rate of climb, hence the rocket. The airplane could afford limited endurance, since (unlike the lower-altitude fighter) it would not have to orbit on Combat Air Patrol. SR177 was cancelled in the next (1957) Defence Review.

The US view of these issues was quite different. In 1945, it, like the Royal Navy, operated mainly day fighters with small numbers of night fighters. Unlike the Royal Navy, it considered a single-seat night fighter satisfactory, developing versions of the standard Hellcat, Bearcat and Corsair. Postwar night fighter development led both to the two-seat Skyknight and to a variant of the single-seat Banshee. The Skyknight had such poor carrier performance (it tended to smash catapults as it took off) that it was soon relegated to land operation.

That left the twin-engine, single-seat F2H Banshee. As in the case of the Royal Navy, the US

Helicopters were clearly valuable, but their deck cycles had little in common with those of conventional aircraft. They also consumed considerable deck space, as *Hermes* shows here. The aircraft are paired Scimitars and Sea Vixens forward, Gannet AEWs aft. [*USNI*]

Navy tended more and more to require all-weather performance. However, given its interest in the strike mission, it could not really afford two distinct classes of fighter. Its day fighters were replaced, not by new fighter-bombers (like the powerful Scimitar), but by pure attack bombers (Skyhawks) with some minor residual fighter characteristics. By the late 'fifties, the chosen Fleet Air Defense weapon was a long-range fighter-launched missile, the Sparrow, carried first by the single-seat Demon and Cutlass, but very soon by a heavy two-seat fighter, the Phantom. The Phantom in turn had such powerful engines that it could operate effectively at high altitudes, despite its weight. It might be argued, too, that maneuverability could be invested in the missile, not the fighter. This idea reached its most extreme form between 1956-1960 in Eagle-Missileer (F6D), a relatively low-performance fighter (Missileer) carrying a very high-performance air to air missile (Eagle). Missileer was later superseded, first by the unsuccessful General Dynamics F-111B, and then by the current F-14 Tomcat. Its missile became the current Phoenix.

Perhaps the highest British postwar priority was reserved for a single-package ASW airplane, GR 17/45, which became the Gannet. It required two crew, beside the pilot, to operate radar, ECM, sonobuoy-receivers, tactical plot, weapon control, and to navigate. The sheer size of the airplane was reduced by gearing its two turbo props together to a single contra-prop. It would not be ready for some years.

Wartime Barracudas were retained in service as an interim measure as well as the wartime two-seat Firefly fighter which was adapted for ASW as the Firefly 6. It in turn had only two seats, and limited endurance. It also had only one sonobuoy receiver, so that it could track a submarine but could not fix it by cross-bearing. In 1949 Fairey proposed a three seat version, Firefly 7, as an interim solution to slow Gannet development. It achieved better endurance by using a smaller engine, and could operate from unmodernized light fleet carriers, but showed poor stability, and a poor forward view. It had to be relegated to training duty. In 1953, the US Navy provided 100 Avengers as an interim replacement.

Meanwhile, a much less capable aircraft, which became the Short Seamew, was developed specifically for operation from future converted merchant ships, or from unmodified light fleet carriers. Suggested in the same 1949 memorandum which had produced the cruiser-destroyer, it could carry only a single torpedo or a load of sonobuoys. The Gannet could carry both sonobuoys and two homing torpedoes.

Strike aircraft were also a problem. The 1945 cancellations left the most promising project, the turbo-prop Wyvern, in development. By 1952, however, it was suffering from engine surge, and no cure was in sight. Nor did the US Navy have any surplus modern strike aircraft: Skyraiders were in short supply. Wyverns entered squadron

service only in 1955, replacing an earlier piston single-engined strike fighter, the Firebrand. No Wyvern successor was ever designed because by the early 'fifties no suitable new torpedo was under development. By that time, however, the Royal Navy had won its battle for a more strike-oriented role, and a new carrier bomber, the NA39, (which became the Buccaneer) was under development. The latter was justified partly as a counter to future Soviet surface raiders, which (like their German forbears) might contrive to lose themselves in the wide Northern seas. No surface ship could be relied upon to find a fast Soviet cruiser. It was vital, then, to have a fast, long-range airplane which could carry a sinking weapon (such as Green Cheese or a tactical atomic bomb). The Buccaneer's ability to fly considerable distances at low level made it an effective strike bomber against land targets, eg, in support of the Army.

*   *   *

In 1945, the Royal Navy operated three major types of carrier, the six large armored flight deck fleet carriers, the 12 *Colossus* class light fleet carriers, and escort carriers, most of which would have to be returned to the United States upon the conclusion of lend-lease agreements. The British-converted *Campania* was retained as an aircraft transport. The carrier-like aircraft repair ship *Unicorn* reverted to auxiliary status, as a maintenance ferry carrier. The even less capable MACs (Merchant Aircraft Carriers), converted in wartime, had retained their tanker or grain-carrier hold space. All reverted to commercial service postwar.

Only the big fleet carriers could be modernized to take substantial numbers of modern aircraft. Of

For task force ASW, the obvious solution was to move the helicopters from the carrier to some alternative platform. The County class missile destroyers were probably the first attempt in this direction. By the late 'fifties, preliminary work was proceeding on an escort cruiser, which would carry task force helicopters and a task force area defense missile. It would leave the new carrier, CVA01, free to operate as many airplanes as possible. The escort cruiser died with the big carrier, but two cruisers were modified to fill its intended role. *Blake* is shown. The escort cruiser sketch designs later formed the starting point for what became the VSTOL carrier *Invincible.* [USNI]

Helicopters were also extremely useful for limited amphibious assault, a point taken by the US marines in the early 'fifties. Helicopter-borne marines from the light fleet carriers *Ocean* and *Theseus* attacked successfully at Suez, inspiring the conversion of larger ships. Marines man their helicopters aboard *Albion*, December 1965. [*USNI*]

the six, the three *Illustrious* class (*Illustrious, Formidable,* and *Victorious*) were the oldest and least capable, with their single hangars. They would also be the easiest to modernize, since their hangars were relatively deep. Moreover, since they were a class of three, a single reconstruction design would suffice for the maximum number of ships. In this sense the two-ship (double-hangar) *Implacable* class was the next most attractive, and the odd ship of the group, the transitional *Indomitable*, the least attractive. *Illustrious* was refitted in 1945 to operate heavier aircraft, and served postwar as a trials and training carrier. *Formidable* was to have been the first rebuilt, but she was in bad condition, and was laid up unmaintained from 1948 onwards. Thus *Victorious* was taken in hand for modernization in 1950. At this time preliminary design work also began on the *Implacable* class, but in April 1952 the Admiralty decided formally that only *Victorious* would be rebuilt. At that time it appeared that a much more satisfactory ship, a new 50,000-ton carrier, would be ordered within a few years.

Moreover, the two big *Ark Royal*s were being completed to modernized designs.

Modernization of the light fleets was discussed, but rejected as too expensive. Several ships did receive slightly strengthened flight decks and stronger elevators and arresting gear to take such intermediate aircraft as the piston-engined Sea Fury fighter and the Gannet ASW bomber. Moreover, the royal Navy did evolve a category of second-line 'trade protection' aircraft, such as the Sea Venom fighter. The Seamew single-role ASW airplane was evolved largely to be flown from unmodified light fleet carriers.

The escort carriers had fulfilled a role which would again be important in any future war. A 1946 study suggested that, within 18 months of the outbreak of war Britain would need 20 trade protection carriers over and above her existing fleet. Declared requirements at this time were 12 escort, four replenishment, and three training carriers. They would have to be merchant ship conversions. However, only fast liners would be able to operate modern (ie, Gannet-like) ASW aircraft, and they would not be available. The alternative was to develop a special lightweight ASW airplane. Although it was not followed up at the time, this was the idea that eventually led to the Short Seamew, a two-seater which could carry either sonobuoys or homing torpedoes, but not both. Existing light fleet carriers would provide convoy fighter defense.

A table of available and prospective merchant ships showed that none fitted the staff requirements for training, escort, or replenishment carrier. The best available would be a 450 to 500ft 14 to 18-knot ship. At this time the future ASW airplane, the GR 17/45 (later the Fairey Gannet) was being credited with the ability to take off in 450ft in 17 knots of wind over the flight deck when fully loaded, ie, from a 14-knot ship into a three knot head wind. It was to have been equipped with RATOG (rocket-assisted take-off gear) for launching if no catapult were fitted. One might realistically expect staff requirement weight (16,000 pounds) to rise 2000 pounds, so the airplane might have to jettison some of its load when landing in little or no wind to meet arresting gear limits (staff requirements were 20,000 pounds/85 knots air speed for an escort carrier, 17,000 pounds/75 knots for MAC). If, however, the British were reduced to using 12-knot merchant ships as MACs, then they would have to develop new fighters and ASW aircraft.

War experience showed that an 18-knot carrier could operate fairly comfortably with convoys, but that a 16-knot ship could not. The conclusion was that carrier conversion should have prior claim on fast ships, especially as convoys would probably be faster than in the past.

These calculations were complicated by the need to deal with shadowers. The new submarines, operating submerged at all times, would have little independent capability to detect targets at any great range. They would, therefore, have to depend upon reconnaissance aircraft (snoopers). If the latter used radar, they could operate at such great ranges (200nm) as to be virtually immune from interception by escorting fighters. However, 18-knot escort carriers of World War II type could not operate anything better than the existing Sea Fury propeller fighter.

The anti-snooper idea is still relevant. When the British *Invincible* class VSTOL carriers were being designed, the major Soviet blue-water, anti-ship missile was the ship- and submarine-launched SS-N-3, which required targeting assistance in the form of a Bear D radar reconnaissance bomber. The light carriers were provided with Sea Harrier fighters just for the anti-snooper (in this case, anti-Bear) mission which had been discussed at length just after World War II. As in the earlier postwar period, it was assumed that Soviet anti-ship bombers (which the light carrier could not counter) would be limited to submarines and perhaps to a few surface ships. The current US view would be that this lower-threat area will contract as the Soviet anti-ship bomber force is modernized.

In the postwar period, the Royal Navy had to plan to operate large carriers in the high-threat areas, leaving lower-threat ones (such as the Atlantic) to light carriers. One might draw a current analogy and argue that the heavy carriers (now exclusively US) will operate in the highest threat zone, with light ASW carriers reserved for lesser threat areas. However, the British ASW carriers may also support the US heavy-carrier force as a specialized adjunct.

The trade protection situation was so bad in 1947 that exotic solutions were proposed: completing the three *Tigers* as carriers, even retaining discarded heavy cruiser hulls (without superstructures) for emergency conversion in wartime. However, by 1949, interest in such ships had declined. Studies of prospective wartime aircraft production showed that it would be difficult enough to fill the existing fleet and light fleet carriers. British policy, then was to assume that in wartime, as in World War II, the United States would have to supply both escort carriers and aircraft. At this time, however, US minimum requirements for an escort carrier were rising, and it seems unlikely that mass production on a World War II scale of the new design (SCB 43) would have been possible.

In 1953, a British shipping line owner tried to convince the Royal Navy to subsidize special merchant ship construction for potential MAC use in wartime, but his arguments were rejected. The Radical Review soon ended interest in such protracted-war projects.

By 1954, the Royal Navy classed its carriers according to their 'standard' of modernization; a 1956 version shows:

A: 984/CDS (Comprehensive Data System)/32 or 48 track/DPT (Digital Plot Transmission); fully angled (approx. 9 degrees; 6½ degrees in *Hermes*) deck; steam catapults; Mk 13

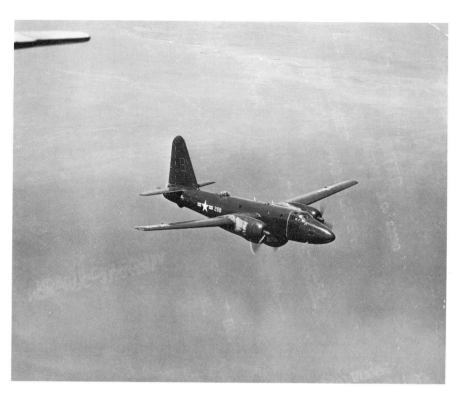

For the US Navy, unlike the Royal Navy, naval aviation includes both ship- and shore-based aircraft. For example, for many years the US Navy operated land-based fleet AEW aircraft. This Lockheed Neptune (P2V-3W), photographed in June 1950, was an alternative to the larger Super Constellation (WV-2 or EC-121). Thirty were built; later Neptunes, like carrier ASW aircraft, used their APS-20s for snorkel detection. [*USN*]

arrester gear; NA 39, N113, DH 110 and earlier. (H) adds HTP (hydrogen peroxide) stowage, can operate SR177.

B*: As A but 982/983/960/CDS/(16 or 24 track)/ DPT

B: Only 982/983/960, no CDS, full angled deck, steam catapult, Mark 13 arrester gear

C: Interim (5½ degree) angled deck, steam catapult, Mark 13 arrester gear

C(H): Plus HTP for SR177

D: 982/983/960 or earlier, interim deck BH 5 or earlier catapult, earlier arrester gear: Sea Hawk, Sea Venom, Gannet

E: Earlier radar, axial deck, earlier arrester gear.

F: Earlier radar, interim deck, present aircraft in training and trials role only.

The 1949 ('restricted fleet') plan formed the basis of the postwar peacetime British operational carrier force: it allowed for two fleet and three light fleet carriers. Other ships remained in commission for non-flying training, which kept them in service for potential mobilization. In 1951, of the fleet carriers, only *Indomitable* was operational, as flagship of the Home Fleet. *Illustrious* was trials carrier. *Implacable* and *Indefatigable* served as non-flying training ships, the former just having been relieved by the modernized *Indomitable*. The new *Eagle* entered service late in the year.

In 1951, the planned wartime (M plus six months) carrier force was two fleet and four light fleet carriers, the latter reduced to three in 1952. At this time the Global Strategy paper showed a requirement for seven to ten trade protection carriers in the Atlantic, of which the United Kingdom was to provide five. This, however, was based on an obsolete analysis. As the Soviet naval air arm was re-equipped with jet bombers of greater range, the air threat to the eastern Atlantic and to the northern part of the North Sea increased. That in turn would have to be countered by fleet carriers. The Global Strategy paper did not even mention the Mediterranean, but the earlier analysis from which it worked called for two fleet carriers there. A proposed cut from one fleet carrier and a light carrier to a single light fleet carrier would leave a weak ship facing a very strong air threat – or depending very heavily on the US Sixth Fleet to win the initial battle for maritime air superiority. At this time the US and British governments were competing for the NATO Mediterranean command, and some in the Admiralty feared that any further reduction would weaken the British position.

Moreover, as long as the Korean War continued, a light carrier would have to operate in the Far East until M plus three months. It might then be allocated either to the Atlantic or to the Mediterranean – and shown in lists as allocated to the latter, to help politically. DAW (Director of Naval Air Warfare) rejected such tampering altogether: 'the plain fact is that we haven't enough air strength to meet even vital commitments and must therefore lean heavily on the US Navy. However much we may try to delude ourselves to the contrary, we cannot delude the Americans'. Certainly existing British piston-engine fighters (this was 1952) would be of little use against Soviet jets.

Tactically, it was argued that single fleet carrier operations would be risky. Better to keep them together as the nucleus of a carrier task force. The war plan, then, showed both fleet carriers operating together in the Atlantic. Total withdrawal from the Far East would free a fourth light carrier. Three could therefore operate in the Atlantic in defense of trade, leaving one in the Mediterranean to reinforce the two squadrons of (RAF) maritime aircraft there, with their inadequate fighter cover.

The planned (1952) wartime (D plus 30 days) composition of the NATO strike fleet shows just how large a part of the total British contribution her two heavy carriers represented:

	US	UK	Total
HEAVY CARRIERS	4	2	6
BATTLESHIPS	1	1	2
CRUISERS	4	—	4
DESTROYERS	21	15	36
SUBMARINES	2	—	2

Of the surviving war-built light fleet carriers, *Glory* and *Theseus* alternated off Korea. *Vengeance* was fully operational in the Mediterranean Fleet. *Triumph* served as training carrier, alternating with *Warrior*. *Vengeance* was lent to the RAN in November 1952, for service while HMAS *Melbourne* was being completed to a modern design.

In 1953 *Indomitable* then in the Mediterranean, suffered a severe gasoline explosion. She was patched sufficiently to participate in the Coronation Review, but was never repaired, and was placed in the lowest reserve category.

The first effect of the Radical Review was to force the Royal Navy to choose between maintaining two non-operational fleet carriers (against wartime needs) or maintaining three non-operational light fleet carriers. The latter could actually operate somewhat heavier aircraft, and none of these ships could serve as anything more than a trade protection carrier. In that role, numbers were more important than size. The two big training carriers were reduced to un-maintained reserve, and three light carriers (*Ocean, Theseus* and *Triumph*) were converted for non-flying training in 1953-54. *Glory* remained in service as a trooping and ferry carrier. British mobilization plans called for her to return home in an emergency, to be equipped with her own air group.

The next economy was to lay up the fourth fleet carrier, *Illustrious*, which (under earlier plans) would have served at least through the 'fifties. One ship, *Warrior*, would have to suffice for trials and training. She in turn would become surplus when *Hermes* replaced *Bulwark* as the third modern light fleet carrier. In fact, she was retired earlier, and sold to Argentina in July 1958.

The refit schedule often reduced operational strength below the planned level. For example, by the end of 1954 there would be only one fleet carrier (*Eagle*) and three modern light fleet carriers (the three original *Hermes* class).

Eagle, the first postwar fleet carrier to be completed, began with an axial deck. She was refitted with an interim angled deck (Standard D) in 1954-55, and was then to Standard A in 1958-60. Her sister ship *Ark Royal* was completed to Standard C (steam catapult, interim angled deck). She was to have had a large refit to Standard A after *Eagle* emerged, but that was cancelled, and she was never fitted with Type 984 radar.

Victorious was completed to Standard A in 1958.

The light carriers *Albion, Bulwark,* and *Centaur* (*Hermes* class) were completed with interim angled decks and hydraulic catapults (Standard D). Prior to the Radical Review, *Albion* and *Centaur* were scheduled for refit with full angled decks and steam catapults (Standard B) in 1958. *Bulwark* would not be refitted, as she would be replaced by *Hermes* (Standard A) upon completion.

Hermes was completed to Standard A in 1959.

After her return by the Royal Canadian Navy in 1948, the light carrier *Warrior* was brought up to Standard E at Devonport (1952-53), and then was refitted (1955-56) with an interim angled deck (Standard F).

As of 1954, the British naval program envisaged, in addition, laying down a medium carrier in 1958 for completion in 1963. In 1957, then, the Royal Navy would have no Standard A carriers in service. However, the first fully satisfactory ship

(*Victorious*) would enter service in 1958, with others following in 1959 (*Hermes*), 1961 (*Eagle*), 1963 (the new carrier), and 1964 (*Ark Royal*). On the other hand, options studied under the Radical Review included the cancellation of work on *Hermes* and *Victorious*, as well as the reduction of the fleet carriers to light carrier air groups.

In fact, *Bulwark* reduced to flying training duty earlier than might have been expected, leaving four operational carriers (*Ark Royal, Eagle, Albion,* and *Centaur*). In 1959-60, both of the *Ark Royals* were refitting, and there were only three operational carriers (including the new *Victorious*). *Bulwark* had already been withdrawn from flying training, for conversion to a commando (helicopter assault) carrier. She was not replaced. *Ark Royal* was never raised to full A standard, but she was refitted with the full angled deck and then with more powerful steam catapults. One reason why was that Type 984 itself, like ambitious contemporary US radars, proved extremely difficult to maintain.

The total British carrier force was then set at five ships, at least one of which was always refitting. For example, in 1961-62 *Eagle* was refitting, and *Ark Royal, Victorious, Hermes* and *Centaur* were operational. *Albion* was undergoing conversion as the second commando carrier. The last of the original *Hermes* class, *Centaur* was withdrawn only in 1966. A proposed commando ship conversion was cancelled, and she served as an accommodation ship before being broken up.

*   *   *

The *Victorious* modernization showed just how difficult it would be to rebuild the existing fleet carriers. She had been built to operate 14,000-pound airplanes; now she was to fly off the same 30,000-pound (40,000 pounds for take-off) types for which the newer *Ark Royals* and *Hermes* class light carriers had been designed. Similarly, the new aircraft needed roomier hangars (hangar height increased from 16ft to 17ft,6in), which in this case required that the flight deck – the upper strength member of the hull – be bodily raised 4ft, so that a complete gallery deck could be worked in beneath it. The full 3in flight deck armor was, moreover, retained, although side armor (including side projection of the hangar) was reduced from 4½ to 2in. Part of the reduction in side armor thickness was required because the armor had to be extended aft to cover bulk avgas stowage.

Modern catapults (two BS4) and arresting gear were installed, the flight deck widened and cleared so far as possible, and the island substantially reduced in length. At one point the long-range air search radar (then a Type 960) was to have been carried atop a separate mast, as in some later US carriers. However, when Type 984 was chosen during the reconstruction process, it was sited atop the island structure.

The new jets needed much more aviation fuel:

the ship had been designed with only 50,000 gallons, compared to 80,000 for the small light fleet carriers, and 103,300 for *Ark Royal* – which was still far short of the 240,000 (US) gallons of an *Essex* or the 120,000 (US) gallons of a small US light fleet carrier.* The Naval Staff wanted a total of 348,000 gallons, including 150,000 gallons of avgas. This was based on four days of maximum air operations, with 6000 gallons for each of 58 aircraft. However, the initial design (1950) showed only 285,000 gallons, 140,000 of avgas and 145,000 of heavier avtur, a jet fuel which could be burned in a ship's boilers, and which could be handled (and stowed) like oil fuel. DAW was willing to accept a reduction to 4800 gallons per airplane (a total of about 280,000 gallons). Unfortunately, these calculations were made just when the US government was demanding total reversion to avgas. Since British fuel supplies were tied to US production, it was essential to increase avgas stowage. However, armored volume was very limited. The best DNC could do was to trade off avgas against bomb room (magazine) volume, to increase to a total of 185,000 gallons. Avtur stowage, on the other hand, could be traded off against ship endurance.

Within a few years, the Royal Navy had switched back to a special high-flash-point jet fuel, avcat, and was stowing most of its fuel in unarmored tanks. Thus *Victorious* emerged from

---

* The Royal Navy would argue, with some justification (based on escort carrier experience), that its fuel stowage was more secure.

Note that one Imperial Gallon (British) was equivalent to 1.201 US gallons, so that the *Essex* was equivalent to about 200,000 British gallons, and the *Independence* to about 100,000, ie, to the fuel stowage of the much larger British *Ark Royal* of the 1943 program.

The Neptune became the symbol of postwar US shore-based naval aviation. Although it was widely used for ASW, it was designed, during World War II, as an anti-shipping bomber, a characteristic still evident in early postwar versions. This P2V-3 was photographed in August 1949. Note the solid (attack) nose carrying four 20mm cannon. Eleven of 53 ordered became P2V-3Cs for carrier take-off as interim nuclear attack bombers. They would fly to their targets, drop their 10,000-pound weapons, and then ditch alongside specially placed submarines. This tactic was actually demonstrated on 7 March 1949, when a P2V-3C took off from the large carrier *Coral Sea,* carrying a dummy weapon (at a total weight of 74,000 pounds), flew 2000nm to a target, dropped the weapon, and then flew 2000nm more to a landing. [USN]

modernization carrying only 60,000 gallons of avgas – and 279,000 of avcat, very nearly the total originally envisaged. The larger *Eagle*, which had been credited with only about 100,000 gallons of avgas, was completed with 165,000 gallons of avgas and 302,000 gallons of avcat. Note that by divorcing aircraft fuel stowage limits from internal armored volume limits, the shift to avcat made it possible to stow very large amounts of fuel aboard relatively small carriers. Thus HMS *Centaur*, a large light fleet carrier, was completed carrying 61,200 gallons of avgas, but 290,500 gallons of avcat – more than the larger *Victorious*.

The other hallmark of modern carriers is electronics. In the case of *Victorious*, electric power was initially almost doubled, to 4200kW, and then increased again, after the ship had been completed, to 5000kW.

Initial plans showed a new battery of six twin 3in/70 and four sextuple 40mm. However, the ship was actually completed with six twin US-type 3in/50 and with one sextuple 40mm. She thus became the sole British warship actually to receive the MDAP gun.

The original modernization plan of 1949-50 required that the ship be bulged by about 4ft on each side. Requirements were revised in 1953, and *Victorious* was completed with both a fully angled deck and the Type 984 fighter control radar. As completed, her prospective air groups were as set out in the following table: (the air group planned for HMS *Eagle* after modernization is included for comparison.)

explain the quick decline of the less modern ships.

The comparable US modernization (SCB 27A) of *Essex* class fleet carriers was not quite so drastic, partly because hangar height already seemed sufficient. It did add topweight (eg, in two H8 catapults), and, like the British project, it did clear the flight deck, in this case by removing the twin 5in/38 and 40mm mounts at either end of the island structure. However, the US ship had no flight deck armor to disturb, and her hull strength was not affected by changes in the flight deck – which, from a structural point of view, was merely a superstructure.

In 1952, it appeared that the British rearmament program might well include a new carrier for construction from 1956 onwards. Her main roles were stated as:

— Fighter defense,
— Strikes against targets on sea and land to a range of perhaps 1000nm,
— ASW,
— helicopter operation,
— army support.

Of these, the second alone would required new heavy attack aircraft. It was justified on the ground of the expected evolution of strike aircraft, which would require a carrier to remain further out to sea to be safe from enemy attack. In addition, this range would allow the Navy to use the new tactical nuclear weapons most effectively, striking deep into enemy territory.

Doctrine called for carriers to operate in task groups of four, with a total of 300-350 aircraft,

1959	1961-2	1963	Eagle
12 N 113	12 N 113	8 SR 177	12 SR 177
	8 NA 39	12 NA 39	
12 SEA VENOM	10 DH 110	10 DH 110	10 DH 110
8 GANNET	8 GANNET	8 A/S HELO	8 A/S HELO
4 AEW SKYRAIDER	4 AEW GANNET	4 AEW GANNET	6 GANNET AEW
2 SAR HELO	2 SAR HELO	2 SAR HELO	2 SAR HELO

Similarly, the modernized *Hermes* can be compared to the interim-modernized *Centaur* (also given in the table).

HERMES	CENTAUR
8 N 113	
9 DH 110	12 DH 110
8 AS HELO	8 GANNET
4 AEW GANNET	4 SKYRAIDER AEW
2 SAR HELOS	2 ASR HELOS

These air groups are only examples, but they show the effect of major modernization, and

hence a capacity per carrier of 80-90 aircraft. Echoing American practice, the tentative staff requirements suggested that the ship be designed to carry perhaps one squadron of eight atomic bombers. Several smaller aircraft might be displaced when they were aboard.

Given progress in VSTOL and flexible deck techniques, it seemed likely to be the last designed primarily to operate fast-landing jets – a phrase often repeated in the following three decades in the US Navy. That did not deter the Naval staff from demanding capability to operate large, heavy aircraft, up to 60,000 pounds/120-135 knots (the US limit at this time was 70,000 pounds). One reason was a desire to be able to operate US naval aircraft from British carriers, either for cross-decking

A P2V-5 (May 1953) displays its ASW features: the big belly radar for snorkel detection and the wingtip searchlight for contact identification. The searchlight could be controlled by the bow turret (lookout) operator. Note that, unlike the current P-3 Orion, it was heavily armed (and armored) for self defense, with two 20mm cannon in the nose and tail, and two 0.50-calibre machine guns in a top turret. A large bomb bay could carry two Mark 41 homing torpedoes; the current P-3, converted from an airliner, has a much smaller bomb bay. Late production aircraft had magnetic anomaly detectors in 17ft plastic fairings which replaced their tail turrets, and from October 1954 onwards aircraft were fitted with underwing jet engines which shortened their take-off runs and increased their dash speed. Their turrets were removed at this time. Neptunes of this type were provided to Britain (and operated by RAF Coastal Command until Shackletons could be provided), Argentina (where they directed Super Etendard attacks many years later), Australia, Brazil, the Netherlands, and Portugal. Additional users of the ultimate P2V-7 were Canada, Chile, France, and Japan (which produced an improved version of her own). [USN]

within the strike fleet, or under some future MDAP program. Fast, heavy, aircraft in turn required a long flight deck, about 1000ft, (later reduced). Draft was limited to 35ft for harbor entrance and docking. An aviation fuel capacity of 1,000,000 gallons, comparable to contemporary US practice, was suggested. Most of it would be low flash-point fuel (similar to kerosene) stowed the double bottom; mixing pumps would also be provided.

Steam catapults would reduce any need for wind over the deck. However, high speed had considerable value for self protection, both against shadowing aircraft and against submarines. Speed was therefore tentatively set at 30 knots (deep and dirty), and economical speed at 20 to 25 knots (endurance 6000m, at 22 knots). The speed was a knot more than that of *Ark Royal*; it would be helpful when working with the (generally faster) US carriers. However, the earlier ship was rated at an endurance of 10,000nm at 20 knots, and it seemed unwise to accept less.

The ship would not be limited (as before World War II) by the dimensions of the Panama or Suez Canals. She would probably displace about 55,000 tons. The last British carrier design, *Malta*, had been severely limited by a requirement that it be dry-docked in existing facilities. However, even then, plans had been made to build larger docks in

the United Kingdom. The new design therefore went ahead without reference to docking restrictions.

Torpedoes and atom bombs would be the main threats. Protection, then, would be based on compartmentation, anti-torpedo armor, and grouped ventilation. Armor as such would be less important than strength against blast. Analysis showed that the maximum practicable flight deck armor was 2in thick; similar armor could be applied to the ship's side down to the waterline. Anything more, like the older carriers, would be prohibitive.

By July 1952, actual characteristics had been worked out sufficiently to permit machinery to be ordered in October 1952 and a sketch design prepared by December. Like existing British carriers, this one would have a closed hangar. Length was now 870ft, endurance 6000nm at 22.5 knots. Hangar area was to be 50-55,000ft^2, height 17½ft under beams (25 crossed out).* Aircraft would take off at 60,000 pounds, and land at 40,000 pounds (70,000 and 45,000 crossed out). Landing and take-off speeds were set at 135 knots (140 crossed out) true airspeed; dimensions at 65 by 65ft (70ft span crossed out); span was 45ft (49 crossed out) folded, height folded 17½ft (22 crossed out). the ship would need at least three catapults, and she would be armed with a main battery of 3in/70 guns. She would have two Type 984 radars. Aviation fuel stowage was cut back to 750,000 gallons (250,000 avgas).

The director of Air Warfare (DAW) suggested

* The excised original figures indicate the characteristics originally desired, which were close to contemporary US practice.

that the carrier should be able to take aircraft of about Canberra size. The new USS *Forrestal* had been designed for the new US 70,000-pound strategic bomber, and at first it was agreed that the British ship should also be capable of operating up to this size for special operations. However, any increase in hangar height would considerably affect overall ship size. the initial folded height of 22ft had led to the 25ft hangar height figure. Similarly, it was agreed that at least 1000ft of flight deck was needed to operate a Canberra and N113 (Scimitar) and its successors. It was desirable to limit draft to 33ft.

At first, two of the three catapults were to have been able to take the heavy bomber; then all three. Four were considered desirable, to scramble four fighters quickly.

On the basis of a 55,000ft^2 hangar, 1000ft flight deck, and 690ft angled deck, DAW established a maximum air group of 90.

By the end of 1952 money was tighter, and the big carrier had to be abandoned. That did not end the need for a new ship, however. In December 1954, as part of his series of design studies for the Sea Lords, the DNC presented two more modest carriers: one of 35,000 tons and one of 28,000 tons.

The 35,000-ton carrier was considered the smallest type which could operate modern aircraft in reasonable numbers with other design features to a corresponding standard. It was a general purpose carrier which, though not so large as to be wasted in trade protection could carry a considerable strike force when needed. Aircraft: 47 of typical types, eg, 12 Scimitar, 12 Sea Vixen (or Scimitar), eight Gannet (or additional Buccaneer), nine Buccaneer (or additional Gannet), four AEW, and two Search and Rescue (SAR, helicopters). Twenty-one aircraft would be carried in the deck park, 26 in the hangar. Armament would consist of four twin 3in/70, and machinery would be three shafts (48,000shp each), for 29.9 knots deep and dirty. Endurance would be about 5000nm at 20 knots. The hangar would be protected by 1.5in top and sides, the top of the citadel outside the hangar by 1.5in, the side in way of citadel 3in, and 1.5in armor would be spread around vital compartments in island and immediately below. The arrangement included a catapult on the hangar deck.

The 28,000-ton carrier was considered the smallest which could operate modern aircraft in reasonable numbers, the type then represented by *Hermes* and her class. Aircraft features had to cost other ship qualities (protection, armament, speed, ammunition, etc). DNC considered it unbalanced, particularly as regards defensive qualities. An air group of about 38 aircraft, would typically comprise 12 Scimitar, 12 Sea Vixen or Scimitar, eight Gannet or Buccaneer, four AEW, and two SAR, of which 18 would be carried in a deck park, and 20 in the hangar. Armament would be limited to twin Bofors. Two-shaft (100,000shp) machinery would drive the ship at 28.4 knots deep and dirty. Endurance would be 5500nm at 20 knots. The

flight and hangar decks and ship's sides over the citadel could be protected with 1in plating.

Even the 35,000-tonner was too expensive. By March 1956, the Sea Lords were considering a 30,000-tonner armed with the '1¾' missile (Bristol Bloodhound, see Chapter 3) then under consideration as a future missile cruiser weapon. Staff requirements were then due early in 1958, for delivery in 1965. This would have been a very limited ship. Instead, by 1959, the Royal Navy had reverted to the carrier strike role. Tactical analysis showed that the kind of small air group which a small carrier could support would not suffice for the roles then envisaged, which included deep strikes. Thus design work reverted to something close to the 1952 design, which became the abortive CVA 01.

*   *   *

The other aspect of maritime aviation was the long-range maritime patrol bomber, both water- (such as the wartime Martin Mariner and the Short Sunderland) and land-based (such as the postwar Lockheed Neptune and the Avro Shackleton). Such aircraft were used for a combination of long-range maritime reconnaissance and attack and anti-submarine patrol. However, because their fundamental naval strategies differed, similar aircraft in the two navies had very different roles, leading to very different postwar lines of development. The fundamental British prewar strategy was defensive. She had to protect a worldwide Empire with limited forces. Inevitably, her strategy was to establish a series of bases from which her mobile fleet could operate. The bases in turn had to be defended, whether or not the fleet was nearby. For example, torpedo bombers were stationed at Singapore to detect and to attack a Japanese invasion fleet. They were as much part of the fixed defense of Singapore as were the heavy guns emplaced nearby, and thus were naturally under Air Force control. Although British flying boats could operate from relatively unprepared positions, their association with the fixed base structure of the Royal Air Force limited any interest in their strategic mobility. Morever, RAF maritime reconnaissance doctrine emphasized anti-ship attack, not fleet cooperation.

By way of contrast, the fundamental prewar US naval problem was to move a fleet across the Pacific to engage and defeat the Imperial Japanese Navy. The United States had agreed at Washington in 1921 not to fortify its few mid-Pacific possessions, and in any case Japan controlled most of the island chains. Thus there was little question of garrisoning key points. Reconnaissance would be vital, and the fleet would have to take its scouts with it. the US Navy, therefore, developed long range seaplanes, such as the PBY Catalina, and a force of fast tenders from which they could operate. Postwar, this kind of strategic mobility remained important in US naval thinking, even though it original impetus, the problem of trans-Pacific warfare, had lost its significance.*

Politically, perhaps, the major wartime issue was naval operational control over maritime patrol aircraft. The Royal Navy gained control over carrier aircraft in 1939, but the RAF retained land-based maritime patrol aircraft and seaplanes. Split operational control over ASW forces caused problems, and in 1943 RAF Coastal Command came under naval operational control, which ceased at the end of World War II. Coordination continued, but repeated Royal Navy efforts to gain control over Coastal Command failed. This purely political arrangement later had important consequences, as the land-based ASW aircraft could be held up as an alternative to trade protection carriers and frigates. The implicit rivalry between bombers and ASW ships and submarines was to resurface in the 1981 (Nott) Defence Review.

By way of contrast, the US Navy had controlled its seaplanes from the first. They were primarily long-range scouts; only in 1939 did the Navy even consider developing a smaller seaplane for ASW patrol out of undeveloped US coastal inlets, in rough analogy to British practice. A prewar compromise limited the Navy to water-based aircraft. However, under the pressure of the 1942 U-boat campaign, the Navy was allowed to

* That is, the United States was already in position in the Western Pacific, and well provided with island bases in the area. It no longer had to contemplate the seizure of a string of such bases as a prerequisite for operation against enemy forces.

operated land-based ASW bombers, initially Lockheed Hudsons. for a time both Navy and Army flew ASW patrols, but by 1943 the US Navy had taken over all of the land-based ASW aircraft, both operationally *and* administratively. As it seized island bases in the Pacific, it moved its land-based maritime bombers forward. By 1945, it was flying prototypes of a new generation long-range maritime bomber, the Lockheed Neptune. Moreover, because there was no administrative division between land- and sea-based naval aircraft, the US Navy was able to develop long-range fleet support (such as airborne early warning) aircraft. Presumably, similar considerations apply to any current US naval interest in space-based communications and reconnaissance.

As a result, although there might be internal naval rivalries between carrier and shore-based aviators, they had nothing of the bitterness of the British disputes. The postwar US ASW (HUK) carriers were a means of bridging gaps between land-based coverage, as is clear from the distribution of land- and sea-centered HUK groups in the 1947-1949 long-range plans (see Chapter 2). As patrol plane range increased, there was less and less need for open-ocean HUK groups built around ASW carriers, and with the advent of the P-3 Orion the latter were finally eliminated altogether. Thus the development of SOSUS and the P-3s changed the distribution of funds within the US Navy, but it did not reduce overall Naval power – including political power. The Royal Navy faced very different considerations.

The DNC notes for Trident (see Appendix III) stress the importance of providing specialized naval aircraft for the Navy. *Vengeance,* a light fleet carrier, is shown here at Oslo in June 1947, with Seafires and two Walrus air-sea rescue amphibians on deck. With its well-known vices, the Seafire was perhaps the greatest example of the danger inherent in adapting even the best land-based aircraft to naval use. However, there was another side to the story. The Fleet Air Arm could never be very large. By using naval versions of land-based aircraft, it could at least benefit from the expenditures of the much larger Royal Air Force. Otherwise, naval aircraft tended to be built in very small numbers, and to cost proportionately too much. The result was an undue limitation of naval aircraft development – as witness the demise of the promising Supermarine Scimitar. [CPL]

5
CRUISERS

In 1945, the cruiser was a dual purpose ship. She was an important element of a fleet or convoy screen, both for anti-aircraft and for anti-ship action. She was also the smallest warship fully effective as an independent unit. For example, the Royal Navy distinguished between cruiser and destroyer standards of maintenance and manning, defining a destroyer as a ship requiring depot or tender support. Armed with 6in or 8in guns and generally carrying a substantial contingent of Marines, the cruiser was the ideal vehicle for intervention in what would now be termed the Third World.

The two cruiser roles diverged sharply after 1945, so that the modern cruiser, at least in Western navies, occupies the high end of a spectrum of fast fleet escorts. Most current US cruisers, for example, were at one time designated large destroyers (DLG; the US Navy, alone in the world, termed them 'frigates'). The only Western approach to a return to the earlier concept of the cruiser as a self-sufficient combatant was the abortive Strike Cruiser (CSGN), too expensive even for the US Navy to build.

The principal vehicles of change were anti-aircraft missiles. In their initial forms they were large weapons, and it seemed natural to consider cruisers or even larger ships to carry them, probably to the almost total exclusion of conventional guns. Unlike guns, the new weapons would be effective only against aircraft, and relatively high-flying ones at that. Radar guidance systems were unlikely to function well against either low-fliers or against ships on the surface. As for shore bombardment, the number of huge missiles a ship could carry seemed ludicrously small. Nor, for that matter, did it ever seem rational to fire an expensive missile across some ship's bow, in the traditional exercise of naval presence. Missiles could kill, but they could not threaten, and they were not useful in low-intensity or low-technology combat.

Thus, a missile-armed cruiser, however well she could survive in the tropics without a dockyard close at hand, was still impotent to coerce the local rulers; her 1903 forebear would have done better. She was tied to a fleet, whose offensive and anti-ship potential resided almost entirely in strike

aircraft. Fleet defensive potential resided largely in defensive fighter aircraft, whence the second major change in cruiser function.

Cruisers made effective platforms for fighter direction. Here US and British practice varied. In the US Navy, although the carrier remained the primary seat of fighter control, it was considered more important to promote maximum flight deck area, ie, maximum aircraft operating conditions. As a result, carrier island size had to be sharply reduced; carrier radar efficiency would necessarily suffer, and with it the efficacy of carrier fighter control. The Royal Navy preferred to place its best radars in its carriers, although, like the US Navy, it did provide some fighter direction outside the carrier.

Missiles added a new burden. Traditionally, fighters had been free to operate relatively close to the ships, whose anti-aircraft range was never more than a few thousand yards. Even the earliest missiles were effective out to ten or 20nm, and planned ranges were far greater, so that it was essential to keep fighters away from friendly anti-aircraft missiles. The obvious solution was to move fighter control to the missile ship. However, that in turn drove up the size of the missile ship. For the US Navy, this was an academic issue: the size was already there, in the war-built hulls which were converted to missile cruisers. For the Royal Navy, however, existing ships were too small. In the (required) new ones, ship cost could be proportional to ship size.

In 1956, for example, in connection with the British missile cruiser, it was argued that future task groups would have to have at least three operating fighter-control radars (984), associated with as many intercept positions as possible, certainly a minimum of seven per ship. Fighter direction facilities in the cruiser were essential, in case the 984 in a carrier should break down. This issue became particularly urgent when, in 1956, it was decided not to modernize Ark Royal. That would leave only three carriers (Eagle, Hermes, and Victorious) with Type 984 radars. Other ships would therefore have to be fitted, even if only to provide two per task group. Moreover, 984 was increasingly seen as necessary to provide sufficient early warning for missile firing.

The loss of traditional cruiser capability seemed to be of relatively little import to a US Navy which, after 1945, was redesigned to fight a new kind of high-intensity war – and which found two low-intensity ones to fight instead. For Britain, however, low-intensity war was extremely important; it was the old Empire or Commonwealth security mission.

The hot *vs* cold war choice had little impact in the period immediately after World War II. Britain had more gun-armed cruisers than she needed, and any hot war (missile-armed) ship would tend to supplement them. It also seemed likely that new gun armed cruisers would be built during the postwar decade, and several design studies were carried out. However, there was never enough money for ships beyond destroyer size. By the late 'fifties it was clear that the existing gun-armed ships would soon be gone. Most had been laid down before the end of 1942; even the *Tigers*, completed in the late 'fifties, had been launched before the end of 1945. Worse, the roomiest of the existing ships, the 'Towns,' had all been completed before the war and thus had all been subject to strenuous war service.

The inherent choice between missile and gun was made more agonizing by the historical accident which forced Britain, rather than the United States, to design new missile ships. Existing British cruisers were just too small to accommodate a missile system, particularly one as massive as Seaslug. All had evolved from prewar designs, most of them limited by the 1936 London Treaty to 8,000 tons or less (standard displacement). Ironically, Britain had proposed this limit in the first place in order to reduce the unit cost of cruisers, and so to be able to afford enough to protect her sea lanes. The United States had tried to follow suit, and in September 1939 her warship designers were just failing to fit a 6in dual purpose armament into the requisite displacement. The many problems of this design were resolved by the outbreak of war. With the treaties suspended, the US Navy could revert to the much larger designs it preferred. As a result, it ended the war with large numbers of new 10,000-ton light cruisers and 13,600-ton heavy cruisers, all of them available for conversion.

A much poorer Royal Navy had either to convert much larger ships, such as carriers or battleships, or to design a new cruiser. In the latter case, it would have to face the issue of the role of the cruiser: was it to be limited to fleet functions, or was it to operate in the traditional role as well? How large should it be? How expensive? The US Navy had the luxury of avoiding such questions altogether. The issue of size was settled by the availability of the war-built hulls. Moreover, secure in the possession of large numbers of reserve gun cruisers, the US Navy did not have to

In 1945, the cruiser was already a combination of two very different ships: an independent unit for raiding or for peacekeeping; and a medium to heavy fleet or convoy escort. In the US Navy, the second role was already so clearly predominant that it was natural for the cruiser and destroyer categories ultimately virtually to merge. The Royal Navy had very different priorities, and through the 'fifties it tried to maintain the independent role of its cruisers, largely to police its Empire and its spheres of influence. Large cruisers like *Liverpool*, shown here off Toulon in March 1950, were well adapted to this role. Torpedoed on 14 June 1942, she spent the rest of the war under repair at Rosyth, emerging in July 1945 as shown, with radars of Types 293 (foremast), 277 (foremast), 274 (main director), 279B (air search, aft), and 283 (secondary fire control). When this photograph was taken, she was flagship of the First Cruiser Squadron and Flag Officer Second in Command, Mediterranean, Admiral Mountbatten. She paid off into reserve in 1953, and was broken up in 1958. [CPL]

consider providing substantial gun batteries for its
new missile ships.

Perhaps ironically, neither navy was able to
build new cruisers. The US Navy built one
nuclear-powered ship, the *Long Beach*, but the
remainder of its new-construction missile ships
were large and small destroyers. The Royal Navy
came close to building two missile cruisers, but
ultimately it, too, had to settle for missile
destroyers, but without the comfort of operating
the large converted gun cruisers the US Navy had.
In each case important capabilities were lost, a fact
attested to by several subsequent US attempts to
build new full-sized cruisers.

For the Royal Navy, the nature of the guided
missile cruiser was tied to the question of the role
of the navy itself. Certainly, postwar British
governments considered convoy warfare more
important than carrier strike warfare, so that at
times a slow missile-armed convoy escort was
given a higher priority than the fast missile
cruiser. The air threat would be particularly
severe, the British expected, in the Northern and
Western Approaches. The US Navy of the early
postwar period suffered no such confusion, partly
because it did not expect to escort convoys within
range of enemy air attack.

Of the two major Western navies, only the
Royal Navy actively continued cruiser design
efforts immediately after World War II. The US
Navy had so many war-built ships either in service
or under construction that it was clearly unlikely
that any new ones would be approved. The last
studies, for a new-design anti-aircraft cruiser
(armed with the new 5in/54 gun) were dropped in
1946 on the argument that new destroyers would
do as well at a lower price. Moreover, any new
small cruiser would be so lightly armored as to be,
in effect, unprotected. After this, new design
effort was directed at conversions of existing hulls

for new roles, which turned out to be fleet air
defence (by missile) and fleet command and
control.

The Royal Navy was in a very different position.
Its wartime cruisers were, by 1945, largely
obsolescent. None had effective anti-aircraft fire
control systems. In 1953 the then Deputy Chief of
the Naval Staff observed that ships were still fitted
with systems he had decried as obsolete in 1939.
The only exception was the last of the war-built
cruisers, *Superb*, which, like her Canadian sister
Ontario, had three Mk VI directors. Only the two
most recent cruisers, *Swiftsure* and *Superb*, had
really efficient surface fire control systems, with
the new Type 931 splash-spotting radar. Six large
Minotaur class cruisers (which would have
incorporated fully satisfactory fire controls and
dual purpose weapons) had been approved in
wartime (five in 1944, when a sixth, a *Tiger*
approved in 1941, was switched to this design),
and early postwar plans showed them completed
'in slow time' postwar. They were still carried in
the the Director of Plans lists in 1947-8, but were
killed by the Defence Committee shortly
thereafter, so they did not appear in the February
1948 preliminary Nine Year Plan.

Perhaps worse, only 14 cruisers had Action
Information Organizations or AIOs (CICs in US
parlance). Whatever her fire controls, a ship with
an AIO was considered twice as effective in
anti-aircraft gunnery as one without. However,
both AIOs and modern directors required internal
space, which the relatively small British cruisers,
particularly the *Didos*, lacked.

Of the existing cruisers, the big 8in ships were
too old to modernize, and they were soon
discarded, despite their roominess and large
reserves of stability. The six prewar 'Towns' had
the advantages of size and a superior (prewar)
standard of construction. The ten war-built
'Colonies' (*Fijis*, improved *Fijis*, *Swiftsure*, and
Superb) were generally more cramped.
Unfortunately, the *Tigers*, the only three partially-
built hulls, which were the chief candidates for
radical modernizations, were slightly enlarged
'Colonies' (*Fijis*). Finally, there were ten smaller
cruisers, the *Didos*, valuable for their dual purpose
main batteries (5.25in) but decidedly cramped.

The best prospective cruiser gun was a new
rapid-fire twin 6in (Mark 26), which would be
substantially heavier than the existing triple 6in
Mark 23 (45-degree elevation) or 24 (slow-firing,
but 60-degree elevation). Although it could fire at
high elevation, it did not have a high enough rate
of fire to be considered fully effective for anti-
aircraft fire. The best prospective heavy anti-
aircraft gun, effectively a replacement for the twin
4in or even for the 5.25in, was a twin 3in/70. By
1949, a new compromise weapon, a rapid-fire
high-velocity 5in/70 (later 5in/62), was also in
prospect. It was conceived as the smallest effective
anti-ship weapon, and the largest effective anti-
aircraft weapon, and it formed the basis for a new
cruiser.

Immediately after the war, the best that could be done was to replace the three triple turrets of the three *Tigers* with two Mark 26 twin mounts (for a net gain, in theory, in rate of fire) and to replace her five twin 4in guns with three twin 3in/70. The 4in gun, however controlled, was considered useless against the new jets. This reconstruction plan, with another three twin 40mm added, was approved in 1949. This anti-aircraft-oriented armament required elimination of torpedo tubes, which the Royal Navy still valued as a means of dealing with heavy ships, as in the north Russian convoy actions of World War II.

Three ships could not suffice to meet fleet needs for modern cruisers. The question, then, was to what extent existing cruisers could be modernized. Many ships were too cramped to accept a weapon as large as the twin 3in/70, which was comparable in size to the big dual-purpose 4.5in Mark 6 on *Daring* class destroyers. A *Fiji*, not as beamy as a *Tiger*, could be fitted with only two twin 3in/70 in place of her five twin 4in; a larger *Southampton* could take three. However, the midship magazines in a *Fiji* could accommodate only about 600 rounds per gun for the two twin 3in/70. The *Town* class had no amidships magazine; ammunition would have to be transferred along their decks. Some additional anti-aircraft firepower might be obtained by replacing two of the three existing Mark 23 mounts by Mark 24s manufactured for the *Tigers*, but that would be of limited value.

The 1948 fleet plan envisaged full modernization of three existing ships to *Tiger* (Mark 26, 3in/70) standard. Admiral Edwards argued in June 1949 that this was wasteful, and, moreover, that it did not take into account the needs of the two main fleets. The Mediterranean would need air defense; the Home Fleet, all-round ships which could take on both aircraft and Soviet cruisers. *Swiftsure* and *Superb* would probably have better surface fire control than any Soviet cruiser for the next eight years (ie, through 1957, the crucial year). All other cruisers would need modernization. Their 4in

high-angle guns would be useless, even with Flyplane; perhaps they could be replaced by a single version of the new 3in/70.

For the Mediterranean, then, Admiral Edwards envisaged the three *Tigers* and four modernized *Didos* (retaining their 5.25in guns, but controlled by Flyplane). The Home Fleet would have five 6in cruisers with modernized surface fire controls and new 3in anti-aircraft guns (including *Swiftsure* and *Superb*). However, the 'Revised Restricted' fleet plan of 1949 showed two *Dido* and three 6in cruiser modernizations, the latter still to *Tiger* standard.

The Tiger Class

Modernization of three older 6in ships to full *Tiger* standards was rejected on the basis of cost, given the advanced age of the ships, which would age more before they could be fitted with the new Mark 26 and 3in/70. It might be necessary to replace existing DC by AC generators: the 6in was an AC gun. Modernization of existing ships would require the development of parallel AC and DC designs for the twin 3in/70. The existing 6in cruisers were limited to new 4in fire controls (which in any case would be inadequate), to improvements in 6in fire control which, it was hoped, would more than balance the larger size of Soviet cruisers.

The smaller *Didos* were an even more depressing proposition. Although twin 3in/70s could replace their twin 5.25in mounts, magazine space was so limited that it was estimated they would be able to fire for no more than three minutes. At best they could receive new fire controls (Mark VI directors with Flyplane predictors).

Full modernization of the cruiser force, then, would be limited to completion of the three *Tigers*, pending new construction. Even they could not be altogether satisfactory; in 1947, serious consideration was given to cancelling them, on the basis that there was little point in putting 1948-50 systems into a 1938 hull, and that they might not show much of a margin of superiority over

Design Z4C for the large cruiser *Minotaur*, presented to the Admiralty Board as Sketch D, the one actually selected in 1946. Standard displacement was 15,280 tons (645 LWL x 75 extreme beam x 20ft,9in mean draft; 23ft,3in freeboard to top of deck at side amidships; GM 3ft,3in). Deep displacement was 18,415 tons (mean draft 24ft), and speed in deep condition (clean) 31.5 knots on 100,000shp. Complement would have been 1090 (private ship). The guns shown are 6in twins Mark 26 and 3in twins; earlier versions had twin 4.5in guns instead of the newer 3in.

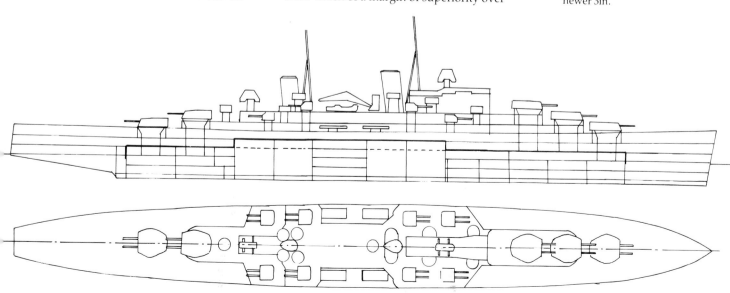

These sketches, drawn by the British DNC department in 1948, represented a first approach to a future cruiser design. They in turn formed the basis for early estimates of the size and cost of a missile-equipped cruiser.

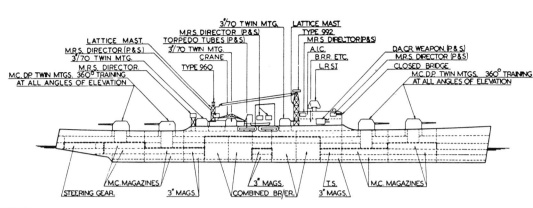

THE LARGE CRUISER OF 1960

SKETCH I

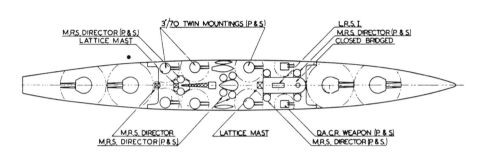

LENGTH, W.L.	645'-0"
BREADTH.	74'-0"
DRAUGHT.	23'-0"
SPEED. (DEEP CLEAN.)	31 KNOTS
S.H.P.	95,000
DISPLACEMENT. (STANDARD.)	14,500 TONS
" (DEEP)	17,500 "

ARMAMENT 8 – MEDIUM CALIBRE GUNS IN 4 TWIN MOUNTINGS
          12 – 3"/70   "   " 6   "   "   "
          2 – D.A. CLOSE RANGE WEAPONS
          4 – Q.R. TORPEDO TUBE MOUNTINGS

RADAR TYPE 960
       TYPE 992 WITH T.I.U. III

COMPLEMENT 900 – 950

THE LARGE CRUISER OF 1960 WITH "SEASLUG"

SKETCH II

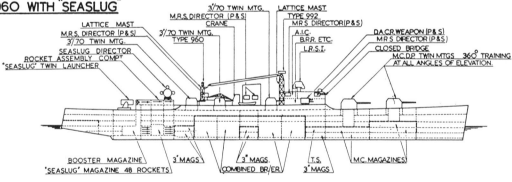

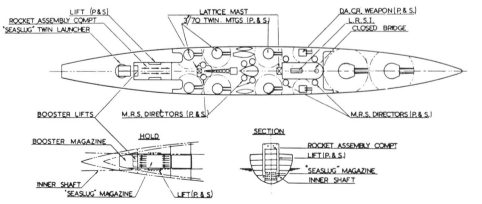

LENGTH W.L.	630'-0"
BREADTH	73'-0"
DRAUGHT	22'-0"
SPEED (DEEP CLEAN)	31 KNOTS
S.H.P.	95,000
DISPLACEMENT. (STANDARD)	14,000 TONS
" (DEEP)	17,000 TONS

ARMAMENT 4 – MEDIUM CALIBRE GUNS IN 2 TWIN MOUNTINGS
          12 – 3"/70   "   " 6   "   "   "
          2 – D.A. CLOSE RANGE WEAPONS
          "SEASLUG" TWIN LAUNCHER
          48 ROCKETS

RADAR TYPE 960
       TYPE 992 WITH T.I.U. III

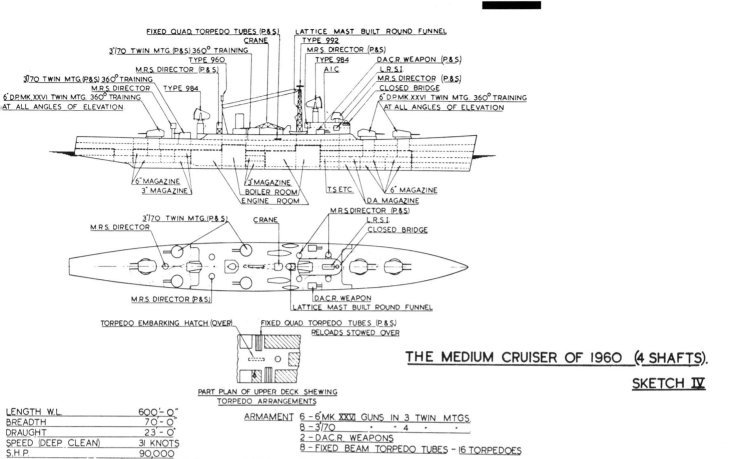

THE MEDIUM CRUISER OF 1960 (4 SHAFTS).

SKETCH IV

			ARMAMENT	6 – 6"MK. XXVI GUNS IN 3 TWIN MTGS.
LENGTH W.L.	600'- 0"			8 – 3"/70 " 4 " "
BREADTH	70'- 0"			2 – D.A.C.R. WEAPONS
DRAUGHT	23'- 0"			8 – FIXED BEAM TORPEDO TUBES – 16 TORPEDOES
SPEED (DEEP CLEAN)	31 KNOTS			
S.H.P.	90,000		RADAR	2 – TYPE 984
DISPLACEMENT (STANDARD)	12,250 TONS			1 – TYPE 992 WITH T.I.U. III.
" (DEEP)	14,750 TONS			1 – TYPE 960

existing gun cruisers when completed (as then planned) in 1952-3.

One possibility was to complete all three as prototype missile cruisers. An October 1947 study suggested that if the after main machinery, the after turret, all 4in guns and all torpedo tubes were removed there would be space and weight for a missile installation and possibly two 3in/70 twins. This was so terrible a price that DNC much preferred completion with dual-purpose guns when the latter became available. Moreover, the missile (then called GAP) was not expected to be ready until about 1958, whereas it was assumed that the ships could be completed with guns about four years earlier. In fact, they were completed in 1959-61, but the missile was also late.

An alternative proposal to complete them as light carriers was also rejected, as they offered very little capability at a high price.

At first the three ships were to have been completed as orginally designed, with single-purpose 6in guns and 4in medium range weapons. In that case, however, their efficiency as gun ships would be limited. It was estimated that, if the most efficient ship which could be built in 1953 was rated at 100 in gun power, a *Tiger* would equate to only 40. However, *Superb*, with the best existing fire control system, was rated at only 20, and existing cruisers only nought to five. Rearmament of an old 8in- or 6in-cruiser might bring it up to an efficiency figure of 80, purely on the basis of gunnery equipment. However, hulls and engines, which had already seen hard war

service, would be even older in 1953. The conclusion was that it would be worth while to complete the three *Tigers*, and to arm them from the first with the new-generation weapons.

The three *Tigers* were modernized to a 1951 staff requirement which emphasized their role in providing surface and anti-aircraft cover for convoys and carrier task forces. They were completely gutted, and new AC (rather than the earlier DC) generators installed, to provide for roughly double the electrical load initially contemplated. However, a proposal that they be reboilered was rejected. That in turn limited the extent to which the ships could be closed up against fallout or chemical attack, since the original boilers could not be isolated from the air supply to the machinery spaces.

The design called for two dual purpose 6in Mark 26 (400 rounds per gun), three twin 3in/70 (851 rounds per gun), twin Bofors L70 (1500 rounds per gun), one quadruple torpedo tube (no reloads), 15 depth charges (one track), and a long-range rocket flare launcher (50 rockets). The ships were actually completed with only the 6in and 3in guns, as the L70 Bofors never appeared. Illumination requirement was added to the basic staff requirement in 1952. The Staff Requirement never included torpedo tubes, but the SDPC proposed that they be fitted, at the after end of the quarter deck, as a post-completion alteration and addition, if the necessary margin of 20 tons still remained. One of the Bofors mounts could be sacrificed to provide topweight for an anti-torpedo weapon.

The combination of new generators, distilling plant, and air conditioning was considered equivalent to about four per cent of total installed shp, and it would cut endurance by about 440nm (compared to the original figure of 4190nm at 20 knots with a clean bottom).

The new requirements of naval warfare were reflected in a much-enlarged and fully enclosed (against fallout) bridge structure which accommodated the AIO and the gunnery direction room on the same level as the navigating bridge (compass platform). An admiral's covered bridge was provided immediately below.

The weights given below show the way in which the design grew to accommodate modern equipment:

TABLE 5-1: THE *TIGER* CLASS AS REBUILT

	TIGER (tons)	*ORIGINAL DESIGN* (tons)
GENERAL EQUIPMENT	799	631
MACHINERY	1494	1431
ARMAMENT	1101	1134
RADAR AND RADIO	110	—
ARMOR AND PROTECTION	1370	1345
HULL	4883	4553
FUEL OIL	2015	1902
RESERVE FEED WATER	128	131
DEEP DISPLACEMENT	11,900	11,127

NOTES: The *Tiger* data are taken from a 1954 legend. Original design weights were from the book of calculations in the National Maritime Museum. Note that armament weights originally included radars and radios. Increased machinery weight reflects increased generator power, and increased hull weight partly reflects the need for more internal volume, hence more structure to cover it.

The existing cruiser force would almost automatically be reduced to subsidiary and 'cold war' duties, although two ships (*Glasgow* and *Jamaica*) had been fitted with YE aircraft homing beacons to serve as 'pylon pickets'. *Newcastle, Birmingham,* and *Newfoundland* were modernized in 1950-52, and the smaller *Royalist* in 1954-56, primarily with new enclosed bridges, new radars, new fire controls (Mk VI, modernized existing GDS 2), and modern AIOs. These ships could barely defend themselves, and were considered the minimum acceptable for the strike fleet. *Sheffield* later had a large refit, her bridge being roofed over, and Mk VI directors installed. The existing Mk IV HACS (high-angle control system) was so ineffective that it was removed altogether (for topweight compensation) in the 'Colony' class cruisers *Bermuda, Ceylon, Gambia,* and *Kenya*. US Mark 63 directors were supplied under MDAP, and Mark 34 radars fitted to the 4in mounts, in analogy with contemporary US twin 3in/50s. By 1953, the MRS 6 system (including Mark VI) was no longer in production and so was no longer an option. Only three were available: one surplus from the Canadian *Ontario*, and two from the Australian *Hobart*.

In 1953, at the outset of the Radical Review, fuller modernization was planned for the big *Belfast* and for the two newest pre-*Tiger* cruisers, *Swiftsure* and *Superb*. *Belfast* would have retained her 4in secondary battery (but with six rather than four twin mounts with two MRS 3, and six twin 40mm L70). She could not take the new 3in/70 for structural reasons. The other two ships would have been rearmed with three twin 3in/70. In each case, the object of modernization was for the ship to be able, not only to defend herself but also to protect a consort under both visual and blind-fire conditions. This was far too expensive, and less expensive refits on the lines of the earlier ships were considered. There was also an intermediate standard, in which the ship could defend a consort in some limited fashion (MRS 3 installed for existing anti-aircraft weapons, L70 Bofors installed). Only *Belfast* was actually modernized, and she was not fitted with the planned Mark 26 mounts. *Swiftsure* was included in the program because she had recently been damaged. Work began in February 1957, but stopped before completion in August 1959. She was later considered as a potential single-ended missile cruiser or helicopter cruiser. However, she was broken up instead.

Modern cruiser requirements, as they were understood immediately after the war, really demanded a much larger ship, a point appreciated even during World War II. In 1944, the Admiralty chose for its new cruiser a large ship armed with 6in guns rather than an enlarged *Dido* armed with the new 5.25in (which led to the postwar 5in; see Chapter 3). The 1944 program included five such *Minotaur* class ships. So serious was the perceived deficiency of the existing 8,000-ton design that early in 1945 the last of the *Tigers* (ordered under the 1941 program) was re-ordered to become the sixth *Minotaur*. These ships were to be armed with a combination of high-angle triple 6in guns (Mark 25) and twin 4.5in guns, on the theory that the 6in was too large for fully anti-aircraft fire. At the end of the war, however, the Royal Navy was working on an automatic twin 6in dual-purpose weapon, Mark 26. The *Minotaur* design was therefore re-cast to incorporate the new weapons: the Mark 26 and also the new twin 3in/70. Traditional concerns showed in the retention of a heavy torpedo battery.

The new design was approved by the Admiralty

Blake reconstructed, shown on 27 March 1962. The three *Tigers* were the chief fruits of the ambitious cruiser modernization plans proposd in the late 'forties. Reconstruction was not authorized until 1954, and it was not completed until 1959-61, *Blake* being the last ship completed, in March 1961. The delay was largely due to delays in the production of the twin rapid-fire 6in and 3in guns. *Blake* was the first to be refitted with a helicopter pad aft (see Chapter 4) in 1965-69, followed by *Tiger* in 1968-72; the third ship, *Lion*, was never rebuilt again. *Blake* was laid up in January 1980. Note that the only directors visible are five MRS 3s, one to each twin gun mount, 6in or 3in. The big radar on the foremast is Type 992, with a long-range 960 on the mainmast (note the bar of its IFF below it) and a 277Q height-finder below. Note, too, the row of inflatable life rafts (of an early pattern) along the side of the forward superstructure. [*MoD*]

Board in August 1946, and work continued for some time beyond that. Even at that time the design was criticized as relatively old-fashioned, due to its wartime origins. In 1946, for example, some on the Board argued that it should have been scrapped altogether, and it was abandoned in about 1947. That did not eliminate the need for cruisers, and in 1948-49 new cruisers were included in the Nine Year fleet modernization plan.

Table 5–2 shows the final wartime design (Design Y) and also the postwar design approved by the Board in 1946; both are compared to the US cruiser *Worcester*, which was armed with a similar (and slightly heavier) twin 6in gun. It was often argued that deficiencies in British electrical plant (making for heavier weights) cost the *Minotaur* a

twin 5in mount, compared with the US cruiser. However, the British secondary battery consisted of the much heavier 3in/70, the mount for which was estimated to weight 35 tons, compared to 14 for the US twin 3in/50.

Given the necessary lead times, it was natural to explore the requirements of a next-generation cruiser. Although the resulting study was labelled '1960 cruiser', and thus might have been considered a long-term proposition, it must have been conceived as the immediate successor to the *Minotaur*. Moreover, it explicitly excluded a variety of exotic ideas, concentrating on the weapons and other systems expected to be available during the next decade.

As of December 1948, the likely menu of new systems (with dates of availability) was:

MAIN ARMAMENT	6in Mark 26 DP turret	end 1953
	Medium calibre DP (5in/70?)	1957
SECONDARY	3in/70	1957
CLOSE RANGE (CR) ARMAMENT	New (DA) weapon	1957
FIRE CONTROL	LRS I Director and TS equipment	1953
	MRS III Director and Predictor equipment	1953
	MRS IV Director and Predictor equipment	1957
	TIU Mark III	1954
RADAR	Type 960	Existing
	Type 992	1954
GUIDED MISSILE	Seaslug	1958

For propulsion at the powers involved, there was, in the relatively near future, no practicable alternative to the steam turbine. The type of machinery envisaged for the *Minotaur* design (improved *Daring* Class type) would be used. Funnels could not be dispensed with, but their number could be reduced to one if the arrangement of upperworks so required, and if the loss of the degree of dispersal given by two funnels was acceptable.

DNC tried to develop a series of sketch designs to show what could be achieved in the near future. He assumed that Britain could not longer build capital ships, and that cruiser size would have to be held down so that sufficient numbers could be built. Their main functions would be the protection of seaborne trade against surface and air attack; protection against submarines was ruled out on the ground that cruisers would necessarily by too large to be built in sufficient numbers, and that they would be too vulnerable (because they would not be sufficiently maneuverable) and also too attractive as targets in themselves. The numbers argument was based on the limited range of existing ASW weapons and sensors. The British noted, however, that the US Navy had taken the opposite point of view in building the submarine killer (at one time designated an ASW cruiser), *Norfolk*.

Perhaps the most important cruiser characteristic was its logistical independence of bases or a fleet train for an extended period, which in itself had to force up cruiser size. Other requirments clearly included a good surface gun armament; good long and short range AA armament (ultimately missiles); good speed; good endurance and seakeeping qualities; good protection – at least splinter protection – to all vital parts; good torpedo armament, or alternatively anti-ship guided missiles; ability to detect aircraft and submarines; ability to direct aircraft; and accommodation for a force flag staff and good communications. This combination seemed to demand substantial size.

Three sketch designs were drawn up. In each case the main armament would consist of dual-purpose weapons, although their calibre was as yet undecided. Moreover, no single sketch showed all the features, as that would have made it too large.

Sketch I was a large cruiser armed with eight medium calibre DP weapons in four twin mountings (controlled by one LRS 1 forward, one MRS 4 aft plus four sided MRS, two forward and two aft, for separate control); 12 3in/70 in six twin mountings (two MRS 4 and four MRS 3 directors). Overall gun direction would be by a TIU 3 with Type 992 radar, and the ship would also have Type 960 for air search. Her battery would be completed by two DA close range weapons and four quintuple 21in torpedo tubes. Protection would consist of 3¼in side belt; box protection to machinery spaces, magazines, (gunnery data) transmitting stations, bridge, steering gear, etc.

Power would be 95,000 shp, to give 31 knots deep and clean (to give 30 knots deep under any condition); endurance 7500nm at 20 knots deep and clean, in temperate conditions.

The main features of the design were:
— All-round training of the main battery. The individual mounts were arranged to avoid physical fouling between guns of adjacent mountings or with fixed structure at any angle of training, elevation or depression. This was considered necessary to overcome the difficulties arising from the high training speeds and automatic control of gun mountings.
— A combined boiler/engine room. The machinery was divided into four self-contained units, with sufficient separation between the forward and after pair to give strong probability that no one torpedo hit could immobilize the ship. The machinery would be of the improved *Daring* Class destroyer type.
— A single funnel to provide all-round training without having to lengthen the ship. This would require much space for the long horizontal uptakes.
— A Closed Bridge. A low bridge structure with a closed bridge at the fore end adjacent to and on the same level as the AIO would probably be a requirement.
— Space requirements. The enclosed space below the upper deck, after allowing for armament, operational, and machinery requirements, including workshop and office accommodation, etc. would provide accommodation to modern standards, including cafeteria messing, for only about 650 men. If, as was more likely, the complement turned out to be 900–950 men, the provision of such accommodations would require more enclosed space, obtained by working a superstructure deck amidships at the expense of raising the level of the secondary and close range armament, and incidental items such as boats, crane, etc. This would also provide the necessary space on the upper deck for the torpedo armament, which otherwise could not be fitted.

This cruiser would not displace less than about 17,500 tons deep (14,500 std) with a waterline length of about 650ft, unless the weight and space requirements for the new armament, fire control equipment and radar were much less than anticipated – a most unlikely contingency – or unless complements and standards of accommodation and maintenance were drastically reduced.

Sketch II showed how a guided missile armament might be fitted in the first design at the expense of the after pair of MCDP mountings. The weight and space requirements for Seaslug were as yet very tentative, but based on existing knowledge it would be feasible to provide a twin launcher with stowage and handling arrangements for an outfit of 48 rockets in a ship of slightly less length and displacement (17,000 tons deep, 14,000 tons std).

TABLE 5–2: *MINOTAUR* DESIGN

	Design Y	1946 Design	Worcester
LWL (ft,m)	655	645	664
BEAM (ft,in)	76	75	70,7¾
DEEP LOAD (tons)	—	18,415	18,008
DRAFT (ft.in)	—	24	25
STANDARD (tons)	15,350	15,280	15,210
DRAFT (ft,in)	21	20,9	21,6
SHP	108,000	100,000	120,000
SPEED (DEEP) (knots)	32	31.5	32
FUEL OIL (tons)	2850	2780	2354
ENDURANCE (nm/knots)	7500/20	6000/20	7460/20
COMPLEMENT	1050	—	—
6in GUNS	4 x 3 (250)	5 x 2 (400)	6 x 2 (425)
4.5in GUNS	6 x 2 (400)	—	—
3in GUNS	—	8 x 2 (800)	12 x 2 (600)
40MM TWIN	10 x 2 (1440)	—	—
20MM TWIN	16 x 2 (2400)	—	—
TORPEDO TUBES	4 x 4 (17)	4 x 4 (17)	—
AIRCRAFT	—	—	4
WEIGHTS (tons):			
GENERAL EQUIPMENT	810	1060	1240
ARMAMENT	2050	2270	2270
AIRCRAFT	—	—	74
MACHINERY	2000	2100	2150
(ELECTRICAL)	—	(320)	(187)
PROTECTION	2340	2480	3110
HULL	7850	7240	6600
RESERVE FEED WATER	—	180	184
MARGIN	300	305	—

NOTES: Speeds and endurances are at full load but with a clean bottom. For example, Design Y was credited with only 29.5 knots deep and dirty, ie, fully loaded, six months out of dock in the tropics. Figures in parentheses are rounds per gun, except in the case of torpedoes, where they are totals carried. Design Y also carried 15 depth charges, which are not listed. By 1945, her 20mm battery had been replaced by eight single 40mm.

Sketch III was a 'small' cruiser similar to I, but with the armament reduced to four medium calibre, dual purpose guns in two twin mountings; six 3in/70 in three twin mountings; four DA close range weapons; four quintuple revolving torpedo tube mountings.

In this design the beam would probably be insufficient for the combined boiler/engine arrangement of Sketch I, and it might be necessary to revert to a *Fiji* arrangement, except that the forward and after machinery units would be separated so that there would be a strong probability of not being immobilized by one torpedo hit. The deep displacement would be 13,000 tons; standard 10,500 tons.

This was, in effect, the *Tiger* (11,700 tons deep) with improved machinery layout, 31-knot speed, higher endurance, and with heavier close-range armament; a two per cent Board margin was included. It showed just how cramped the *Tiger*s were, given even the earliest postwar ideas on cruiser characteristics.

On paper, each of these ships must have seemed very lightly armed for its size. One reason

SENSORS
1   FH 11 (HF/DF)
2   RADAR 992 (OUTFIT AHS)
3   RADIO: OUTFIT APH FOR 87 M/S (UHF)
4   RADAR 974 (HDWS)
5   MRS 3 DIRECTOR
6   MF/DF COIL
7   HULL OUTFIT 9A (SONAR TYPE 184)
8   AERIALS FOR THIRD TRANSMITTING ROOM
9   IFF MK X
10 RADAR 960
11 OUTFIT ANL FOR RADIO TYPE 87M
12 BROAD-BAND DIPOLE FOR HF TRANSMISSION
13 RADAR 277Q
WEAPONS
14 6in TWIN MK 26
15 3in/70 TWIN MK 6
16 LOWER 6in MAGAZINE
17 'A' MOUNTING CONTROL COMPARTMENT
18 3in MAGAZINE
19 6in UPPER MAGAZINE
20 6in TRANSMITTING STATION
21 GUN DIRECTION ROOM
22 AIRCRAFT DIRECTION AND BRIDGE OPERATIONS
     ROOM
OTHER
23 BOILER ROOM
24 ENGINE ROOM
25 CAPTAIN'S SEA CABIN
26 ADMIRAL'S SEA CABIN
27 COMPASS PLATFORM

28 CPO MESS
29 RADAR ROOM
30 PO MESS
31 CANTEEN AND SOFT DRINKS BAR
32 SEAMEN'S HEADS
33 SEAMEN'S MESS
34 TELEPHONE EXCHANGE
35 STORES
36 COLD/COOL ROOM (PROVISIONS)
37 CAPSTAN MACHINERY
38 PRISONS
39 PAINT SHOP
40 PAINT STORE
41 INFLAMMABLE STORE
42 ROYAL MARINE MESS
43 WARDROOM AND EMERGENCY OPERATING STATION
44 WARDROOM ANTEROOM
45 CABINS
46 ADMIRAL'S DAY CABIN
47 ADMIRAL'S DINING CABIN
48 STEERING GEAR
49 BOAT CRANE
50 SHIPWRIGHTS' WORKSHOP
51 LAUNDRY
52 GALLEY

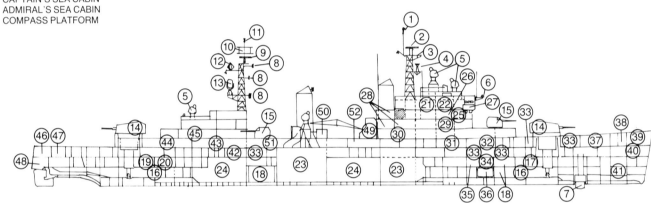

Tiger Class as modernized.

was the demand that turrets not interfere with each other, which had to be costly in overall length. A 5in/70 would have a muzzle sweep of 35ft, so that turrets would have to be 70ft apart, and 35ft from the nearest fixed structure. Moreover, given a very high rate of fire, they would need large magazines, both to accommodate shells and to accommodate the machinery responsible for that rate of fire. Even the 3in/70 would have a muzzle sweep of 21ft, and would require 400 square feet of magazine per mount. Each medium calibre turret would require 600kW of electrical power, and the ship would probably have a total generating capacity of 6000-8000kW.

Centreline space would also be consumed by the directors, particularly if each mounting was to have its own.

These were not, moreover, the largest conceivable cruisers; they were only large enough to accommodate the staff of a cruiser squadron. Nor could they serve as fleet aircraft direction ships. DNC estimated that radar picket equipment would cost about half the 3in/70 and close range armament. On the other hand, DNC did think space could be saved by eliminating torpedoes,

'unless the ships are definitely required for A/S duties'.

This was not an entirely idle series of speculations, as it appeared, late in 1948, that two cruisers might be laid down within the next eight years, the first perhaps as early as 1954. The 1960 cruiser therefore became the basis for tentative staff requirements. Sketch I seemed too large, and Sketch III too small, so the Ship Design Policy Committee (SDPC) opted for an intermediate cruiser, armed with six medium-calibre guns, and displacing perhaps 14,000 to 15,000 tons fully loaded. The Committee rejected the 5in because it doubted that its shells could seriously damage a Soviet cruiser. Nor did it expect the gun to be ready much before 1957. In January 1949, therefore, the SDPC listed tentative staff requirements: six 6in in three Mk 26 DP twin turrets; eight 3in/70 in four twin mountings; two multiple close range weapons; four fixed torpedo tubes on each side; Type 984 radar.

This was a considerable retreat from the *Minotaur* (two fewer 6in turrets, half as many 3in/70, half as many torpedo tubes), yet it was still expected to cost about 15,000 tons fully loaded.

In April 1949, DNC produced Sketches IV and

V, showing this equipment with alternative four- and three-shaft machinery schemes. The four shafts would be powered either by a new 22,500 shp unit or by a mixture of *Daring* (30,000 shp on outer shafts) and A/S frigate (15,000 shp Y 100 on inner shafts) units. This 15,000-ton cruiser would be 600ft long on the waterline, and because of its smaller beam would have to have separate boiler and engine rooms rather than unit machinery. The Engineer-in-Chief wanted to standardize on the existing 30,000 shp *Daring* plant, on three or four shafts. DNC remarked that this might mean accepting more or less power than the ship really needed. Thus, although the 15,000-ton cruiser could be driven at the required speed by a 90,000 shp plant (three shafts, as shown in Sketch V), four shafts (Sketch IV, 120,000 shp) were generally favored on grounds of arrangement. DNC could either force the adoption of a totally new 22,500 shp plant, or else he could combine standard 30,000 shp units on the outer shafts with the new Y 100 unit (15,000 hsp) developed for the new ASW frigate on each of two inner shafts.

In a three-shaft arrangement, there would probably be enough beam for combined engine/boiler rooms for each of the two outer shafts forward. They would be separated from the after engine and boiler rooms by magazines. Enough space would be saved to shorten the ship by about 20ft, compared to the 600ft Sketch IV. However, the after 6in turret would have to be raised one deck to keep it clear of the center line shaft. Moreover, experience with the three-shaft carrier *Ark Royal* had shown that a center line propeller could cause heavy stern vibration.

Perhaps worse, the centerline propeller would have to be limited in diameter, and hence would have to rotate fairly rapidly. However, much effort during and after the war had gone into silencing, which required large-diameter slow-turning propellers.

All of these designs provided enough weight for the scale of protection planned in 1946 for the *Minotaur*, which included a 3¼in belt. However, some redistribution was possible. One possibility was to give up belt armor (with its attendant design problems) altogether in favor of separate armored boxes over the magazines, machinery, and steering gear. After all, cruisers had rarely been hit on their belts. DNC argued otherwise, that a cruiser without a belt might have her bouyancy or stability destroyed by small shells and rockets tearing up her side. The combination of belt and deck would prevent oil fuel fires, and it would also protect much important equipment which might otherwise find itself outside the proposed boxes. DNC therefore argued in favor of a somewhat thinner belt (2in at least) with additional box protection for the magazines and steering gear. Splinter protection would be provided for the guns, AIC, radar offices, and important cable leads.

A program for a future 6in cruiser, then, would have envisaged Sketch IV or V. Rear Admiral Edwards, the Assistant Chief of the Naval Staff, proposed a radical alternative, the cruiser/destroyer. He argued that it would never be possible to build enough conventional cruisers or, for that matter, enough conventional destroyers, to meet the required numbers. The primary threats at sea would be air and submarine attack, supplemented, perhaps, by surface raiders. The new 5in rapid-fire gun might make it possible to combine useful anti-air and anti-surface capability in a hull small enough to be worthwhile for ASW as well. Such a ship could replace both cruiser and fleet destroyer. Low unit cost would demand that the ship be built to destroyer rather than cruiser standards, unarmored, and without a double bottom. Armed with three of the prospective 5in guns, she could displace about 4500 tons (over

Earlier cruisers were considerably refitted, but not rebuilt to the extent imagined in the late 'forties. *Belfast*, the largest British cruiser, presented the greatest potential for reconstruction, and was to have emerged from Portsmouth with new vertical funnels and L70 Bofors guns. Instead, she received a more modest modernization (1956-59), leaving her with an enclosed bridge and six twin 40mm Mark 5 mountings, controlled (with her 4in battery) by MRS 8 directors. She is shown, newly completed, in June 1959. *Belfast* has been preserved in London as a museum ship, in much this configuration. [*MoD*]

The large cruiser *Newcastle*
illustrates the standard of
reconstruction achieved in the
early 'fifties. She is shown in
Malta on 20 October 1948, just
before reconstruction, and on 7
May 1954, two years after
completion of reconstruction.
Note the entirely new bridge
structure, the uniform anti-
aircraft battery of 40mm guns,
and the installation of Mark VI
secondary-battery directors to
replace the obsolete HACS.
Note, too, the retention of anti-
ship torpedo tubes: the Royal
Navy might use its cruisers to
police the Commonwealth, but it
also took the anti-ship role
seriously, and torpedoes were
valued equalizers. They were
very nearly installed in the
reconstructed *Tiger*s. The radar
suit has also changed. In 1948, it
was still the early wartime 281
(using separate transmitting and
receiving antennae), and the
main battery director had the
early wartime 284. As rebuilt, the
ship has the long-range 960 aft,
293Q and 277Q on her new lattice
foremast, and 274 on her main
battery director. The antenna on
the shorter pole aft is a YE aircraft
homing beacon; the ship could
serve as a limited radar picket or
pylon. [*MoD and USN*]

At Malta in October 1958, *Bermuda* shows the effect of a slightly more modest modernization. She retains her original bridge, but it has been enclosed. She has the uniform 40mm battery applied to *Belfast* at this time, and CRBF directors for her 4in battery (with 262 radar dishes on the mounts themselves). Only *Ceylon* and *Newfoundland* were rebuilt completely; the other ships of the class ended their careers in much the configuration shown here, accumulated over normal refits. *Bermuda* paid off into reserve in 1963, and was broken up in 1965. [*CPL*]

5000 tons if to cruiser standards). Edwards argued that, given good speed and maneuverability, the best possible sonar, and a Limbo type weapon or A/S torpedoes, she would be adequate for the hand-off role which was all that was required for this job, and would be able herself to operate in submarine threatened waters without A/S escort.

The new 5in gun was the basis of the design. Given its very high rate of fire, and a new armor-piercing shell, the gun might well compare with that of a 6-inch gunned *Tiger*. Two light cruisers, with their high speed, superior gunnery technique, and better seamanship, would be more than a match for one 180mm (7.1in) gunned Soviet *Kirov*. Note that unless the 5in gun succeeded, it would have been impossible to build a small cruiser, since a ship would have had to combine the best anti-ship weapon, the twin 6in Mark 26, and the best anti-aircraft weapon, the twin 3in/70, both of them quite large and heavy. Thus it was risky for Admiral Edwards to base his new cruiser program on a gun as yet only incompletely designed.

Edwards hoped to replace the planned combination of 18 cruisers (ten 6in and eight 5.25in) and 58 destroyers with a total of 50 cruiser/destroyers (30 of which would be active in peacetime); he saw the obsolescence of the existing cruisers as an opportunity rather then a disaster. The existing 6in cruisers would not be modernized. Only those required for peacetime police duties would be refitted. Instead, the *Dido*s would be updated, with improved fire controls and anti-submarine weapons, and the later Battle class destroyer fire controls also modernized, to bring the cruiser/destroyer force towards the desired goal of a single type.

This radical program was not accepted, at least at the time. The First Sea Lord, Admiral Fraser, did propose to build a 5in cruiser/destroyer in 1955, but he also hoped to start a 13,000- to 14,000-ton 6in cruiser the following year. However, Edwards was proven correct in the long run, in that the large cruisers were squeezed out in favor of what amounted to large destroyer, the Counties, albeit in much smaller numbers than he had foreseen. In addition, the advent of the cruiser/destroyer concept stopped work on a proposed improved *Daring* incorporating all postwar requirements, and armed with four (rather than three) twin 4.5in guns.

The 5in cruiser was tentatively included in the 1953-54 program, and DNC was asked to develop sketch designs on the basis of two twin 5in dual purpose guns (directed by one LRS 1 and two MRS), two STAAG Bofors (four preferred), eight torpedoes (anti-surface and ASW), and a single Limbo. Speed was to be 31 knots (30 knots minimum) and endurance 4500nm at 20 knots deep and dirty. Edwards had asked for four guns, but he had pressed for single mounts, presumably for survivability in action. They would have been too heavy. Even with two twins, DNC estimated that the ship would displace 4600 tons deep (465 x 48 x 34ft depth), which seemed too large.

The SDPC met in February 1950, to prune back the design by reducing requirements to a minimum. The ship had been conceived primarily as a carrier escort and as an anti-aircraft escort for ocean convoys. Hence she would have a dual-purpose gun battery (using the new 5in gun); enough anti-submarine armament to hand off a submarine; and an anti-ship torpedo battery. The Gunnery Division expected that the ship could be provided with three single dual purpose mounts, each weighing up to 90 tons; they would be controlled by one dual purpose and two anti-aircraft directors. There would also be three 30-ton close-range mountings. The latter weight limit would preclude installation of the new twin 3in/70, and the ship would have to have US-type single 3in/50, which were inferior weapons.

Four torpedoes was consider the minimum anti-ship salvo; a broadside of eight torpedoes would be best. It could be argued further that the tubes should be on the centerline, since the alternative would be eight fixed tubes on each beam. However, a cruiser was too beamy for centerline tubes. Given this problem, it was tentatively decided to dispense entirely with the anti-ship torpedo.

ASW requirements, however, were much more urgent. They included both Limbo with ten salvoes (considered next in importance after the 5in guns) and a pair of fixed ASW tubes with reloads, At this stage the ship was also to have been fitted with Ruler, a torpedo-killing rocket. The other side of ASW was a long-range sonar, which would have to be retractable to simplify drydocking.

Then there was radar. As a carrier escort, the cruiser would have to provide fighter control facilities, with at least Types 982 and 983 radars, as well as the usual 960 for long-range search and 992 for gun target acquisition (in combination with the GDS 3 weapons direction system in a six-channel version). Clearly, however, it would be better to provide the ideal fighter-director system, the huge Type 984.

DTSD tried to cap growth at 4600 tons, separating essential from desirable requirements. The essential list included both Limbo and two fixed ASW torpedo tubes with reloads. Desirable features would include a salvo of at least four surface torpedoes, with eight preferred; the three close-range weapons; and Type 984 for fighter control. One possibility was to reduce endurance to 3000nm at the striking force cruising speed of 22.5 knots.

DNC produced three alternative designs in March 1951. Each was 450 (LWL) 465 (LOA) x 48 x 34ft depth; the best variant, Scheme II, displaced 4770 tons at a draft of 14ft, 6in. Armament was three 5in single mounts, two single 3in/50, and eight fixed torpedo tubes with eight reloads. A 60,000shp YEAD 1 plant (two units separated by a 50ft block) would drive her at 30.75 knots deep and dirty.* Sonar equipment would have been elaborate: 177 for long-range detection, 170 for weapon control, 180 for contact maintenance, 175 for Ruler (anti-torpedo weapon) control, and 176 for passive warning. The three alternatives represented different levels of austerity. Scheme I showed minimim radar (960 and 277Q) and carried one 5in mounting forward, one amidships, and one aft; she displaced 4710 tons. Scheme II had the full outfit: 984, two guns forward, and two guns aft, and Limbo forward of the bridge. III was a compromise, with 960 and 982/983, and all three guns forward, at 4770 tons.

After all the agony, the Royal Navy obtained, not a full-fledged cruiser, but rather a large destroyer, the County. It did have a substantial shore fire potential in the two twin 4.5in guns forward, and it had spaces roomy enough for many Third World cruiser assignments, but it lacked a cruiser's command and control facilities, including air control. However, the ingenuity of the DNC Department did provide nearly as many missiles as had been squeezed into designs three times its size. Here, *Devonshire* escorts *Ark Royal* in the Mediterranean, May, 1963. [*CPL*]

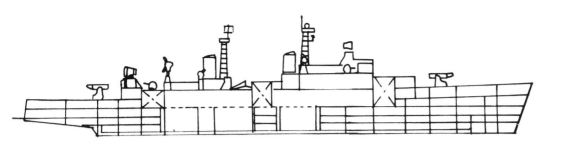

Missile cruiser, January 1955: 530ft LWL (541ft LOA) beam 69ft draft, 18ft 6in, 10,700 tons deep load; 90,000shp, 30.75 knots deep and clean (30 knots deep and dirty); endurance: 4500nm at 20 knots. Armament: two missile launchers, 54 missiles (30 forward, 24 aft; note the three missile elevators). Protection: 1in side and deck except 2in side, 1 1/2in deck over machinery. She has Radars 960 and 983 aft, and 992 forward. Accommodation: 60 officers, 720 ratings.

None was entirely satisfactory, given the short endurance. The next step was to increase displacement to 5000 tons, using the difference to add oil fuel. 'A' was Scheme II with maximum fuel, for an endurance of 3550nm. 'B' surrendered one 5in gun (4050nm); 'C' surrendered Ruler and the eight torpedo tubes as well, retaining one fixed tube on each side, with eight reloads (4350nm). The conclusion was that 4500nm at 22.5 knots would leave only 5.9 per cent of total displacement for armament at 5000 tons, a poor bargain. 'A' was the best of a poor lot.

It would take 1500 tons of oil to drive a 4600-ton ship for the desired 4500nm at 22.5 knots. This weight in turn would not leave anything like enough for a balanced design, and planned endurance was reduced to 3000nm at 22.5 knots, which would be about 25 per cent shorter than the range of the larger *Superb* but slightly longer than that of the existing large destroyer, the *Daring*, and considerably better than that of the modernized *Dido*.

Tentative staff requirements were revised in February 1952, to reflect these studies. The ship would be armed with three 5in guns (with three MRS 3) and two sextuple Bofors (two MRS 3), with a GDS 3 six-channel gun direction system, and one stripped-down 4in or 4.5in gun for illumination. The torpedo battery would be six tubes on each beam or one set of eight, with a limited training arc, aft, in each case without reloads. The ship would have a single Limbo. Ruler development having failed, the anti-torpedo system was now specified as four triple-tube sets of a new torpedo

system called Camrose. As in Scheme II, she would have Radar 984.

Even these more limited requirements were too ambitious. The new sextuple Bofors, with its 2500 rounds per barrel and MRS 3 director, would consume 200 valuable tons; it was replaced by a pair of twin 40mm L/70 Bofors. Radar 984 was abandoned as incompatible with the 5in gun (presumably due to vibration), and the ship was reduced to the compromise radar suit, 960, 982, and 983. The torpedo tubes were deleted. Even then the ship was expected to displace an excessive 4800 tons.

DGD argued, late in 1952, that no system of switching shell types could be entirely satisfactory in a two-mount ship. Nor could he guarantee the reliability of each mounting. Far better, then, to abandon the two-mount ship entirely in favor of a larger medium cruiser with four, or even three, twin 5in.

Early estimates showed stowage for about 400 rounds per gun in a two-mounting 4500-ton (later 4750-ton) cruiser/destroyer.

Against ships, very rapid fire was expected to shatter the lightly protected part of a cruiser, It was argued that British ships probably would have little margin of superiority in fire control; there was, after all, relatively little margin of improvement left to make. Hence, superiority would depend on an ability to develop and maintain a higher rate of fire. That in turn would favor a smaller calibre, which would make for the highest possible rate of fire.

The correct tactical handling of ships in a surface action would be, then, to close to effective range as soon as possible, withholding the maximum rate of fire until that range was reached. Thus the highest possible speed would be desirable. Wartime experience suggested that it would take 35 5in hits to disable a Soviet cruiser. If seven per cent of shells fired hit, a total of 500 rounds (125 for each of four guns) would be required. About ten hits would disable a Soviet destroyer, two or three of which might be engaged in rapid succession. The hitting rate would fall to four per cent, so a total of 500 to 750 shots would be required, ie, 125 to 188 rounds per gun.

Against aircraft, the gun would have to fire five or six bursts (15-20 seconds each) at 10- to 15-second intervals. Minimum interval between attacks would be 15-30 minutes. This entailed firing about 70 rounds within two and a half to three minutes at intervals of 15-30 minutes.

* British postwar steam and some COSAG plants were designated in a Y series: they were designed by Pametrada, an organization set up by the Admiralty and the shipbuilding industry. YEAD resulted from collaboration between Yarrow and English Electric, an organization (designated YE 47A) having been established in December 1946 to develop three major variants of the 60,000 shp two-shaft *Daring* plant, the most efficient high-power type then available in Britain. That plant itself was patterned on existing US destroyer practice (high temperature high pressure steam), since the US plants were known to be reliable and were also far more efficient than existing British low-pressure plants. YEAD I was a further advance (950 degree rather than 850 degree steam, running at the same 650 lb/sq in pressure). The prototype completed its trials early in 1958, but a projected YEAD II was abandoned in view of the greater promise of gas turbine boosted machinery. The Y series included Y 100, for the Type 12 frigates, Y 101 for the single-shaft Type 14, and Y 111, for the third-rate and then the common hull.

SENSORS
1   RADAR TYPE 992
2   RADAR TYPE 277Q
3   ALO (AIR LOOKOUT) SIGHTS
4   HDWS (RADAR 974)
5   MRS 3 DIRECTOR
6   TORPEDO SIGHT (PORT AND STARBOARD)
7   RADAR TYPE 932 (SPLASH-SPOTTING)
8   ASDICS (SONARS) TYPES 177, 170, 180, 175, 176
9   RADAR TYPE 960
WEAPONS
10 LIMBO HANDLING ROOM
11 LIMBO MAGAZINE
12 LIMBO HOIST
13 3in MAGAZINE
14 MRS 3 AA/SU3 ROOM
15 MRS 3 AA/SU2 ROOM
16 FIXED TORPEDO TUBES (8 TUBES,
    4 EACH SIDE, TOTAL 8 RELOADS)

17 5in MAGAZINE
18 3in/50 SINGLE GUNS (PORT AND STARBOARD)
19 5in GUN (MCDP MK 1)
20 ROCKET FLARE LAUNCHER
21 LIMBO
22 RULER (ANTI-TORPEDO WEAPON,
    COVERS 45 DEGREE
    ARC EACH SIDE ASTERN)
22A RULER LOADING BAY
22B RULER MAGAZINE
23 TYPE 992 POWER ROOMS
24 TYPE 992 OFFICE
OTHER
25 LAMP AND PAINT ROOM
26 CABLE LOCKER
27 CREW SLEEPING
28 ASDIC INSTRUMENT ROOM
29 PROVISIONS
30 DIESEL GENERATOR

31 PO SLEEPING
32 WARDROOM
33 STABILIZER
34 GYRO
35 COMMAND
36 BRIDGE OPERATIONS ROOM
37 CAPTAIN'S SEA CABIN AND CHART ROOM
38 SIGNAL DECK
39 GALLEY
40 BOILER ROOM
41 ENGINE ROOM
42 OIL FUEL
43 FRESH WATER
44 STEERING GEAR

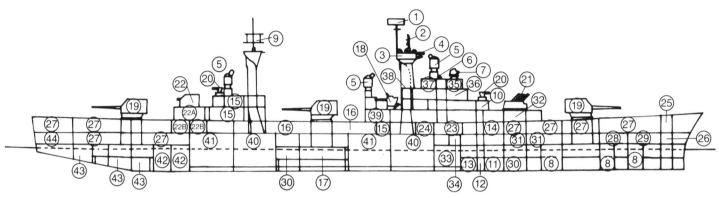

Schemes 1 (plan) and 2 (artist's impression) for the cruiser/ destroyer of 1950. Note the Ruler anti-torpedo weapon in the Scheme 1 sketch; it was common to all versions of the design. The guns in the waist are single US-type 3in/50 to be delivered under MDAP. Hull openings were erroneously included in the painting of Scheme 2. [*MoD*]

The high rate of AA fire would be required to build up the best possible cumulative chance of a kill in the short period during which the target would be within range. The requirement for five to six bursts in rapid succession was based on a forecast of future Soviet tactics. It was assumed that the Soviets would continue to use conventional anti-ship weapons, rather than (as they actually did) develop long-range anti-ship stand-off missiles. Numbers of attacking aircraft were calculated on the basis of Soviet fleet

strengths; it was assumed that they would attack by squadrons, aircraft from any one squadron attacking on the same line of bearing, in succession. Earlier estimates had shown that 12 dive bombers (the most effective, if the most costly, anti-ship weapon) would suffice to sink a heavy cruiser.

The estimated scale of attack which might be expected from the aircraft of one Russian fleet within 300nm of their airfields. A serviceability of 50 per cent was assumed.

— Two squadrons of dive bombers – 24 aircraft at intervals of two to three seconds, followed five seconds later by:

— One or two squadrons of conventional torpedo bombers – 12 or 24 aircraft dropping with an interval of 10 seconds between the first and second formations of 12 aircraft.

A well co-ordinated attack would involve 60 or 72 aircraft, and from the first rocket or cannon shell to the last torpedo it would take two and a half to three minutes. The strike force would have fighter escorts. A further attack of about half this size could be mounted a few minutes later.

This would involve a special effort. However, under some circumstances two fleets might co-ordinate, or a fleet might be heavily reinforced by tactical aircraft. A small task group might expect a three-squadron attack.

The combination of air and surface requirements was equated to 150 HEP and 250 HE shells per gun.

By 1953, the cruiser/destroyer had been downgraded to destroyer status. Although it was eliminated from the building program that September, a slightly updated version of this 5in destroyer was included in a selection of designs presented to the Sea Lords in November 1954. By this time the design showed no weight margin to allow for development of either its gun or its machinery, neither of which had yet been completed. The gun in the design was the twin 5in of 1952, which had already been abandoned due to excessive weight and complexity. Further growth would have to cost ammunition or endurance.

The 5in destroyer would be armed with two such weapons (forward and aft), each with its own MRS 3 director and with 400 rounds per gun, as in the earlier studies. A single 4.5in gun, mounted between the forward 5in and the bridge, would fire starshell. The secondary battery would be two sided twin 40mm guns, each with its own MRS 3, and there would also be a powerful ASW battery: two sided quadruple torpedo tubes and one Limbo (ten salvoes). The radar outfit combined relatively simple aircraft direction sets (960 for search, 277Q and 983) with the standard target acquisition (992) and surface search (974) sets. YEAD 1 machinery (60,000 shp) would drive her at 30 knots (deep and dirty; 31 knots clean) and endurance would be 2900nm at 20 knots (dirty; 3800nm under trials conditions). Protection would be limited to destoyer standards, and complement would be 475.

The small cruiser was still alive. DGD's preferred medium cruiser, an updated *Dido*, was perhaps the last gasp of the pure gun cruiser in Britain. An 8000-ton light cruiser, protected on much the scale of the *Dido*, was submitted to the Sea Lords in November 1954. It was not intended as a reply to the *Sverdlov*, but rather as a light cruiser of moderate size and cost, armed with a new simplified twin 5in gun, mounted two forward and one aft. Each battery would be controlled by its own MRS 3 director, so that the ship would be able to engage two targets simultaneously. The secondary battery would consist of one sextuple 40mm mounting forward (between B 5in mounting and the bridge) controlled by an MRS 3 director, and two twin 40mm aft, covering the after arcs, with TOMs. These guns would be supplemented by four sets of triple torpedo tubes and four reloads, sufficient for her to maintain salvoes of three anti-ship and three anti-submarine torpedoes ready on each beam. Radar would be limited to sets required by the ship herself: 960 for warning, 277Q for height-finding and surface search, and 992 for target acquisition (with the GDS 3 gun direction system).

The powerplant was the Y 102 COSAG (30,000shp steam turbines and 30,000shp gas turbines) under development for the contemporary fast anti-submarine escort, the corresponding full power speed being 29.5 knots deep and dirty or 30.5 knots clean. Similarly, endurance would match that planned for the A/S fast escort: 3600nm at 20 knots dirty under operational conditions with connected auxiliaries; 4700nm at 20 knots dirty under trials conditions with connected auxiliaries; 5500nm at 20 knots clean on trial (compared to 4400nm for *Dido*).

Protection would match that of the last small cruiser, the *Dido*, with the addition of 1in all around AIO compartments. Magazines would have 2in crown, 1.5in side, machinery 1in crown, and 2.5in side. Accommodation for 675 would be provided. (For details, see table overleaf.)

The gun-armed cruiser (and the 6in guns on British missile cruiser designs of this period) reflect continuing concern with the threat of Soviet cruisers, which might attack convoys just as the German capital ships and cruisers had during World War II. British carriers had had to specialize in anti-aircraft and anti-submarine weapons, with very little deck or magazine space left over for anti-ship purposes. Similarly, postwar development effort had gone almost exclusively into anti-aircraft and anti-submarine weaponry. To find the Soviets building old-fashioned gun cruisers alongside their submarines and jet bombers was, therefore, an unpleasant surprise. It was not that the new *Sverdlov*s were particularly impressive, but rather that they presented a kind of threat which had seemed to recede after 1945.

In September 1954, for example, the Director of Plans called for gun ships in the new long-range construction program. They would have to be able to engage a *Sverdlov* on reasonable terms, while defending themselves against the aircraft of the 1960s. This implied 6in guns, although an improved 5in turret (as on the 8000-ton cruiser) could perhaps be developed reasonably quickly if confined solely to surface fire. It was almost certain that no new large-calibre dual-purpose weapon would appear; the 3in/70 seemed to represent the end of that line.

The Director of Naval Ordnance considered construction of any new large cruiser unlikely; at best Britain could afford ships armed with a new

WEIGHTS FOR COMPARISON (tons)

	Light cruiser	5in destroyer
HULL	3630 (45.4)	2030 (42.7)
EQUIPMENT	640 (8.0)	390 (8.2)
ARMAMENT	850 (10.6)	530 (11.2)
PROTECTION	850 (10.6)	—
MACHINERY	880 (11.0)	850 (17.9)
OIL FUEL	1000 (12.5)	900 (18.9)
BOARD MARGIN	150 (1.9)	50 (1.1)
	8000	4750

RFW is included in machinery.

twin 5in DP armament, the mounting being simplified compared with the 5in mounting considered for the cruiser/destroyer, and its reduced performance accepted. Even so, seven to eight years would be required for its development.

The other possibility was to use the advanced technology of the fast-firing 6in gun to combine sufficient gun fire power with a powerful missile battery in the same ship. If *Sverdlov*'s guns were equated with those of conventional British cruisers, they could achieve a total of 96 rounds per minute, eight per gun. The new twin mount was rated at 40 rounds per minute, so that two turrets (as on *Tiger*) would surely give a cruiser a chance.

Ultimately, the Royal Navy would have an anti-ship missile, Blue Slug, compatible with Seaslug handling and guidance systems. It would more than even the odds against an all-gun ship, and it was expected to be available in 1961; in fact, it was cancelled in 1957. Blue Slug was command-guided in a shallow, flat trajectory with a terminal dive. The combination of the need for a sufficient gun battery and for anti-aircraft missiles made the large composite cruisers, proposed from 1954 onwards, attractive. All could later be converted to all-missile ships in the event that that was necessary (eg, if Blue Slug proved successful), although it had to be admitted that ships designed from the beginning for all-missile operations would probably be less expensive.

As conceived in 1947, Seaslug was designed to be fitted in the *Minotaur* class cruisers still carried in the British shipbuilding plan, and later aboard Town and Colony class cruisers and battleships after major reconstruction; there might also be special vessels designed for fleet and convoy AA defense. As of February 1948, DNC was unwilling to make estimates based on a missile of uncertain size, but he expected that missile ships would be much larger than 10,000 tons; 17,000 tons seemed a reasonable guess for a cruiser. It was soon evident that, in contrast to guns, missiles stressed ship volume more than ship weight-carrying capacity. Like airplanes, they required hangar space. Thus, by 1949, DNC had concluded that the best fast missile ship would probably be a

converted aircraft carrier; the best slow missile ship (for convoy defense) would be a converted fast merchant ship. Battleship conversions were also considered, and it was at this time that the First Sea Lord, Admiral Fraser, decided that the guns and fire controls of two of the four *King George V* class battleships in reserve would not be preserved, based on the theory that they would ultimately be replaced by missiles.

In December 1950, the Ship Design Policy Committee defined a missile ship program:
- — A: Task force ship, 30 knots, two triple launchers.
- — B: Ocean convoy escort, 17 knots, two triple launchers.
- — C: Coastal convoy escort, 12 knots, one triple launcher.

The order of priorities – C before A and B last – reflected British naval concerns of the time, in which convoy operations came first. Throughout the development which followed, the Admiralty would turn back and forth between convoy and fleet operations.

At this time, too, it was decided that, instead of the previously proposed LST (3), a fleet auxiliary, *Girdle Ness*, would be converted for missile trials. She might then become the Type C prototype. However, she could not accommodate a full war complement, and in 1952 the design was converted as a dedicated trials ship, without guns, armor, or other operational features. Meanwhile (see below), the Type A project had stalled. The Type C failure therefore left the Royal Navy without any planned operational missile ship, and a new series of studies began.

Type A was to operate with the fleet and with special convoys. Its main requirements were speed and missile stowage capacity, although fighter direction would also be desirable. Three carrier classes were investigated: the existing *Colossus* class light fleet carrier, which was too slow; the *Majestic* class, no faster, but still under construction and so perhaps less expensive to convert; and the armored fleet carrier *Formidable*, which in any case would have to be rebuilt to operate modern aircraft.

Tentative staff requirements were drawn up in

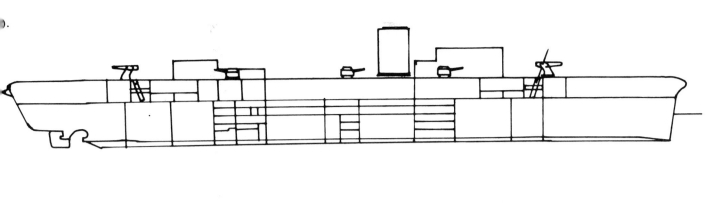

).

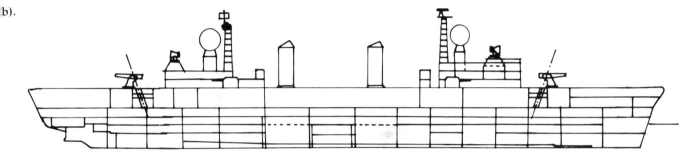

b).

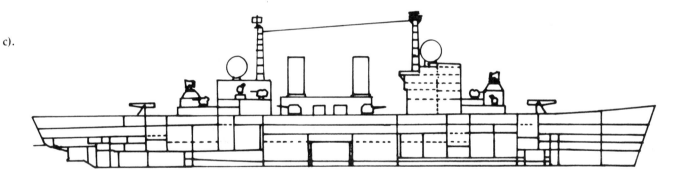

c).

1949 for a light carrier conversion. She would be armed with two triple launchers (90 missiles each) each with its GMS 1 (Type 901 radar) director; four twin 3in/70 controlled by the new MRS 4 director (905 radar), and four close-range weapons (unspecified) with their director. The search radars would be limited to a 960 long-range unit and a 992 target acquisition radar (working with the GDS 3 system); there would be no fighter control facilities. The light carriers were entirely unprotected; 2in splinter protection would be applied to their missile magazines. Such ships were also too slow, at about 25 knots (40,000shp). They would have to be re-engined. It was estimated that they could make 31 knots on 68,000shp at an increased displacement of 21,000 tons. Endurance would be 4500nm at 22.5 knots; the standard figure in the later designs was 4500nm at 20 knots.

Apart from the large number of missiles to be accommodated, these figures and systems were typical of later British studies. The 3in/70 was the best available anti-aircraft gun, and it was needed to deal with attackers who might evade Seaslug.

Even a double-ended Seaslug could, after all, deal with only two attackers at once. Nor could it be assumed that a British fleet would include more than one or two such ships. Its missile defense could, then, be defeated by saturation attacks, either by several aircraft striking simultaneously or by a stream of attackers in very close succession. British tacticians considered the simultaneous attack difficult if not entirely impractical, given its cost in assembly time and thus in jet endurance. The stream, however, was taken far more seriously.

As actually sketched in 1950-51, *Majestic* incorporated both fire control radars and the 984 required for fighter control, all on a new centerline superstructure. However, she could stow only 52 missiles for each of her two launchers, occupying available hangar deck space outside the combined boiler/engine rooms. Even so, she would be top-heavy, without an adequate reserve of stability in the light condition. Nor could she be protected beyond 40 pounds (1in) plating around important equipment in the bridge and superstructure.

Proposed conversions of British aircraft carriers to missile ships, 1951. The guns are twin 3in/70 and (in c) twin STAAG 40mm. The large circles represent Type 984 radars. (a) *Formidable*, 25 June 1951 (b) *Majestic*, 28 June 1951 (c) *Majestic*, 9 June 1951.

Missile ship sketch designs prepared for presentation to the Sea Lords, November 1954. In each case, crossed broken lines indicate the missile elevators(s).
(a) Missile cruiser, with two twin 6in, 2 twin 3in, 4 twin 40mm, 48 missiles; 645ft LWL (657 LOA) x 79 x 22ft, 6in (deep), 18,300 tons; 120,000shp, 32.25 knots deep and clean (31.25 knots deep and dirty). Endurance 4500nm at 20 knots.
(b) Fleet escort, with two twin 3in, four twin 40mm, and 90 missiles (note the long magazine between the end elevators); 530ft LWL (540 LOA) x 70 x 19ft, 11,000 tons deep load; 60,000shp, 28.5 knots deep and clean (27.5 knots deep and dirty); 3in sides and 2in deck over machinery, 2in sides and 2in deck over missile stowage. Endurance 5600nm at 20 knots. Note the use of 982/983 instead of 984 in this and smaller designs.
(c) Convoy escort, two 3in (abreast), four twin Bofors, 90 missiles, 520ft LWL (530 LOA) x 70 x 17ft, 10,000 tons deep displacement, 30,000shp, 24.75 knots deep and clean (23.75 knots deep and dirty), endurance 6400nm at 12 knots. Protection as in the fleet escort.
(d) Missile conversion of a *Fiji* class cruiser, 550ft LWL (556 LOA) x 62 x 20ft, 9in, 10,950 tons deep load; 80,000shp, 30.5 knots deep and clean (29.5 knots deep and dirty); endurance 3900nm at 20 knots. One triple 6in Mark 23, two twin Bofors Mark 3 (rather than L70, as in the others, and with STD rather than MRS 3 directors), 24 missiles; no additional protection for the missiles.
(e) Destroyer, 360ft LWL (372 LOA) x 43 x 12ft, 6in, 3550 tons deep load, 60,000shp, 30.75 knots deep and clean (29.5 knots deep and dirty); endurance 3000nm at 20 knots. Armament: three twin Bofors L70 (Mark 11) with MRS 3 directors, two fixed ASW torpedo tubes (adjacent to the missile launcher, on the quarterdeck), 12 missiles. No protection at all.

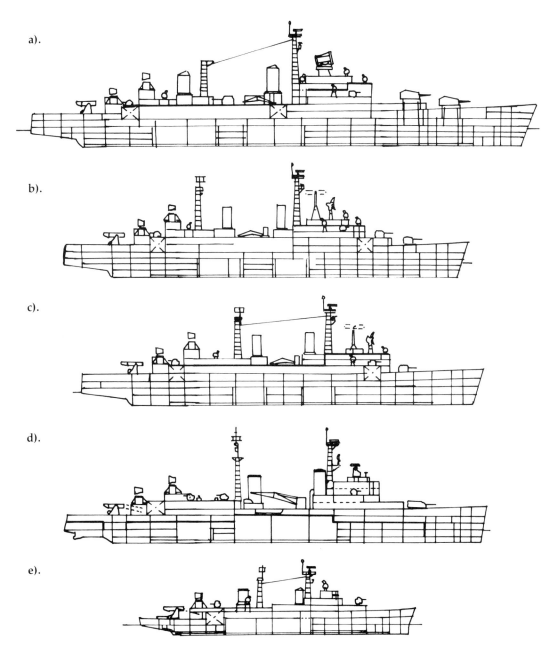

The alternative was a much more radical reconstruction, in which the magazines would be buried deep in the ship. All structure above the gallery deck would be removed, and a new strength deck, the new upper deck, built at the gallery deck level. Magazines forward were to be below the original main deck; four would serve the three lines of supply to the triple launcher through a lift and testing and tuning space below the new upper deck. Magazines aft would have to be higher in the ship to clear the lines of shafting; three magazines would serve the three lines of supply. Stowage would be 90 weapons forward, 80 aft. There was enough margin of stability to provide some 60 pounds (1.5in) protection, including a belt extending between the outer ends of the magazines, covered by a deck of equal thickness.

As for speed, it appeared possible to substitute two unit systems, each of 30,000shp (persumably based on the new Y 100 frigate plant) for the existing 20,000shp units, and so to realize a speed of 28.5 knots deeply loaded.

DNC concluded that the light carriers could meet the staff requirements, but only at a horrendous cost. But the design studies had not been wasted: they showed the rough outlines of a practicable Type A missile ship. It would have to be 80-100 feet longer than a *Majestic* to allow for the increased power required; deep displacement would be about 23,000-24,000 tons. Additional secondary armament could be accommodated. DNC suspected, however, that even a new design would be unlikely to accommodate more than the number of missiles in the much-modified *Majestic* 90 and 80, respectively. He considered it far too small for so large a ship and asked whether such small numbers might not bring into question the entire concept of a large ship armed entirely with Seaslug.

The alternative conversion candidate was the fleet carrier *Formidable*, no longer capable of

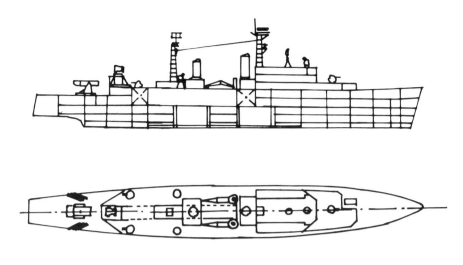

Small convoy escort missile ship, November 1954: 450ft LWL (460 LOA) x 53 x 12ft,6in, 5000 tons deep load, 30,000shp, 27 knots deep and clean (25.75 knots deep and dirty); endurance 4500nm at 15 knots. Three twin 40mm Mark 11 (L70), six fixed ASW torpedo tubes (12 torpedoes), 1 Limbo (forward, in the cut-out shown, with 20 salvoes, 30 missiles. No protection.

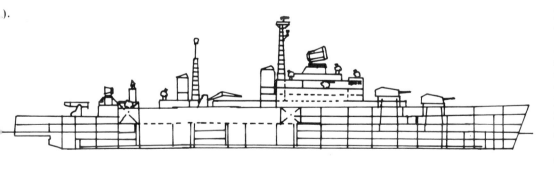

Cruiser sketch design dated May 1955, armed with two twin 5in guns, four twin Bofors L70 (Mark 11), and 48 Seaslugs: 590ft LWL (600 LOA) x 76 x 19ft,3in, 13,500 tons deep displacement. Protection: 1½in sides, 1½in decks (1in deck over machinery). The dashed line defines the bottom of the missile magazine, with a lift at either end. The twin Bofors guns can be seen under the second MRS 3 director forward, and under the missile telemetry dish aft. Missiles would have been embarked through hatches in the deck between the MRS 3 and the telemetry dish aft. The foremast carries 992 and 974 radars.

).

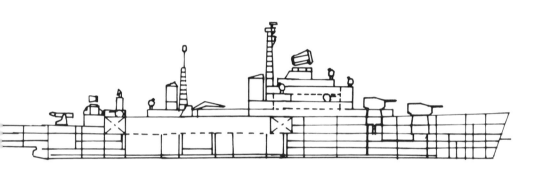

Missile cruisers with alternative anti-aircraft armaments, May 1955.
(a) **Cruiser** armed with two twin 6in and four twin 40mm Mark 11 (L70) and 48 missiles: 615ft LWL (625 LOA) x 77 x 19ft,6in, 14,500 tons deep load; 105,000shp, 31.5 knots deep and clean (30.75 knots deep and dirty); endurance 4500nm at 20 knots; protection 1½in deck and side except 1in deck over machinery.

ɔ).

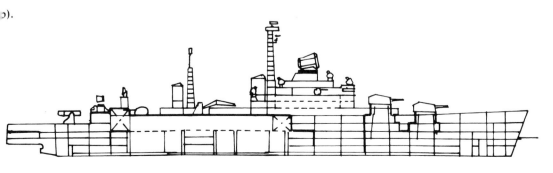

(b) as (a) except two twin 3in/70 Mark 6 instead of the two after twin 40mm guns: 626ft LWL (635 LOA) x 78 x 19ft,9in, 15,100 tons deep load; speed and endurance as (a). Accommodation 76 officers and 970 ratings, vs 78 officers and 970 rating in (a). Missiles are embarked into the small deckhouse over the missile elevator.

Missile cruiser (GW 60), August 1955: 645ft LWL (657 LOA) x 78 x 20ft,3in, 15,800 tons deep load; 105,000shp, 32 knots deep and clean (31 knots deep and dirty; noted in pencil on this drawing: 120,000shp, 33/32 knots deep and clean/dirty; endurance: 4500nm at 20 knots. Armament: two 6in Mark 26, two 3in/70 Mark 6, two Bofors Mark 11 (twin L70), 48 missiles. Note the 'fish' of the variable-depth sonar forward, streamed from the bow. Protection: 1 ½in side and deck, except 1in deck over main machinery spaces. Missiles would be embarked through a hatch under the big boat crane aft.

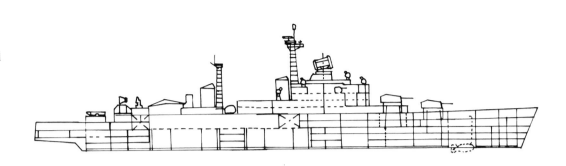

Missile cruiser, January 1957, the final version developed: 675ft LWL (687 LOA) x 80 x 22ft, 18,450 tons deep load; 110,000shp, 32 knots deep and clean (31 knots deep and dirty); endurance: 4500nm at 20 knots. Armament: two twin 6in Mark 26, four twin 3in Mark 6, 64 missiles. The foremast carries radars 978 and 992. Protection: 1½in side, 1½in deck (except 1in side and deck over AIO, and 1in deck over machinery). The dish amidships is for missile telemetry. Each machinery unit consists, forward to aft, of a boiler room, a machinery room, and a gearing room; the two units are separated by a 3in magazine above stabilizer machinery. Emergency generators are located under the missile loader aft, and a gas turbine generator room abaft No 2 6in magazine. Sonar equipment occupies the two-deck level space in the bottom of the ship forward of the 6in magazines. In the forward superstructure, the level below the enclosed compass platform (with windows) is an operations room, with the wardroom below that.

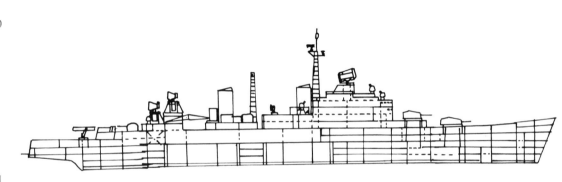

operating modern aircraft and thus requiring some form of modernization in any case. Unlike the light carriers, she clearly could attain the desired speed, and she was already well protected. She was large enough to eliminate any likely stability problem, and her hangars could easily accommodate 72 missiles per launcher. However, any conversion (including modernization as a carrier) would have to deal with the fact that her thick flight deck was also her strength deck: cuts through it would have to be limited. Moreover, she had been completed in 1940, and had seen hard war service. Only later was it discovered that she had suffered irremediable structural damage. Even in 1951 she had been proposed for scrapping, and was described as 'in an indifferent state structurally, mechanically, and electronically'. DNC rejected her, finally, for her excessive freeboard, which presumably would have made handling difficult.

As for cruisers, DNC concluded that they would not readily carry large numbers of missiles, due to the fineness of their hull form. Moreover, placing the missiles aft would subject them to vibration, while volume would be limited by the run of the propeller shafts beneath missile magazines. Note that the US Navy solved this problem in its *Cleveland* class conversions by building a hangar-like magazine structure entirely outside the hull aft. The later British missile cruiser designs also

showed long magazine spaces well above the waterline, as an alternative to short, deep magazines serving a launcher by way of a special missile elevator.

In 1951, however, a missile conversion of the new *Tiger* was rejected on the basis of hull age and because, although a triple launcher could replace the twin 6in mount forward or aft, there would be no more than 30 missiles. The *Tiger* hull was, moreover, so cramped that it would be difficult to provide the requisite radars. The much larger (17,000-ton, 31-knot) 1960 cruiser actually could accommodate the full 90 missiles aft, but it would have to make excessive sacrifices in other ship functions, such as accommodation – which would prove so difficult to provide in the later specialist missile cruiser designs. It would, however, be possible to develop a balanced design with a twin launcher and 50 missiles aft. This approximated the missile cruiser ultimately proposed five years later.

Three years later the DNC would comment, in connection with the US cruiser conversions, that there was no British ship even approaching the US ships in size. For example, the volume which could be made available in a *Tiger* by removing the after 6in turret and magazine would be just under one-third of that used in the American ships *Boston* and *Canberra* (CAG 1 and 2) for missile magazines alone (each 36 x 28 x 57ft). Since each o the US magazines accommodated 72 Terriers, the *Tiger* would be limited to about 20 such weapons, in a magazine which would, moreover, extend above decks. Nor would Seaslug, designed for horizontal stowage, fit.

DNC also considered battleship conversions. These large hulls could be expected to accommodate about 70 missiles forward, 50 aft. Here the number of missiles was limited by the internal protective bulkheads, which were fixed. It might also be difficult to find enough volume for missile controls and for the weapon direction system and modern CIC (AIO) required for a missile ship; nor was it clear that there would be enough length to accommodate both the new missile directors and the necessary radars. In these ships twin 3in/70 would replace the existing 5.25in guns. It appeared to be impracticable to provide eight MRS directors in addition to the four required by the GWS. DNC concluded that a battleship would be unsuitable; her small outfit of missiles would be uneconomical on so large a displacement.

This negative report did not quite kill the possibility of conversion. The Deputy Chief of the (British) Naval Staff visited the United States in October/November 1953, and was most impressed by the US cruiser conversion program. What could the Royal Navy do to match? Fresh studies were, therefore, made of conversions of the two battleship classes and of the large fleet carrier *Implacable*. The DNCs main counter-argument was that production of the guidance radars and control equipment would be so limited that relatively unsatisfactory conversions could be carried out only at the expense of the much more satisfactory new-design ships: the best is always the enemy of good enough.

All three existing ships would been considerably more electrical power. A thorough modernization would extend the life of these ships by about a decade, and missile numbers were far more optimistic than those which had been developed three years earlier. Thus the after two turrets of the *Vanguard* could be replaced by 140-150 missiles behind 2in armor; in a *King George V*, 90-100 missiles would replace Y turret. Both battleships were, however, rejected on the grounds of needing far larger generator capacity, for which space would be difficult to provide. The *Vanguard*, for example, could only just feed her existing DC generators at top speed, and she would have to reduce speed to provide sufficient steam to add AC power.

As in 1951, the fleet carrier was far more attractive. Two twin launchers (with two directors each) would be served by 200 to 250 missiles. As in 1951, the gun armament would be four twin 3in/70. The ship would also operate three ASW helicopters, which would be Sikorsky S-55s or later types. The *Implacable* study was considered particularly urgent because a decision on the future of the class had to be reached shortly, as the new light fleet carriers were being completed.

Three schemes were drawn. In the simplest, Scheme 1, the launchers were at forecastle and quarterdeck level, exposed to sea damage, and fed by missiles stowed in the hangar. The lower hangar would accommodate the transmitters for the four Type 901 missile guidance radars, and the helicopters stowed in a lightweight hangar on the old flight deck. This would be a very austere conversion: the uptakes would remain on starboard side, balanced by a Type 984 on the port side. A new superstructure on the centerline would carry the four 901s.

In Scheme 2, the missiles were protected from sea damage; they were moved to the old flight deck and the forward 3in guns mounted on the forecastle. The helicopters would have to be stowed in the hangar at the expense of some missiles. They would have to land on the quarterdeck, a much livelier platform than the flight deck, but they would be protected from the weather.

The third alternative was to move the after missile launcher to the flight deck, the after 3in being lowered to the quarterdeck. The helicopters would now land on the flight deck.

In any case, the carrier hull would need extensive attention, particularly in view of the bad state of parts of inner bottom and bulkheads. Equipment would probably not be ready until 1963, when the ship would be more than 20 years old. DNC doubted that it would be worth the very large design effort involved. The clinching argument was that a conversion would preclude construction of new ships. Given the continuing crisis in British finances, the issue was really the long-term future of the Navy. A new ship might last another thirty years; a conversion, no more than ten. Better, then, to provide the longer-term solution.

By the time the 1951 studies had been completed, missile size had increased to the point where stowage in a carrier hangar was no longer practicable. Given the failure of the cruiser conversion studies, the Type A ship would have to be a wholly new design. As for B, very preliminary studies showed that a fast refrigerator ship of about 17,000 tons was promising. Since C was the first priority, it seemed logical to seek a compromise between B and C as the British operational missile prototype ship. Tentative staff requirements of July 1952 showed a speed of 18 knots, and an endurance of 4500nm at that speed. One launcher (single, twin, or triple) would be served by a 90-missile magazine, and controlled by two 901 radars. Other radar was initially limited to the 960 and 992 required for search and target acquisition, but fighter direction radars (982 and 983) and facilities were added when the design was reviewed. The weapon system was, except for directors, half the conceived for the Type A, and included two twin 3in/70.

Eighteen knots was quite slow, even for a convoy escort, given the range of speeds required for the new frigates then under construction. In

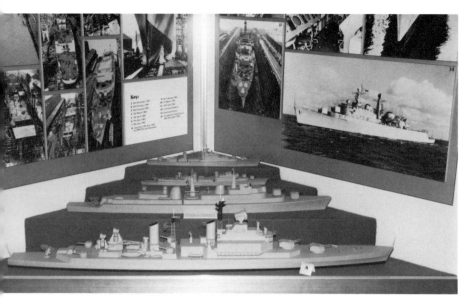

Models at the Centenary Exhibition of the Royal Corps of Naval Constructors show several of the British missile ship designs. These models were built in the 'fifties to display features of proposed ships to the Admiralty Board. The large one in the foreground is the large missile cruiser described in the text, armed with Seaslug, and twin 6in and 3in guns. Behind it is a model of a County class missile destroyer, with two earlier approaches to the County class design behind that. In the cruiser model, note the paired 901 control radars, the telemetry dish amidships, and the two MRS3 gun directors atop the bridge. The big radar is Type 984. [*Author*]

January, therefore, the SDPC asked that the design be developed for speeds up to 25 knots. DNC found that such a ship, whether with hangar or deep missile stowage, would displace 9500-10,000 tons, figures which seemed extremely large for a convoy escort. The ship could be cut by eliminating the 3in guns, or by reducing missile stowage from 90 to 60, or by eliminating provision for fighter control. Her cost, however, would very largely be a consequence of the nature of the missile control system. Thus cuts in size might well leave the ship more vulnerable, and probably little cheaper.

Revised staff requirements of January 1954 therefore matched those of 1952, except for higher speed (25 knots deep, six months out of dock) and reduced endurance (4500nm at 12 rather than 18 knots). The 3in/70 would be supplemented by four twin Bofors, the close range weapons of the earlier studies. The two fighter control radars of the earlier study were replaced by the now-standard 984.

This convoy escort seemed rather large and expensive. Surely something substantially smaller could be built. In April 1954, DGD (director, gunnery department) called for a minimum ship, with one twin launcher (and one director), two twin Bofors guns (no 3in/70), and no fighter control facilities. The number of missiles would be determined by the minimum size of the ship, 'consistent with a well-balanced design'. Although the new minimum escort was conceived as a replacement for the 10,000-ton convoy escort, there was pressure for fleet rather than convoy speed, for maximum flexibility. By this time, after all, British policy was turning towards the short, sharp, war, in which convoy operations would be substantially less important than carrier strikes. There may also have been the first hints of a post-1957 policy in which the carrier task force was the central naval unit, hence in which virtually all ships would have to be task force compatible.

This was not the ideal ship, as the naval staff

saw it, but it was a first approach to a minimum. For example, an analysis in May 1954 equated task force escort with both fleet speed and a double-ended arrangement, the latter to permit the ship to launch in any direction without having to leave her station. However, the low expected rate of production of missile control systems would clearly prohibit anything so lavish on the prototype, which was code-named BLUE 01.* Almost by definition, then, BLUE 01 would be a convoy escort. Even so, the staff argued for fleet speed, unless that speed would be prohibitively expensive.

Similarly, it would be desirable to provide two directors per launcher, so as to take maximum advantage of launcher output, which was estimated at two to three missiles a minute. This was particularly worrying, since it was estimated that a coordinated attack by about 20 aircraft (or a fast stream attack by a similar number) could overwhelm the system. However, in 1954, it was still not clear that directors could be duplexed. Moreover, it would be vital to keep down ship size so as to keep up the sheer number of missile-firing ships. DGD therefore accepted the single-director arrangement.

Similar arguments were made for a minimum gun battery. Bofors twins were chosen because the next larger weapon, the twin 3in/70, would be prohibitively expensive in terms of space, operating, and particularly maintenance personnel. As it was, the 40mm guns would be controlled by the best available British director, MRS 3.

The impressive reduction in size compared to earlier designs was achieved by scaling up from frigate and fast minelayer practice, rather than down from cruiser practice. Instead of a double bottom and 2in armor over vitals, the ship would be virtually unarmored except in the top range of displacement, where 1in armor and a 'tank top' to the bottom could, under certain conditions, be provided. DNC believed in May, for example, that he could provide 36 missiles and no protection (at 24 to 25 knots) on 4500 tons. Complement would be 370. An increase to 5500 tons bought fleet speed (28 knots plus), with a complement of 400, or 44 missiles and a complement of 370. Fleet speed plus 1in protection required 7000 tons (44 missiles, complement of 500).

On the basis of this estimate, presented at a May 1954 DTSD meeting, Controller and DCNS proposed that the 7000-ton study be carried out, and that the proposed staff requirements for the 10,000-ton ship be suspended. A more detailed study showed that 36 missiles and frigate machinery (30,000 shp) could be accommodated on 5000 tons, with a complement of 500 (*vs* 750 to

---

* British charts of the expected rate of missile ship introduction showed convoy escorts as blue bars, and fleet escorts as green bars. Hence the statement that BLUE 01 would be the prototype meant that convoy escorts would come first.

The US Navy was fortunate in having a large supply of cruisers suitable for conversion to missile ships. Their characteristics in turn largely decided the details of the conversions. The earlier ones were single-ended not so much to preserve the gun firepower of the fleet, but because the early missiles were not considered very reliable. By 1956, US policy had turned to all-missile ships, such as the *Albany* class conversions. This is an earlier single-ender, *Oklahoma City*, February 1965. She combined the functions of long-range missile cruiser (Talos) and fleet flagship (at the expense of one of her forward twin 6in turrets). Note the large boom swung out to starboard, just forward of her after lattice mast, for missile replenishment at sea. She carried only 46 missiles. All were stowed in the deckhouse aft, below the pair of missile control radars (SPG-49) and the stub mast. *Oklahoma City* was ultimately valued more for her flagship than for her missile capabilities, and as such she was the last of the converted US cruisers to be decommissioned in 1979. [*USN*]

885 for the 9000- or 10,000-ton ship). The small ship would, however, be quite limited. She could not accommodate fighter control comparable to that of an Aircraft Direction (A/D) frigate. That would be acceptible, on the theory that other fighter director ships (A/D frigates or carriers) would generally be available in company with the missile ship. The issue of de-conflicting missiles and aircraft was not raised at this time.

The Director of Plans justified fleet speed in this limited escort in a June 1954 memorandum. Missiles would clearly represent a revolutionary advance in naval warfare; how could they be provided for convoys, and not for the fleet itself? Even if single-ended, these ships would be far more effective than ships armed only with guns. After all, fleet speed was not so much more than convoy speed: 28 knots *vs* 24, so the cost could not be so very great. Surely even a single-ender was worth while. This argument succeeded. Sketch staff requirements issued in September 1954, called for 28 knots in deep condition, six months out of dock, an endurance of 4500nm at 20 knots, and at least 30 missiles with one twin launcher. All round cover by Bofors L/70 twins would be required, with at least two fire control channels. There would be no fighter control. However, there was some skepticism; 7000 tons was at the upper limit of lightweight hull practice, Moreover, some suspected that any missile convoy escort would be worth protecting with the 3in/70 gun, to provide for self-defense against aircraft getting past Seaslug. As a last gasp, DNC proposed to trade

missiles for guns in an 8000-ton cruiser (December, 1954), but it was clearly a poor bargain.

The alternative was a full cruiser, with fighter control and with a useful anti-ship main battery. The latter reflected a gradual shift back towards interest in means of countering the growing Soviet gun-armed cruiser force, following a reassessment early in 1952. It paralleled increased emphasis on strike aircraft.

In September 1954, the DNC began feasibility studies of both the full cruiser and what he called a missile destroyer, alongside yet another cruiser conversion (of a *Fiji*). They were to form part of the basis for the 1955-56 new construction program, and in November were presented to the Sea Lords as part of a book of sketches: carriers, a light (gun) cruiser, a 5in gun destroyer, and a range of missile ships: 18,300-ton cruiser, 11,000-ton fleet escort, 10,000-ton convoy escort, 10,930-ton converted *Fiji*, 3590-ton destroyer, 5000-ton small convoy escort.

The missile/gun ship displaced 18,300 tons deep load (657 x 79 x 22.25 feet), and was armed with two twin 6in Mark 26, two twin 3in Mark 6 sided amidships, four twin Bofors L/70 (two forward and two aft at the corners of the superstructure). It would have full fighter direction with a 984, and the hangar type missile stowage for 48 weapons aft. In the event of it being rearmed with missiles forward, the hangar could be extended forward under the bridge. Meanwhile, it was considered useful for accommodation, as the ship would actually have a greater complement as a gun/ missile ship than as a double-ended missile ship. The 120,000shp all-steam plant would drive her at 31.25 knots deep and dirty, and endurance would be 4500nm at 12 knots. Armor protection would comprise a 3.5in - 4in side belt over machinery and magazines, covered by 3in armor on No. 2 deck. Missile stowage and operational spaces in the bridge would be protected by 2in armor. The complement would be 100 officers and 1200 ratings.

The fleet escort missile (GW) ship was the next step down; it was an expanded version of the small fast escort. Alternatively, it could be regarded as a fast version of the convoy escort of 1953-54. Two 3in/70 were mounted superimposed forward, with four twin 40mm at the corners of the superstructure, and a twin missile launcher aft (with two guidance radars), with most of the missiles stowed three high and two abreast in a hangar extending well forward, and the remainder in the after part of the stowage. In effect, then, it was a cruiser without anti-ship or bombardment capability, and with a more austere fighter direction capability (982/983 rather than 984). These cuts greatly reduced the size of the ship, to 530 x 70 x 19ft.

Two 30,000shp frigate-type machinery units were separated by a 40ft block; they would drive the ship at 28.5 knots deep and clean, but no more than 27.5 knots deep and dirty, endurance would be 5600nm at 20 knots. An increase to the next larger standard machinery unit, 48,000shp, would increase the speed deep and dirty to 29.25 knots, but deep displacement would then be 12,500 tons. The ship would be protected as well as the slower (23.5-knot) version with a 3in side belt and 2in deck over machinery, 1.5in over the 3in gunbays and magazines, and 2in over the missile stowage. Accommodation would be provided for 35 officers and 830 ratings.

TABLE 5–3: BRITISH MISSILE SHIP DESIGNS, 1953–1955

	GW 1	GW 9	GW 14A	GW 18	GW 20	GW 24	GW 25	GW 25B	GW 25C	GW 26	GW 27
DATE	4.3.53	21.5.53	5.54	5.54	5.54	30.9.54	30.9.54	30.9.54	26.10.54	13.10.54	19.10.5
LWL (ft)	484	490	520	350	450	360	645	645	645	530	450
BEAM/DEPTH (ft)	70/42	70	70	60	56	43/28	79/43.5	79/43.5	79/43.5	70/40	63/41.5
DRAFT (ft)	17-9	19	—	—	—	12-6	23	23	23	18-6	16-0
DEEP LOAD (tons)	10,319	9169	10,376	5745	5400	3550	18,360	18,200	18,300	10,820	7200
TWIN LAUNCHER	1	1	1	1	1	1	1	2	1	1	1
MISSILES	90	90	90	36	44	12	84	84	48	90	36
GMS 1	2	2	2	1	1	1	2	4	2	2	1
GUNS	2 × 2 3in	2 × 2 3in	2 × 2 3in	—	—	—	2 × 2 6in	2 × 2 3in	2 × 2 6in	2 × 2 3in	2 × 2 3i
SECONDARY	—	—	—	—	—	2 A/S TT	2 × 2 3in	—	2 × 2 3in	—	—
BOFORS	4 × 2	4 × 2	4 × 2	4 × 2	4 × 2	3 × 2	4 × 2	4 × 2	4 × 2	4 × 2	2 × 2
MRS 3 DIR	6	6	6	4	4	3	8	6	8	6	4
RADARS	992, 960 982, 983 974	992, 960 982, 983 974	992, 984 — 974	992, 960 277Q 974	992, 960 277Q 974	992, 960 — 974	992, 984 — 974	992, 984 — 974	992, 984 — 974	992, 960 982, 983 974	992, 96 — 974
MACHINERY	ST	ST	ST	ST	ST	Y.102A	YEAD 1	YEAD 1	YEAD 1	Y.102A	YEAD
SHAFTS/SHP	2/15,000	2/30,000	2/30,000	2/30,000	2/60,000	2/60,000	4/120,000	4/120,000	4/120,000	2/60,000	2/60,00
SPEED DEEP	18	24.8	24	24	31	31/30	32.5/31.5	32.5/31.5	32.5/31.5	28.75/27.75	28.75/28
ENDURANCE	12,000/12	—	—	—	—	3200/20	4500/20	4500/20	4500/20	5400/20	4500/2
COMPLEMENT	750	750	895	475	375	20/260	100/1200	100/1200	100/1200	55/830	50/55
WEIGHTS (tons):											
HULL	4140	4213	4470	2520	2100	1518	8040	8080	8040	4940	3190
EQUIPMENT	702	649	760	470	300	230	1260	1260	1260	850	500
ARMAMENT	873	824	1140	565	550	232	1475	1115	1415	840	570
PROTECTION	1667	1406	1500	505	600	—	2852	3012	2852	1190	630
MACHINERY	498	706	706	575	850	780	1800	1800	1800	900	820
FUEL OIL	2154	1115	1470	970	900	700	2550	2550	2550	1920	1300
RFW	83	30	30	30	—	20	200	200	200	20	20
MARGIN	182	180	200	115	100	70	180	180	180	160	110

NOTES: The series of 1953-55 designs ran through GW 80. This is only a selection, to indicate the main lines of development. Cruisers were generally armored with 2-3in decks and 4in sides (2in side over missile magazines and AIO). The slower convoy escorts were less heavily armored, typical levels of protection being 1¾in decks and 2in sides (1in deck, 1in side over missiles and AIO). In the missile list, B is the semi-active Bristol 1¾in missile, a proposed Seaslug successor; TIA is its 4ft diameter tracking illuminator. In 1955, this missile was expected to reach prototype stage in 1965-66, and to enter service in 1969-70. It was to have been powered by two 18in diameter ramjets, taking off with four 15ft long, 12in wrap-around boosters (5200 pounds, for a total of

The convoy escort GW ship was essentially the slow ship of 1953-54. Like the fleet escort, it would have 982/983 instead of 984 for fighter direction; dimensions would be 530 x 70 x 17ft. The short hull could not accommodate two 3in on the centerline, so they would be sided forward, with the 40mm mountings at the corners of the superstructure. One twin launcher with two directors was aft. Two unitized 15,000shp sets, 40 feet apart, would drive the ship at 24.75 knots deep and clean, 23.75 deep and dirty, 6400nm at 12 knots, or 4000nm at 20 knots. Protection would match that of the fleet escort, and accommodation would be provided for 55 officers and 800 ratings.

Weights (tons) provided in the 1954 notes for the Sea Lords show how the three designs compared (see accompanying table).

As in the past, a small cruiser (*Fiji*) conversion was examined and rejected as disappointing. Stability would prohibit both fighter control and protection for the missiles or the AIO spaces. Only one triple 6in mount could be retained, forward, and the launcher aft would be limited to 24 missiles (two directors, however). Even then an additional 500kW alternator would be required to meet the increased demand for electronic power. Speed would be 30.5 knots deep and clean, 29.5 knots deep and dirty; endurance would be about 3900nm at 20 knots deep and dirty.

The Sea Lords decided in December that the new program would include a gun/missile cruiser, hopefully somewhat smaller than the one which had been presented to them. They considered the 6in cruiser (18,000 tons) ideal, but only if sufficient money were available, which was not the case. In January, therefore, they opted for a smaller ship of fleet speed, displacing about 11,000 to 12,000 tons, carrying at least 30 missiles as well as fighter control (984), and two twin 5in or 4.5in guns. The guns could be replaced later by additional

	GW 34	GW 38	GW 40	GW 41	GW 50	GW 51	GW 51 (TALOS)	GW 58	GW 59	GW 70	GW 71	GW 76
.54	10.12.54	25.1.55	24.1.55	2.3.55	29.4.55	3.5.55	21.5.55	8.6.55	23.6.55	.55	.55	.55
0	450	580	390	550	570	590	590	625	540	640	630	645
41	63/41.5	72/45	53/41	74/45	76/45	77/45	77/45	78/45	78/47	80	80	78
-6	16	18-6	12-6	18-9	19-3	19-6	19-6	20-3	17	21-1.75	25	20.15
00	7200	12,200	4300	12,100	13,000	13,900	14,030	15,400	10,550	16,770	20,065	15,728
1	1	1	1	1	1	1	1	1	8 SINGLE	6 SINGLE	6 SINGLE	1
0	36	24	30	48	48	48	46 TALOS	48	28	24 B	54 B	17 B
1	1	1	1	1	1	1	2 SPG-49	1	1 × 985	—	—	—
TT	2 × 2 4.5in	2 × 2 6in	1 × 2 4in	2 × 5in	2 × 2 5in	2 × 2 6in	—	2 × 2 6in	—	2 × 2 3in	—	2 × 2 6in
ORTAR	—	—	6 A/S TT	—	—	—	—	2 × 2 3in	—	—	—	2 × 2 3in
× 2	4 × 2	4 × 2	2 × 2	4 × 2	4 × 2	4 × 2	4 × 2	2 × 2	4 × 2	2 × 2	4 × 6	2 × 2
8	6	6	3	6	6	6	4	6	4	4	4	6
960	992, 960	992, 984	992, 960 982M	992, 984	992, 984	992, 984	992, 984	992, 984	992	992, 984 6 TIA	992, 984 6 TIA	982, 984 6 TIA, BEACO
74	974	974	974	974	974	974	974	974	974	978	978	978
00	YEAD 1	YEAD 1	Y.100	ST + GT	ST	ST	ST	ST	ST	ST	ST	ST
,000	2/60,000	3/90,000	2/30,000	3/105,000	3/105,000	3/105,000	3/105,000	4/105,000	2/70,000	4/105,000	2/40,000	4/120,000
5/25	29.75/29.25	31.5/30.5	26.5/25.25	31.5/30.75	31.5/30.75	31.75/31	31.75/31	32/31.25	29.75/29	32/31	24/22.5	33.25/32.2
0/15	4500/20	4500/20	4500/15	4500/20	4500/20	4500/20	4500/20	4500/20	4500/20	5020/20	6340/20	4470/20
420	50/550	900	29/550	—	75/925	78/970	—	76/970	650	1040	80/990	80/990
95	3160	5770	1995	5790	6170	6590	6590	7490	5900	7757	9685	7240
30	500	930	380	930	1030	1070	1070	1130	740	1090	1175	1090
50	600	1090	460	960	940	1220	1305	1340	750	1215	1273	1248
50	630	1010	—	1080	1000	1050	1095	1170	0	1259	1754	1339
50	880	1390	550	1350	1700	1700	1700	1800	1300	1940	1397	1940
00	1300	1950	800	1800	1900	2050	2050	2150	1650	2590	3480	2260
25	20	40	25	40	60	60	60	100	60	100	340	100
00	110	160	90	150	150	160	160	180	150	185	100	180

10,300 pounds). Length would have been 28 feet, wingspan 16ft, 9in (12 feet folded); maximum range, 85nm (about 200 with active homing), maximum altitude 70,000ft. Since minimum range would have been 10-20nm, it could not have displaced Seaslug. Missiles would have been fired at the rate of one per launcher per minute, and some cruiser designs (not listed here) had as many as four launchers and 100 missiles. An alternative installation showed a single beacon illuminator. In the list of machinery, ST is a steam turbine, GT a gas turbine.

	GW Cruiser	Fleet escort GW	Convoy escort
Hull	8043 (44.0)	4994 (48.1)	4790 (47.9)
Equipment	1260 (6.9)	850 (7.8)	850 (8.5)
Armament	1415 (7.7)	840 (7.7)	840 (8.4)
Protection	2852 (15.6)	1316 (12.0)	1316 (13.2)
Machinery	1800 (9.8)	800 (8.2)	600 (6.0)
Fuel Oil	2550 (13.9)	1920 (17.5)	1434 (14.3)
RFW	200 (1.1)	20 (0.2)	20 (0.2)
Board Margin	180 (1.0)	160 (1.5)	150 (1.5)
DISPLACEMENT	18,300	11,000	10,000

Seaslugs. DNC had briefly pressed for a small gun/missile cruiser (two twin 5in, 20 missiles, 8500 tons deep displacement), but it proved slow (28.25 knots) and was soon abandoned as too expensive to be worthwhile. However, the Sea Lords were impressed by a 10,000-ton ship carrying two 5.25in guns forward and suitable for later conversion to an all-missile ship, and they directed that it be developed further with new 5in guns replacing the old 5.25in. In contrast to the austere light cruisers, this one would have full fighter control, with a 984 radar. Tentative (sketch) staff requirements for an 11,000- to 12,000-ton ship were issued in February 1955. Speed would be 31 knots deeply loaded, six months out of dock; endurance, the usual 4500nm at 20 knots. Armament would be one twin launcher with 30-48 missiles (DNC had offered 30-36 missiles on 12,000 tons) and two twin 5in of a new type (4.5in Mark 6 if 5in not available) plus up to four twin Bofors L/70. Like the larger cruisers, this one would function as a flagship.

This looked like a good compromise, and DNC expected that the first ship would be ordered in April 1957. However, the new 5in gun mount did not yet exist, and it would be impossible to develop it while full effort was being applied to Seaslug itself. Either 4.5in or 6in guns could be substituted; it was estimated that the ship would displace either 13,500 tons with the smaller gun, or 15,000 tons (full load) with the larger. On such large displacements, more Seaslug magazine stowage was available, and the ship would probably be able to carry 48 missiles.

The Sea Lords approved the 6in design in May, and new sketch staff requirements were issued in July. In the interim, it grew 300 tons because a four-shaft (two unit) machinery arrangement was substituted for the earlier three-shaft type. The principal changes were the requirement for 48 missiles, two twin Mark 26 6in turrets, two twin 3in/70; and two twin Bofors L/70. The result was quite large, at 15,800 tons and 645 x 78ft. It became the basis for further studies, and for further growth. Thus by February 1956, deep displacement was 18,500 tons. Improvements included a more powerful secondary battery (four twin 3in or two twin 3in and two sextuple Bofors),

and up to 25 per cent of the missiles might have special (ie, nuclear) warheads.

Almost 2000 tons seemed to have bought nothing; the Controller tried to set a limit of 16,000 tons. In fact, the ship had crept up due to unexpected increases in the weight of the 6in mounting and in the size of the missile. Stowage now had to be revised from three high by two wide to two levels of one high by four wide tube

stowage. The cruiser was expected to displace 17,000 tons and measure 645 x 79 x 21.5 ft. An alternative study showed that the 16,000-ton limit could be met (barely) by eliminating one of the two 6in guns, at a great cost in anti-ship capability, and in usefulness in cold wars. That was not really acceptable, and by April DNC was suggesting that even 18,000 tons might not be enough. The ship was back to the high end of the scale as understood at the end of 1954, and that was much too expensive.

The problems of the gun/missile ship threw the Naval Staff back towards the double-ended all-missile concepts of the past, and in May 1956 DNC was asked to develop designs for a 16,000-ton double-ender. Part of the rationale was the hope that nuclear warheads would make Seaslug an effective anti-ship weapon and so eliminate the requirement for the 6in gun. Even so, the ship would have a secondary battery of four twin 3in/70 or twin 4.5in Mark 6. The tonnage target was attained, but total missile capacity (for both launchers) was only 64, matching that of the mixed-battery ship. With only two 3in mountings, the ship would displace 15,848 tons (610 x 78ft). Adding two 3in mounts brought displacement to 16,671 tons. Replacing them with 4.5in mounts brought the ship to 16,529 tons (630 x 79ft).

The Sea Lords considered the 6in gun too valuable to abandon, and reverted to the larger ship. DGD argued that they would be required to meet the staff requirement calling for the ship to be effective against surface raiders. Two turrets was the minimum accceptable. For the bombardment role the 4.5in gun was only just adequate and the 6in ideal. In the AA role the 6in was superior in that it fired a larger shell a greater distance with a higher muzzle velocity, and had a better rate of fire. DGD was not willing to accept anything smaller than 6in and less than two turrets. The standard estimate was that two twin 4.5in or one twin 6in mount could deal with a single airplane. Thus replacement of the two 6in turrets by two twin 4.5in would replace two channels of AA fire with one less effective one.

The second turret was required to make the ship effective (in the absence of any ship-to-ship missile) in surface action against *Sverdlov* class cruisers when aircraft were not available. In the AA gunfire role it provided an additional and 'very effective' AA gun channel.

Moreover, without her lesser guns, the ship

The cruisers *Lion* and USS *Springfield*, and the missile test ship *Girdle Ness* lie at anchor at Malta, August 1961. The conversion of *Springfield* showed that, with a properly designed missile and a ship only slightly larger than *Lion*, something close to a satisfactory missile ship could be achieved. The design of the *Girdle Ness* conversion seemed to show that, at least with the Seaslug as designed, a very special design was needed. Note that *Girdle Ness* was initially to have been the prototype British missile convoy escort. [CPL]

would have a large blind gun arc aft. The absolute minimum was therefore two 3in/70 with MRS 3 aft; it was desirable also to have two twin 40/70 with MRS 8.

The only sacrifice left was to give up the standard of two directors for the launcher. Although this was attractive on grounds of cost, it would have represented a major sacrifice. By this time, the guided missile destroyer described in the next chapter was well underway. It differed from the cruiser in that it had only a single director, and in that it lacked fighter control facilities. Surely, the cruiser should have the better fire control system. It was argued that providing two missile directors for the first cruiser would deny one to the first destroyer; the proposed compromise was to fit the cruiser with one director but provide space and weight for the second.

By August 1956, the cruiser seemed too expensive to buy, and design work was cut back. The Controller formally put back the planning dates, so that the first of three ships was now to be ordered in April 1959, to complete in October 1963;

the second in June, 1960 for March 1965; and the third in April 1962 for October 1966.

Some design work did, however, go forward, and new draft staff requirements were issued in November 1956. The ship would have one twin launcher with 64 missiles (25 per cent special warheads) and two directors; two 6in turrets; four 3in twin mounts, and fighter control radar (984). Like previous British cruisers, she would be fitted with sonar (Type 184; a variable depth sonar had been considered as an alternative). The 3in guns could be replaced by the new American Tartar missile system at a later date.

All work was stopped, at Controller's instruction, in January 1957. In April, the Board of Admiralty decided to announce cancellation, and to justify it on the grounds that in building missile destroyers instead of missile cruisers the Admiralty would be making the best use of the limited resources now available. Perhaps it was symbolic that the cruiser design team became the British nuclear submarine team.

HMS *Sirius*, Portland, August 1947. [*CPL*]

6

Destroyers and Frigates

Before the end of World War II, destroyers, which were fast fleet units designed largely for surface action, were clearly distinguished from slow trade protection escorts such as sloops (and, later, frigates). The gap between the two categories began to close even before the outbreak of war, as older British and then US destroyers were modified for escort duties. In 1943, for example, all surviving British destroyers of the prewar A through E classes were redesignated as escorts. Postwar, the high speed of the new submarines required higher speed in ASW ships, and the gap between destroyer and ASW escort narrowed considerably. For example, the British first-rate ASW escort, the Type 12 (*Whitby*), could be (and was) used as a fleet escort. Ultimately, the Royal Navy would build Type 42 (*Sheffield* class) destroyers somewhat smaller than its Type 22 (*Broadsword* class) frigates, both having about the same speed and endurance. In the US Navy, the chief distinction sometimes seems to be that a destroyer is larger, and has twin screws and slightly higher speed (as in the *Spruance* vs the *Knox* class).*

The two navies ended the war with very different destroyer fleets, a consequence of their very different prewar naval industrial bases. Britain had a large existing shipbuilding base, consisting of yards with a considerable range of capacities. All of her destroyer yards could build the ships under construction in 1939, and through most of the war she continued to build emergency destroyers based on the prewar J-class hull (with much reduced main batteries and increased fuel stowage). However, the wartime demand for a

* For the period covered by this book, the primary distinction (in Britain) was probably that frigates were single-purpose ships, whereas destroyers were not. Thus, the Royal Navy built separate anti-submarine (Types 12 and 14), anti-aircraft (Type 41), and air direction (Type 61) frigates. That was why the general purpose Tribals were initially designated sloops, not frigates. They were redesignated frigates to help honor a British government commitment of a fixed number of frigates to NATO. However, note that the Royal Navy concluded early that no destroyer of acceptable size could really fulfill the general-purpose fleet escort role. Certainly, the French and US Navies buit specialist air direction or radar picket destroyers.

ship armed with 4.5in dual purpose guns, the Battle, made for a hull too large for some slips. The smaller (intermediate) hull therefore remained in production, for the Weapon and *Gallant* (1944 Weapon) classes, the second of which was not, in fact, built. Similarly, escort production resulted in two categories: a full-size frigate and a smaller and slower corvette. In all but the prewar J class (nine ships), each class was ordered as an eight-ship flotilla. War and associated postwar production, apart from some ships to foreign order taken over in 1939, therefore amounted to 23½ flotillas, 189 ships:

— the largest of the prewar classes (the big J, K, L, M, and N classes), all designed to be armed with three twin 4.7in mounts and two quintuple torpedo tubes;

— two smaller early-war emergency flotillas (O and P) designed for four single 4.7in guns and two quadruple torpedo tubes;

— twelve intermediate classes (Q through, W, Z, Ca, Co, Ch, and Cr flotillas), designed for O and P class armament (but with 4.7in limited dual purpose guns capable of 55-degree elevation in the S through W classes, and with 4.5in guns capable of 55-degree elevation in the Z, Ca through Cr series);

— three Battle class flotillas (two of the 1942 and one of the 1943 series armed with two twin 4.5in dual purpose guns (plus a single 4.5in gun in the 1943 ships); another two 1943 flotillas were cancelled;

— one 1944 Battle class flotilla (*Daring* class; with another flotilla cancelled in 1945) armed with three twin 4.5in dual purpose mountings;

— half a flotilla of 1943 Weapons (four ships completed, of 20 ships ordered) of intermediate size, armed with three twin 4in anti-aircraft guns.

Of all of these ships, only the Battles had fully satisfactory dual purpose main batteries reflecting war experience. The modern British Mk VI director was fitted only in the Ch, Cr, and Co, Battle (some of which had US Mark 37) and Weapon classes. None had the modern (ahead-throwing) ASW weapons and matching sonars required to deal with modern (intermediate) submarines. However, towards the end of the war, British destroyer designs

Experience with the Weapon class destroyers *Scorpion* and *Crossbow* showed that Squid could be fired over a ship's bridge. *Scorpion* is shown in October 1947. In 1954, she was refitted with a single Limbo aft, as in the projected modernization of the entire class. [*CPL*]

generally made provision for several alternative armament combinations, including ones with ahead-throwing weapons. For example, one version of the *Gallant* class was to have incorporated a pair of Squids in place of their torpedo tubes. Two others showed heavier depth charge batteries (four rather than two throwers to double the size of the pattern, 100 rather than 50 charges in place of one set of torpedo tubes, 150 in place of both). At this time, Squids had to be mounted forward, generally on the weather deck, and they obstructed the firing arcs of the main battery. In both the 1943 and 1944 Weapon classes, the Squid alternative was rejected because it so reduced gun fire that the destroyer was no longer really a general purpose ship. Postwar Squid installations aft were acceptable because they had much less impact on other destroyer capabilities.*

The US Navy was far better equipped with anti-aircraft fire control systems, although in 1945 they were already becoming inadequate. Like the Royal Navy, its modern destroyers mounted no ahead-throwing weapons and therefore could not effectively counter fast submarines. Given the huge size of their existing destroyer fleets, neither navy could afford wholesale replacement. Each therefore had to develop an austere modernization program.

The British, with more urgent requirements,

* The four Weapons were, however, converted to an ASW configuration. Their wartime design had included an alternative in which Squids replaced one of the two forward twin 4in guns, and two ships were completed to this configuration. The other two, however, had their Squids aft, as a test of the possibility of firing Squid over the bridge of a destroyer. Their success showed that it was possible to modernize the entire British active destroyer force by adding Squids aft, without sacrificing a large fraction of their main batteries.

came first. They replaced depth charges with single or twin Squids aft, experiments having shown that these weapons could safely fire forward over the bridges of the ships. The four surviving Weapons were completed with four rather than six 4in guns, and with double Squid (later single Limbo in *Scorpion*) either in B or in X position. In earlier classes, modernization also sometimes entailed installation of a new main battery fire control system (Mark VI director), even though ships were armed with relatively low-elevation (55-degree) 4.5in weapons. A complicating factor here was that postwar manning was sometimes so tight that the smaller and much less capable emergency destroyers could deploy abroad, while the big Battles and Weapons had to remain in home waters.

Thus, in 1947, the Controller established the pattern of British destroyer deployments:
— Home Fleet: 16 Battle, four Weapon;
— Mediterranean: eight Ch, one T, three V – may be raised to eight Ch, eight other emergency classes when manning permits;
— Pacific: eight Co class;
— Also 21 Battles, emergency class in local and training flotillas, etc, First-line reserve: eight Battle, eight Ca, two Cr, eight Z, remaining two V.

As modernized to a 1951 staff requirement, the Ca class emergency destroyer retained three of her four 4.5in single guns and one of her original pair of quadruple torpedo tubes. Her anti-aircraft battery was reduced to one twin Bofors controlled by an STD and two single Bofors guns. However, her 4.5in guns were radar-controlled by an FPS 5 fire control system (GDS 2*) including a Mark VI director, and she had a double Squid (10 salvoes) controlled by Asdic 164/174. Her bridge was replaced with a square-fronted structure similar to that of a *Daring*, the added internal space being needed for an enlarged operations room. As modernized she displaced about 2685 tons fully loaded, with a sea speed of 28.25 knots, and an endurance of 2700nm at 20 knots or 3700nm at 12 knots.

At this time the Royal Navy planned to fit all post-Z class destroyers (ie, all not scheduled for conversion to frigate) with Squid aft, as in the new *Daring*s. Existing sonars (Asdics Type 144 and 147) would be modernized with Asdic Type 166. It might even be possible to fit larger, less maneuverable, ships with Limbo and anti-submarine torpedo tubes, which required little in the way of maneuvering.

There was also a less visible improvement: silencing to improve sonar performance by reducing self-noise, particularly machinery and propeller noise which might enter a sonar transducer from the rear. Destroyer machinery was generally designed to run at high (ie, relatively noisy) speed; the ideal quiet propeller had a large diameter and ran relatively slowly. It could not be applied to existing ships. During World War II, for example, the Royal Navy found that US-supplied *Captain* class frigates, which had destroyer-type fast-revving propellers (30 turns per knot), could not effectively operate their sonars above about 12 knots, whereas British frigates (with slower-turning propellers, 10 turns per knot) were still effective at 18 knots. The Royal Navy developed silencing, first in the form of Nightshirt, and later in the form of quieter propellers (which were less efficient hydrodynamically). Nightshirt generated a screen of bubbles to trap propeller noise. The installation consisted of a spider web of air tubes mounted just in front of the propeller. In service, vibration quickly broke the tubes, and this particular system was unsuccessful. However, the bubble screen idea was quite widely used later on.

The only other wartime British destroyers were the Hunts, effectively fast, short-range anti-aircraft escorts, and were soon redesignated as frigates. They had been considered limited even in wartime, when Hunt construction was stopped in favor of the slower but much longer-range *Black Swan*. Postwar, they clearly had only very limited potential, as they were too small to accommodate an ahead-throwing weapon or a modern fire control system. Nor was their 4in gun considered particularly effective. Modernization was considered (and only briefly, in the 'fifties) primarily as a means of making up the enormous emergency frigate numbers demanded by NATO planners.*

The equivalent US modernization programs consisted of the installation of pairs of fixed Hedgehogs forward (on the 01 level, below the bridge) and replacement of existing 40mm guns with single and twin 3in/50. During the 'fifties many US destroyers were also fitted to fire lightweight Mark 32 or Mark 43/44/46 homing torpedoes, in many cases by lobbing them over the side. The most elaborate form of this modernization was applied to *Fletcher* class destroyers, which had one 5in gun and one bank of torpedo tubes removed in favor of three twin 3in/50.

The United States, with a small prewar shipbuilding base, created a series of new yards specially tailored to build the new large standard destroyers and destroyer escorts (frigates). The smaller prewar *Benson/Gleaves* class was built only until yards could shift over to the larger ships without slowing production, so that a total of 175 *Fletchers*, 70 *Sumners*, and 93 *Gearings* were completed. Another four *Gearing* hulls were later completed to modified designs as prototype ASW ships. Most of these ships survived the war. Indeed, the postwar US Navy had so many modern surplus destroyers that it could defer consideration of new-construction escorts.

Instead, destroyers could be converted into prototype fast ocean escorts, while retaining sufficient destroyer capability to remain useful for fleet work. In 1948, for example, rather than seek a new 30-knot destroyer escort, the Navy planned to convert all 150 surviving *Fletcher* class destroyers to escort (DDE) configuration. *Gearing* class destroyers would have been converted into submarine killers (DDK) like two of the four 1949 prototypes. Most would not be needed for active service in peacetime, so the plan was to convert ships taken from reserve and then return them to the reserve fleet. Not until 1950 was there a new frigate (ocean escort, or DE) design, and it began as a successor to the wartime coastal escort (the 173ft PC).

The *Gearing* hull was also large enough to accommodate the US version of air control (FADE) facilities. A total of 24 ships were converted to this DDR configuration in 1945, another 12 following in 1952-53. The US Navy was also fortunate in that many of its surviving frigates more closely approximated postwar requirements. The US destroyer escort was conceived as a 24-knot steam turbine convoy escort. The sheer size of the wartime program (which at one time included a thousand destroyer escorts) placed enormous strains on turbine and gearing manufacturers, and many of the destroyer escorts had to settle for half their designed power, for a speed of 19 knots (diesel-electric or geared diesel), but all enjoyed much longer range than the slightly faster Hunt. All also had a simple ahead-throwing weapon, a fixed Hedgehog, and the fast turbine-powered units were long enough to accommodate further weapons. They were clearly not wholly satisfactory, but they were a valuable interim force, and they were worth modernizing (on a modest budget) postwar.

Cavalier, now preserved as a museum, was one of eight Ca class fleet destroyers modernized in 1953-61, beginning with *Carron*. A modern Mark 6M main-battery director was fitted (remote power control for the three 4.5in guns), and the after torpedo tubes and No 3 4.5in gun replaced by a deckhouse carrying two Squids and a twin 40mm gun. The bridge was replaced by a *Daring*-type structure which provided an enlarged operations room. *Cavalier* recommissioned in 1957, and in 1964-66 was refitted at Gibraltar (Seacat fitted). She is shown on 16 March 1966. Her Squids and Seacat launcher are shrouded, and her torpedo tubes have been removed. [*MoD*]

---

* Norway and Denmark did manage to install Squids aboard their Hunts. Similarly, the US Navy made devoted considerable effort to developing an air search radar specifically for the weight-limited war-built destroyer escorts, which (it claimed) could not accommodate the standard SPS-6 search set. Several foreign navies found otherwise.

For the Royal Navy, the postwar dilemma was that adequate destroyers were too large to mass-produce. The ultimate wartime destroyer was the *Daring* (*Duchess* is shown), a ship so large (at 2800 tons) that for a time the Royal Navy officially considered it intermediate between destroyer and cruiser. From an American perspective, she was little larger than a *Gearing*, with a similar battery of three twin dual purpose guns (4.5in here, 5in/38 in the US ship). The class as a whole introduced US-type high-pressure, high-temperature machinery into the Royal Navy, and *Duchess* was one of four ships which introduced alternating current (AC). She and her three sisters (*Decoy*, *Diamond* and *Diana*) therefore served longer than the four direct-current ships. *Duchess* herself was transferred to Australia in 1964 to replace the Australian-built *Voyager*, cut down by the Australian carrier *Melbourne*. She is shown in her original configuration, with two STAAG 40mm mounts abeam her bridge, a lighter weight (Utility Mark 5) twin 40mm aft, two sets of torpedo tubes, and a single Squid on her quarterdeck. This class introduced a new bridge shape, the squared-off portion below the open bridge accommodating an enlaged CIC. Beginning in 1959, all four ships were modernized; both sets of torpedo tubes were landed, the STAAGs replaced by simple twin 40mm guns, and a lightweight MRS 3 director replaced the big Mark VI atop the bridge. Provision was made for installation of the Seacat missile (with 12 reloads), but it was fitted only in *Decoy* (for trials). [*USNI*]

The US Navy did not consider its existing ships entirely satisfactory. Even the big *Gearings* were already badly overloaded, hence somewhat slower than designed, a serious failing in ships intended to operate with fast carriers. Nor did they have the endurance considered desirable. The Navy then discovered that it had to choose between an ideal destroyer and a ship suited to mass production. This was not a uniquely American problem. Both the final US and British destroyer designs directly associated with the war, the *Mitscher* (which actually completed in 1946) and the *Daring*, were substantially larger (hence more expensive) than their predecessors, at, respectively, 3650 and 2700 tons (standard).

The *Mitscher* design emphasized anti-aircraft rather than anti-submarine warfare, on the expectation that fast carrier task would generally be too fast for diesel submarines to attack. For example, they achieved their high speed by using compact machinery with fast-turning propellors, rather than the specially silenced, slow-turning propellers of contemporary British practice. Their gun battery combined the best available anti-aircraft weapon, the twin 3in/70 (twin 3in/50 were actually temporarily fitted when the ships were completed) with the best dual-purpose gun, the new single automatic 5in/54. Although this combination (two 5in, two 3in) seemed far less impressive than that of the smaller wartime destroyers, it was equivalent to a much more (visually) impressive conventional battery.

The design had begun in mid 1945 with the entirely conventional destroyer battery of three twin semi-automatic 5in/54 (equivalent to three of the new single automatic mounts), four twin 3in/50, and two quintuple torpedo tubes. To save centerline space, the conventional revolving tubes were replaced by four fixed tubes with a total of fourteen reloads. By this time ASW seemed more important than surface operations, and the design showed a better sonar as well as Weapon Alfa placed amidships. The tubes were all to fire ASW homing torpedoes.

The conventional arrangement of two 5in mounts forward made for some wetness (through bow-heaviness), and could be justified only by the conventional destroyer role of surface pursuit. In Scheme D, therefore, two of the mounts were placed aft and the Weapon Alfa moved forward (to A rather than B position). In the next scheme, a second Weapon Alfa replaced one of the after 5in/54 mounts (by this time single automatics).

This 3671-ton ship was considered quite expensive, and a smaller alternative, armed with three twin 3in/70, was considered. The uniform (pure anti-aircraft) battery was rejected on the grounds that it would not deal with a surfaced submarine. At the same time, early in 1947, the radar picket (British: aircraft direction) role was incorporated in the new fleet destroyer, a large air intercept (height-finding) radar, SPS-8, being placed amidships. After some study of alternatives, the battery was finally fixed at two single 5in/54, two twin 3in/70, two Weapon Alfa, and two twin fixed torpedo tubes.

The new anti-aircraft battery had the advantage of fore-and-aft symmetry, for full coverage of the 360-degree circle around the ship. Although not as efficient as four twin 3in/70 in anti-aircraft fire, it was more effective for surface fire and for shore bombardment, and so was considered better suited to a general purpose destroyer. Similarly, the ships were fitted with Mark 67 directors, which were better suited to surface fire than the Mark 56 preferred for anti-aircraft fire.

The US Navy accepted increased destroyer size as inevitable, and expected that money would be found to build four *Mitschers* per year (see Chapter 2). However, when postwar destroyer construction money became available during the Korean War, the Navy discovered that the *Mitschers* were too complex for mass production. It had to settle for a much less sophisticated (and much smaller, at 2800 tons) destroyer, the *Forrest Sherman*. They could not accommodate the heavy 3in/70, and so had to settle for three single automatic 5in/54 (more than equivalent to the three twin 5in/38 of wartime ships), two twin 3in/50, four fixed torpedo tubes (with four reloads), two fixed Hedgehogs, and depth charges. Again, although superficially unimpressive, their weapons and their ammunition each weighed much more than those of the apparently more heavily armed wartime *Gearing*. Perhaps more significantly, they had to omit the air control (height-finding) capability of the *Mitschers*.

Nor did the story have a clear moral. In 1954, a new US Navy study (the report of the Schindler Committee, on the Long-Range Shipbuilding and Conversion program) concluded that the austere general purpose destroyer was much too austere to be useful. Better to concentrate on more satisfactory fleet escorts and on ships specially adapted to ASW (fast escorts and slower, cheaper, convoy escorts). The fast fleet escorts would be up-graded *Mitschers* armed with four single 5in/54, the fast ASW ships, existing small destroyers in which one boiler room would be turned over to fuel stowage. These corvettes (DDC) were never produced, but the *Mitscher* successor became the much larger *Dewey* class missile destroyer (DLG). Ironically, production of *Forrest Sherman* class destroyers ended because the design was adapted to carry Tartar missiles, evolving into the larger *Charles F. Adams* class, which gained many of the sensors otherwise associated with the somewhat larger *Mitscher*. However, the ship's powerful combat system had to be squeezed in, with little margin for future development. These *Adams* class missile destroyers, little short of the *Mitscher* in size, have, then, always been considered cramped.

The Royal Navy built no postwar destroyers, but that was not for any lack of interest. Two prototype designs were available in 1945 for further development: the large *Daring*, and the much smaller *Gallant*, the 1944 Weapon class. The latter were, in effect, the smallest hulls which could accommodate the new standard British dual purpose weapon, the twin 4.5in Mark 6. They were all cancelled, and some argued that they were too small altogether. Even so, the postwar studies described in Chapter 2 showed that large numbers of such ships would be needed, and early in 1946 the DNC sketched a smaller minimum destroyer based on the *Gallant*.

He argued that the only way to achieve a smaller ship was to revert to the very early destroyer concept of a stripped ship heavily dependent on depot ships, using forced, ie, light weight (short lifetime) machinery (eg, high rpm) and hull. Adopting unit machinery would save some weight by eliminating two compartments. Such a policy would impose its own costs: the ship could not survive a single torpedo hit, and it would require more maintenance over its relatively short lifetime. It would also be a worse sound platform (for ASW). Extensive reliance on underway replenishment could also reduce the ship's size. For example, reducing endurance from 4900nm (for *Gallant*) to 3500nm at 20 knots would save at least 20ft of length and 260 tons. Stores and the scale of ammunition supply could also be cut, although ultimately the ship might suffer from a lack of internal space, and might therefore need a long forecastle or even US-style flush deck.

Armament would be cut to a minimum: two twin 4.5in, six Bofors barrels (two twin STAAG, two single), one set of pentad (quintuple) torpedo tubes, and one Squid. By way of comparison, *Gallant* had the same two twin 4.5in, but also two STAAG, two twin Oerlikon (equivalent in weight to single Bofors), two quadruple torpedo tubes, and could lay five depth charge patterns.

The 320ft length and 2000-ton deep displacement of the A and B classes of 1928-30 was probably a minimum for worldwide fleet work. The new light destroyer would displace 2204 tons (deep; compared to 2756 tons for *Gallant*) on a waterline length of 320ft (350) and a beam of 38ft, 6in (39, 6). Accommodation would be reduced to 250ft (304). DNC thought he could do even better if efforts were made to reduce the weights of standard equipment, weapons, and fittings. Although each ship would develop 40,000shp, machinery weight would be reduced from 570 to 450 tons (and fuel oil from 650 to 400 tons). Sea speed would actually increase, from 29.75 knots to 30.5 or 31.5 knots.

No postwar destroyer staff requirements were formulated. Work therefore continued on the light destroyer. In August 1948, DNC described a future destroyer, armed with two single 5in (replacing the two twin 4.5in), the new close-range anti-aircraft gun, up to eight torpedoes (probably fired from fixed tubes), and a single Limbo, all on 2700-2900 tons. The alternative general purpose fleet destroyer (in effect an updated *Daring*) armed with existing weapons would require 3500 to 4000 tons for four twin 4.5in, close range anti-aircraft weapons, two pentad TT, and a single Limbo.

This comparison was used a few months later to justify Admiral Edwards' cruiser/destroyer, the proposal for which effectively terminated conventional destroyer design for a time. On 4000 to 5000 tons it could be armed with four 5in (four single preferable to two twin), close-range anti-aircraft weapons, eight torpedoes, a single Limbo, and air control radar. At this time it was expected that the 5in single would weigh about as much as the 4.5in twin Mk VI, with a much smaller crew (15 *vs* 38).

A tabulation of expected comparative effectiveness of fire (*Tiger* defined as 1.0) is given

Mitscher (DL 2) embodied the US view of lessons learned in World War II destroyer operations. She is shown in August 1957, carrying her full designed gun battery of two single automatic 5in/54 and two twin automatic 3in/70. One of the original pair of Weapon Alfas, as well as her single depth charge track, had to be surrendered as weight compensation when the 3in/70 replaced 3in/50 which had been fitted as an interim measure. Not visible here are four fixed torpedo tubes (with a total of ten torpedoes). Note the Bell 47J (HUL-1) light helicopter on her fantail. Experiments in landing such aircraft on unmodified destroyers inspired the DASH drone helicopter torpedo delivery project. The big SPS-8 radar, on a short tower abaft her after funnel, was considered essential for picket duty. The *Mitscher* thus united in a single hull the roles of fleet aircraft direction ship (FADE in British terms), fleet anti-aircraft escort (with what was thought to be the best existing heavy anti-aircraft gun, the 3in/70), and fleet anti-submarine escort. At 3650 tons, however, she exceeded the size limit set by the Royal Navy. [*USN*]

in the table below:

	Surface	AA
NEW LIGHT CRUISER (three single 5in DP, three MRS)	More than 1.0	4.0
TIGER (two twin 6in with FPS) (three twin 3in/70 with MRS)	1.0 0.5 to 1.0	1.0 1.0
FIJI (three triple 6in, one APCT) (five twin 4in, three MRS)	0.6 0.3	0.0 1.8
DIDO (four twin 5.25in, two FPS)	0.8	0.9
DARING (three twin 4.5in, one FPS)	0.8	0.7

In 1948, too, DGD tried to estimate characteristics of three destroyer types:

— AA and anti-surface, a single unified type possibly carrying anti-ship torpedoes, but limited to the ASW equipment required for screening, as it would be too large, at 3000 tons, for submarine hunting (two twin 4.5in, one twin 3in/70, Limbo);

— ASW destroyers with the best possible AS characteristics; it would be desirable, but not essential, for the weapon to be dual purpose (say one twin 4.5), but if this would cost ASW characteristics, then an all AA armament (say one

or two twin 3in/70) would suffice.

— Aircraft direction ships would surely be small cruisers (FADE); this may have been the paper which originated the FADE designator.

The Director of the Operations strongly opposed the term 'gun destroyer' and much preferred 'fleet destroyer'. They would still be armed primarily with the torpedo for offensive anti-ship action, and such action would still be possible as long as an enemy possessed battleships, cruisers, and destroyers of his own. War experience showed that a flotilla or even less could sink an enemy heavy ship either as part of a balanced fleet or even independently (as in the *Haguro* operation, 1945). The Director of Plans considered specialized ships undesirable, since Britain could not afford enough of each type. This was essentially the argument the US Navy always used in favor of individually large but flexible ships of various types.

Even though the cruiser/destroyer was cancelled in September 1953, some new program of fleet escort construction was required to replace existing war-built destroyers, which would begin to wear out around about 1958. The obvious alternative was a smaller specialist ship, which could be built alternatively in anti-submarine and anti-aircraft or air direction versions. As in the case of the postwar frigates (see below), it was essential to minimize machinery weight and volume: the first British COSAG power plants were designed specifically for this fleet escort. The ASW version would have been the first ordered, and it was sometimes described as a fast hull carrying *Whitby* (Type 12) armament and sensors.

The alternative was a general purpose ship, admittedly with less than full capability in any single area. It would be modelled on the last such ship, the *Daring*. In December 1954, the improved *Daring* (rather than the specialist ASW fleet escort) was included in the 1955-65 long-range program, together with the new general purpose escort (later designated Type 81 or Tribal class frigate).

At this point the improved *Daring* mounted three twin 4.5in guns, plus a twin 3in/70 and Bofors guns, single Limbo, and twelve fixed anti-ship/anti-submarine torpedo tubes. It was powered by the new Y102 (COSAG) machinery originally developed for the fast ASW escort. Although it might be considered little more than an updated version of the existing ship, it was substantially larger, and the Admiralty Board tried hard to simplify it. First, it eliminated a proposed aircraft direction capability. The ship still retained a considerable radar suit (by British standards): a long range air search set (initially the US SPS-6C)* plus the more usual combination of target designation (the new and very heavy 992), low altitude air search/height finding (227), and surface search (974). The argument at the time was that without some long-range air search capability, the ship would be unable to engage fast (ie, modern) aircraft, since she would have no time to identify them before they appeared within gun range.** Type 992, in particular imposed a considerable cost in weight, and there was considerable interest in replacing it with a much lighter Dutch radar.

In January 1955, the Board ordered one twin 4.5in and all Bofors eliminated to save about 500 tons. The result displaced about 4500 tons, and could achieve a speed of 30.5 knots; endurance matched the nominal figure for the *Daring*, 3600nm at 20 knots. The estimated complement was 475.

Early in 1955, the improved *Daring* was redesignated the fleet escort, and by mid 1955 the Sea Lords had approved a proposal to make it a missile destroyer (see below).

An alternative 5000-ton (450x43x12.5ft) missile convoy escort, the AA cruiser, (later, the GW escort) was much less attractive, because, with almost no gun battery (a twin 4in, which replaced a twin Bofors in earlier 5000- and 5500-ton designs), it would be ineffective in a cold or warm war. Even with maintenance and accommodation reduced to frigate standards, it was difficult to accommodate the 30 missiles, and their one director. They were really too big to be counted as destroyers (ie, to depend on tenders for maintenance), but it seemed unlikely that the Board would accept a 6000-ton self-supporting alternative, as the earlier discussion had shown that 4500 tons was an upper limit. Nor could these ships, with a maximum speed of 27 knots (deep and clean, on 30,000shp frigate machinery), operate effectively with a fleet. Speed would be 25.25 knots deep and dirty, or 26.5/24.5 on 5500 tons. Endurance was 4500nm at 15 knots. These designs showed one Limbo (20 salvoes) and six ASW torpedo tubes (12 torpedoes), one twin 4in gun and two twin Bofors.

This ship had a very high center of gravity, and therefore needed a very large beam to draught ratio (which made for limited speed). As in many later missile ships, the combination of armament and accommodation made space, far more than weight, a deciding factor in the dimensions. Only a marked reduction in complement, ie, in electronics technicians, would much reduce the volume of the ship. The 30 missiles were arranged three high, two abreast in a tube hangar extending well forward.

This escort was entirely unarmored. At the cost of an increase to 5500 tons (beam 55ft, draft 13.5ft), 1in armor could be spread over the AIO (CIC), the Bofors magazines and deck stowage; the machinery would be protected by a 1.5in deck and 2in side. All of this would cost about 3-4 knots, but

---

* Like the 3in/50, SPS-6C appeared in many British designs of 1952-54 because it was available under MDAP. Similarly, like the (US) 3in/50, it was disliked for its operational limitations. By 1955, SPC-6C was obsolescent. Its adoption by the Royal Navy would have required considerable adaptation (anglicization). The alternatives were the new Dutch LW-02 and a Marconi private venture which became the Type 965.

** In January 1955, the Director of Navigation and Direction (DND) argued that long-range air-search radar was as important for any independent surface unit (such as a large destroyer) as for a radar picket. It would take guns five minutes to come to full readiness, and another two minutes to achieve full fire control solutions and begin to fire. This total of seven minutes corresponded to an initial detection range of at least 58 miles against a 500-knot target. By way of contrast, successful control of fighters intercepting only 20nm away required two minutes for tracking and analysis, two minutes for the fighters to reach the intercept point, one minute for them to turn, and one minute for the interception itself, a total of six minutes equivalent to warning at 50nm.

Caprice (foreground) shows the frigate-type bridge fitted to her. [MoD]

The Canadian Tribal class destroyer *Huron* shows the ultimate configuration of the class, with paired Squids on the quarterdeck, and with the two twin 4in guns moved forward. The twin US-type 3in/50 aft weighed slightly more than the quadruple 40mm gun in *Micmac*, and (as in the other ship) four single 40mm on Boffin (twin 20mm) mounts were carried. Note the radar fire control dish on B twin 4in mount, working with a US Mark 63 director. [USN]

The French fleet escort destroyer *Dupetit-Thouars*, as completed. The long tubes aft could fire either prewar-type anti-ship torpedoes or the new short K2 and L3 anti-submarine weapons. The shorter tubes forward were limited to ASW weapons, with three reloads per bank of tubes in the small deckhouses abaft the tubes. Like the US Navy, and unlike the Royal Navy, the French Navy assumed that a single universal destroyer hull could be developed for both the fleet screen and fleet air direction roles. The accompanying inboard profile shows the radar picket version of the standard postwar French *Surcouf* class. *Dupetit-Thouars* was one of four *Surcoufs* converted to missile destroyers in 1962/65; one Mark 13 launcher replaced both after 5in guns. The forward 5in mount was replaced by a sextuple 375mm ASW mortar, and the long torpedo tubes were removed. [USN]

the ship would gain better seakeeping characteristics.

Any further improvement would be expensive. Cold war duties practically demanded a *Daring* type twin 4.5in in place of the twin 4in forward (at the cost of another 120 tons in deep displacement). Higher speed would require doubling the power, with either two 30,000shp steam turbines or combined steam and gas turbines (two pairs, each comprising a 15,000shp steam turbine and a 15,000shp gas turbine). In either case the ship would be a cruiser, displacing about 7000 tons fully loaded.

In about August, 1954, DNC developed an alternative missile ship, the minimum to which a ship with fleet speed could be reduced and still retain a worthwhile missile armament. Sacrifices included fighter direction facilities, one (of two) 901 missile direction radars, protection to machinery and AIO; maintenance facilities and stores would be comparable only with those of a frigate. The result was dramatic: 372 x 43 12.5ft, 3550 tons fully loaded.

Missile armament would be limited to 12 missiles stowed in a hangar in the after superstructure, feeding a twin launcher. Radars would be limited to one 901, a 960 for long-range air search, a 992 target indicator, and a 974 for surface search and navigation. Armament was limited to three L.70 Bofors (one on the forecastle, two aft). Two fixed AS torpedo tubes could be carried at the stern, and, if required, the forward

twin Bofors could be replaced by single Limbo. Machinery would match that of the fleet A/S escort. Speed, deep and clean, was estimated to be 30.75 knots on the full 60,000shp (29.75 knots deep and dirty; endurance 3200nm at 20 knots deep and dirty). This was only a quarter of a knot faster than the much larger light cruiser (see Chapter 5) on the same power, but the missile destroyer was much shorter. Complement would be 20 officers and 260 enlisted men, far short of the figures then being quoted for the GW escort. In the comparative weights below, the 5in destroyer is the ship described in Chapter 5.

	GWD	5in destroyer
HULL	1518 (42.6)	2030 (42.7)
EQUIPMENT	230 (6.5)	390 (8.2)
ARMAMENT	232 (6.6)	530 (11.2)
PROTECTION	—	—
MACHINERY	780 (22.2)	850 (17.9)
OIL FUEL	700 (19.7)	900 (18.9)
RFW	20 (0.6)	—
BOARD MARGIN	70 (2.0)	50 (1.1)
Totals	3550	4750

(when no figure is given for RFW, it is included in machinery)

Converted to an escort destroyer after a 1947 collision, the Canadian Tribal class *Micmac* illustrates the cost of a heavy ahead-throwing ASW weapon in a war-built destroyer. A single Squid occupies A position, while B is occupied by a US-type quadruple 40mm gun. The two after twin mounts are twin 4in anti-aircraft weapons. This photograph was taken in April 1950. Note the US-type HFDF antenna at her masthead, with a British Type 293 below it. (*USNI*]

This missile destroyer was clearly attactive, although it could not replace the missile cruiser, with its aircraft direction and command facilities. It would be the quickest way to get Seaslug to sea; 12 missiles would be enough.

In the spring of 1955 the decision was made to marry its lightweight missile system to the existing fast fleet escort (the improved *Daring*), the Board accepting weight (and cost) growth well beyond the original limit of about 4500 tons.

In May, the Board asked for designs for 4500- and 5400-ton missile-armed fast escorts (later designated missile destroyers). By July, with the cruiser displacement 15,500 tons rather than the hoped-for 11,000 the missile escort was already seen as a means of offsetting limited cruiser numbers in the overall program.

It soon grew to accommodate 4.5in guns (see below). In July, the Board asked to fit Limbo instead of the ASW torpedo tubes and the Bofors guns then planned. DNC replaced the twin 40mm Bofors (L70) with Limbo. Alternative design studies showed it forward or aft. The latter was preferred, since it allowed for main machinery compartments amidships. Flooding due to action damage, then, would not lead to excessive trim. The after location would also make it easier to clear the mortar's cone of fire. Locating the Limbo

forward would push the bridge and hence the large machinery compartments well aft. Flooding would make for trim by the stern. Moreover, little space would be available further aft.

The four early missile destroyer design studies are tabulated below.

By 1956, which is really outside the scope of this book, the missile cruiser seemed less and less likely to materialize. The Admiralty began to ask for more capability in the missile destroyer, which probably would be built. In November 1956, DNC was asked whether the ship could carry a few special (nuclear) warheads. Could Type 984 Radar, required for air control, be fitted in the missile destroyer hull? It was considered essential both to ensure adequate warning so that guided missiles are used in time, and to back up the main units of a carrier task force. If the missile cruiser were not built, the carrier would have to be supported entirely by missile destroyers, one of which should be equipped with 984. Hence DNC was asked whether a destroyer could carry either 984 and Seaslug but no 4.5in guns (984 with three or four intercept positions as compared with seven or eight positions in a full CDS), or 984 with the 4.5in gun but without Seaslug.

At this time the cruiser project was still barely alive, and DNC could not spare the manpower for

	GW54	GW55	GW56	GW57
LWL	430	450	450	470
MAX BEAM (ft,in)	47,6	49	49	50,6
DEEP DRAFT (ft,in)	14,6	15	15	15
DEEP DISPLACEMENT (tons)	4550	5000	4900	5400
DEEP GM (ft)	4	4	4	4
MISSILES	12	12	12	12
TWIN 4.5in	2	1	1	2
A/S TT	—	—	6	6
40mm Bofors	—	1 twin	—	2 twin
MRS 3 Dir.	1	3	1	4
HT FINDER	—	277Q	—	277Q
MACHINERY	Y102	Y102	Y102	Y102
COMPLEMENT	395	475	405	485
HULL (tons)	—	2340	2405	2575
EQUIPMENT (tons)	—	395	360	430
ARMAMENT (tons)	—	475	365	530
MACHINERY (tons)	—	865	850	865
FUEL OIL (tons)	—	825	820	890
RFW (tons)	—	20	20	20
MARGIN (tons)	—	30	30	30

fresh destroyer sketch designs, although both alternatives seemed feasible on a weight and space basis. The 5400-ton destroyer seemed to be the outer limit for a ship to destroyer standards.

As the cruiser project waned, DNC was able to improve the missile destroyer design. By early 1956 it displaced 5980 tons (505 x 52ft) and carried 18 missiles. 60,000shp machinery would drive it at 30.5 knots, and endurance was 3500 miles at 20 knots. At this time the ASW battery consisted of one Limbo and eight dual purpose torpedo tubes, carrying eight Mark 20 cable-set weapons or eight Mark 21 FANCY long-range torpedoes. Radar systems were those ultimately installed: the new 965 for long-range air search, with 277Q for height-finding and 992 for target indication; airborne early warning terminal equipment; 901 for missile control. However, at this stage the design still showed two twin Bofors guns with their MRS 8 directors (262 radars).

The missile stowage was extended forward, as a hangar running more than half the total length of the ship. As finally completed from 1962 on, the eight 5600-ton County class missile destroyers accommodated 30 Seaslugs, although not all of them were fully assembled for instant firing. The two twin 40mm guns were replaced by quadruple Seacat short-range missile launchers. Finally, the Admiralty required that the combination of relatively short-range ASW torpedo tubes and Limbo be replaced by a hangar for a single large ASW helicopter.

Compared to the cruiser, the destroyer had about half as many missiles and one rather than two missile directors. It lacked task force command and figher control facilities.

The growth of the missile destroyer severely limited the number of fleet escorts which could be built. Although the explicit building program called for only four of them, it was clear that more would be needed. The long-range fleet plan of this period showed 12 fleet escorts to supplement the only surviving destroyers, the eight Darings, by 1965. This assumed that all earlier ships would be gone by 1964, having come to the end of their operational lives. Instead, the 1955-1965 Fleet

Plan, evolved in the wake of the Radical Review, called for the moderization of at least the best eight surviving World War II destroyers, the 1943 Battle class, as well as of the four Weapons. In the case of the Battles, modernization was expected to extend their service lives to about 1970. This plan in turn ran foul of the continuing need for pickets.

*   *   *

The fleet aircraft direction escort (FADE) lay halfway between the destroyer and the frigate. Conceived on the basis of wartime experience, it was approved (as a conversion of an existing ship) by the Defence Committee for the 1947-8 program. In theory, to get five ships by the critical date of 1957, a prototype would have to be begun in 1949. Two more could be laid down after trials in 1952, and one more in each of 1954 and 1955. The fast minelayer *Ariadne* and then the small cruiser *Scylla* were proposed as conversion prototypes, but a decision on the cruiser was deferred in November 1948. It was finally rejected in January 1949.

Then a new-construction ship was proposed for the 1948-9 program. It might have been argued, after all, that in a ship requiring so much (probably AC) electric power, conversion would be extremely expensive. Tentative characteristics included two twin 3in/70, 2 Type 984 radars, and a speed of 29 knots dirty. The ship would be somewhat larger than a *Daring*.

It was rejected, but the Ship Design Policy Committee also turned down the conversions. At this time about half the Colony and Town class cruisers could direct aircraft, albeit with quite inadequate air warning, so that they could not be used as pickets. To fit them with the necessary radar (984) would impose a disproportionate cost in their armament.

Director of Navigation and Direction (DND), who was responsible for air control, suggested that it would be wiser to build fast air direction frigates, and FADE died under the pressure of the 1949 budget review.

The failure to build or convert a FADE did not eliminate the requirement for one. Through the

Agincourt displays the original configuration of the 1943 Battles. When this photograph was taken in July 1947, she did not yet have even a pennant number. Three months later, due to a manning crisis, she was one of only four Home Fleet destroyers in service, the others being her sister ships *Aisne*, *Dunkirk* and *Jutland*. The lower-elevation 4.5in gun amidships was intended primarily for night illumination with starshell. Note the twin 40mm gun between the torpedo tubes, and the STAAGs aft. The very small antenna atop the stub mainmast is the 291 destroyer air search set; a 293 for target indication tops the foremast, with an IFF antenna on the foretop. The director is a US Mark 37 fitted with a British Type 275 gunnery radar. Note the single Squid on her quarterdeck. [*MoD*]

Crossbow as a radar picket, 5 May 1959. The result cannot have been entirely satisfactory, since the ship still lacked a height-finder. Note, too, that she retained much of her anti-aircraft battery: two STAAGs aft and two single 40mm in the bridge wings, MRS 8 replaced the earlier Mark 6 director, for 4in fire control. *Scorpion* retained her Limbo as converted. [*MoD*]

early 'fifties, exercises against low-flying aircraft demonstrated the need for fleet pickets again and again. They would not need quite the capability of the air direction frigates, since they would generally operate with carriers which would provide air control. Their essential role, rather, would be to supply early warning of low-flying attackers. The decision to delete air direction from the new fleet escort made matters particularly desperate, as it meant that no picket ships would be built. The main alternative, the Type 62 frigate, also died at about the same time (see below).

Writing in the wake of this double disaster in May 1955), DND argued that airborne early warning could not solve his problems. At least four aircraft would have to be maintained simultaneously airborne to achieve a 60 per cent probability of detection over a 180-degree sector. That in turn would require a total of 12 aircraft to achieve continuous coverage, which would consume the whole AEW complement of a three-carrier task force (24 crews). Such a force, then, would find it difficult to operate very close to an enemy shore, since it would be unable continuously to defend any much larger sector. This was quite apart from the very real operational limitations of AEW, and the problem of relying on US supplied aircraft. At this time the United States was using AEW radars aboard larger aircraft (EC-121s) for Continental Air Defense, and it must have appeared that the demand for this equipment would crowd out British naval requirements.

That left surface pickets. A February 1954 analysis confirmed earlier studies showing that a total of six would be required for all-round coverage of a force.* This figure could be somewhat reduced by combing surface pickets with smaller numbers of AEW aircraft. DND argued, then, that the Royal Navy should convert

a total of six destroyers, so that four pickets would be available for its future carrier task force. Conversion would generally entail removal of one or both sets of torpedo tubes and installation of a long-range radar (SPS 6C, later 965), a low-level air search radar (277Q), an AEW terminal, a larger AIO, and better close-range air defense weapons. The latter was a problem: existing effective weapons weighed almost as much as 4.5in guns. This problem would not be solved until the advent of the L70 Bofors, in the late 'fifties or early 'sixties. (In fact, it never appeared.)

The *Tiger*s would have been the ideal pickets, but there were hardly enough of them, and they could not be spared. That left destroyer conversions, in order of preference:

— the *Daring*s (which were also the best existing general purpose fleet escorts, hence an unattractive bargain for conversion to special purpose ships);

— the 1943 *Battle*s, considered far better than their 1942 predecessors in AA fire control (they would have to surrender their amidships 4in guns);

— the four *Weapon*s, the minimum acceptable standard, which would have to use the SPS-6C air search radar for target indication as well as for fire control;**

* At about this time, US trials showed that two pickets 30 miles from a force plus four AEW aircraft were required to cover a 180-degree arc. This reinforced the British requirement for six pickets.

** SPS-6C (or any British replacement) achieved long-range by scanning relatively slowly; target indication radars (such as 293Q or 992) achieved track-while-scan capability (multi-channel capability) by scanning very rapidly, hence sacrificing range (shorter dwell time). For example, SPS-6C was credited with a range of 50 miles on a Canberra at 15,000ft. Comparable figures for 293Q (a modernized wartime set) and 992 (its successor) were

The four converted 1943 Battles were the ultimate British radar picket destroyers. HMS *Barrosa* is shown on 11 September 1962, having completed conversion at Devonport the previous April. She and her sisters had US Mark 37 directors with British Type 275 radars, a combination considered superior to the Mark 6 directors of the 1942 Battles. Conversion entailed installation of a big air search radar (965 on the foremast) and a 277Q height-finder (on the stub mast aft, abaft the new structure carrying an electronic countermeasures room. The very short lattice atop this new structure appears to carry a US-type ESM antenna. Note also the enlarged bridge structure forward, carrying an enlarged CIC (AIO), which has squeezed out the single 40mm guns formerly carried on the bridge wings. Note the quadruple Seacat launcher which replaced the former 40mm battery, its director atop the aftermost deckhouse. The short mainmast carried communications dipoles and ESM antennas. Conversion entailed installation of separate AC generators for the radars and the Seacat, as the ships had originally been provided with DC power. Note that, as of May 1955, staff requirements for the Battle conversion called for one twin 40mm gun and a single Limbo. Four conversions had been approved, with four more pending. No Weapon class conversions were as yet officially programmed. [*MoD*]

— Type 15 (non-Limbo) frigates, which already had the 277Q low-level set. It could be argued that this set was actually more important than the SPS-6C (or equivalent).

Existing Type 15s were used as makeshift pickets in Exercise Crossbow, and existing cruisers in Exercise Phoenix. Consideration of Type 15 picket conversions continued up through about 1957, but the destroyers were far more satisfactory. After all, a Type 15, with its very limited anti-aircraft battery, could hardly be expected to look after itself. DND argued that it could only be an emergency (ie, hot war) expedient, excluded under the terms of the Rardical Review strategy. By 1957, the Royal Navy would have Type 61 air direction frigates. They might be too slow for wartime, but they would be satisfactory in peace. The Type 15 picket conversion (with SPS-6C in lieu of 293Q, an AEW terminal, and two fighter control positions in the AIO) would be worth while only if it was needed before about 1959. Otherwise, the ships would merely be converted and then placed in reserve, a perfectly acceptable step in the past, but not given the new strategy, which discounted the reserve fleet.

Of the existing destroyers, the Weapons were initially rejected because, modernized with Limbo, they would be the only fully modern ASW ships prior to the appearance of new fast fleet escorts. They re-entered the picket program only after the failure of the modernization design. Limited in weight-carrying capacity, they became a stopgap for full modernization of the 1943 Battles.

At this time, two alternative picket configurations were proposed. The minimum requirements were 277Q and SPS-6C with Mark 10 IFF. An AEW terminal and VHF/DF and UHF/DF (to track friendly aircraft) were desirable. In the proposed minimum conversion, the single (low-elevation) 4.5in gun, one pentad torpedo tube,

and the existing 293 radar would be surrendered. The AIO would support only one interception at a time. A full conversion would add the new surface search radar (974), a new close-range battery (three twin L70 Bofors controlled by two blind-fire directors and one TOM), GDS 2*, and modern sonars (164/174 or 176 in place of the existing 144). Both banks of torpedo tubes would have to be landed, and the forecastle extended aft as in a Type 15 ASW frigate, to gain internal space. The full conversion AIO would support two simultaneous interceptions.

The second option (apart from the L70 Bofors) was the one selected.

Although the 1943 Battle conversion (in a less complete form) was approved, it had to be delayed for some years, as essential equipment was not available. AEW terminals were all supplied by the US Navy under MDAP. Of 37 requested by the Royal Navy, only 26 had been approved, and all were already earmarked for carriers, cruisers, and Type 61 frigates. By 1955, the MDAP program was clearly tailing off, so future sets would cost foreign exchange. In any case, sets ordered in 1956 would not be available until 1958. Delaying the picket program would make some other systems available to the entire Battle picket class: UHF/DF (VHF/DF would no longer be needed, as aircraft would all have converted to UHF radio), Mark 10 IFF, and a new close-range fire control radar (Type 908, which was later cancelled).

In the end, then, the Weapons and then four of the 1943 Battles filled the FADE role first proposed in 1946.

*　　　*　　　*

Destroyer requirements were ultimately limited by the number of major fleet units which had to be escorted. Frigate numbers had to be much larger, based on the enormous numbers of convoys to be expected in any future war. For example, in about 1947 a British study of trade protection concluded that about 12 convoys would be simultaneously at sea in the North Atlantic at any one time. Other convoys would be routed around the British Isles and through the Channel. They would have to be

22 and 30nm (both at 30,000ft). In the case of 992, system weight and complexity presented additional problems (15.5 tons, compared to 21.25 for 293Q or 1.5 for SPS-6C). As of January 1954, SPS-6C was considered effective over no more than two AA fire control channels.

Rocket was one of two prototypes Type 15 conversions; she is shown on trial and at anchor, November 1951. Note the Type 277Q surface/low level air search radar, which justified the later proposal that Type 15s be used as fleet radar pickets. The low bridge was specially shaped to resist the impact of water breaking over the bows at high speed. Note also the 40mm gun installed atop the bridge structure, the twin 4in located aft, controlled by a CRBF (Close Range Blind Fire) Mark 1 director. *Rocket* and *Relentless* had protoype Limbo mortars aboard, but they were not completed with their projected torpedo outfit. [*MoD*]

SENSORS

1. HF/DF
2. RADAR 293Q
3. RADAR 974 (HDWS)
4. MRS 3 DIRECTOR
5. LOOKOUT SIGHTS (PORT AND STARBOARD)
6. 20in SIGNALLING LIGHT (PROJECTOR)
7. 10in SIGNALLING LIGHT (PROJECTOR)
8. LOOKOUT SIGHTS (PORT AND STARBOARD)
9. TARGET DESIGNATING SIGHT (PORT AND STARBOARD)
10. PELORUS
11. SONAR (HULL OUTFIT 7: TYPES 170, 184)
12. SONAR (HULL OUTFIT 5: TYPE 162)
13. MAIN TRANSMITTING AERIAL
14. COMPASS
15. CRBF DIRECTOR FOR 40mm GUNS (ON CENTERLINE)

WEAPONS

16. 4in TWIN MOUNTING
17. ASDIC (SONAR) CONTROL ROOM
18. OPERATIONS ROOM (CIC)
19. SINGLE BOFORS (40mm) MK 7
20. 21in PENTAD (QUINTUPLE) TORPEDO TUBES
21. TWIN BOFORS L70 (PORT AND STARBOARD)
22. LIMBO A/S MORTAR
23. GUN CREW SHELTER
24. LIMBO MAGAZINE
25. BOFORS MAGAZINE
26. 4in MAGAZINE
27. 293Q OFFICE
28. TRANSMITTING STATION
29. ASDIC INSTRUMENT ROOM
30. MAIN RADIO OFFICE

OTHER

31. LAMP AND PAINT STORE
32. CABLE LOCKER
33. PROVISIONS
34. REFRIGERATED COMPARTMENT
35. CREW SPACE
36. PO MESS
37. OFFICERS
38. LOW POWER ROOM, SPO'S MESS
39. FUEL OIL
40. CAPTAIN'S DAY CABIN
41. WARDROOM
42. STEWARDS' MESS
43. BOILER ROOM
44. RESERVE FEED WATER
45. ENGINE ROOM ENTRANCE
46. ENGINE ROOM
47. AUXILIARY BOILER
48. DIESEL OIL
49. POTATO LOCKER
50. (TORPEDO) PISTOL TESTING, WARHEADS
51. BATHROOMS, HEADS, GALLEY, SICK-BAY
52. CPO, ERA MESS
53. SPIRIT ROOM
54. COOL ROOM, PROVISION ROOM
55. STEERING GEAR

Projected modernisation of the Weapon class, September 1953. This result was so disappointing that the ships were released for conversion to radar pickets.

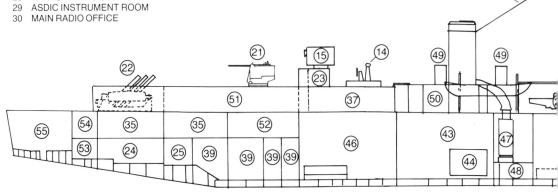

protected not only against submarines and aircraft, but also against mines and enemy fast attack craft. The potential size of the trade protection problem is shown by a 1950 British evaluation of forces required for NATO and overseas operations in wartime (the second column is forces available at D plus six months):

DESTROYERS	53	62
COASTAL ESCORTS	292	145
FAST MINELAYERS	4	3
LIGHT MINELAYERS	5	0
COASTAL ESCORTS	44	33
OCEAN MINESWEEPERS	125	61
COASTAL MINESWEEPERS	627	210
INSHORE MINESWEEPERS	148	118
SUBMARINES	42	53
MIDGET SUBMARINES	18	4
MTBs	36	50

Another 42 frigates in Category C reserve would be available after D plus six months. If disposals were stopped, 47 more would remain. The coastal escorts in the table were trawlers which would be taken up from trade. Minelayers have been included in the table because they were a means of reducing the threat to trade by sealing choke points; the same applies to MTBs and to midget submarines.

These figures explain the urgency of the frigate and minesweeper programs, and the decision to retain four existing O class destroyer minelayers. They do not illustrate the obsolscence of the existing frigate force, on two grounds: lack of effective (ahead-throwing) weapons, and lack of sufficient speed. In 1947-48, the Admiralty could argue that the Soviets did not yet have fast submarines, and that they would be fortunate to have even a prototype by 1950. However, surely that gap would be closed by 1957. Nor does the table suggest another major fear of this period, namely that the Soviets would mass-produce German-style midget submarines for harbor attack. The counter to that threat, the seaward defense boat, presented considerable problems of its own.

The 1950 rearmament program envisaged limited new construction (as tabulated overleaf).

The frigate program amounted to six first-rate (Type 12), 12 second-rate (Type 14), five A/A (Type 41), and four A/D (Type 61).

Plans called for conversation of 35 destroyers to ASW frigates, and six to aircraft direction frigates. Ten destroyers and 22 existing frigates would be modernized; six submarines would be converted for high underwater speed (fast battery drive, in British parlance).

In 1948, it had been assumed that two prototype new-construction frigates would be followed by about eight units per year, for a total projected force of as many as 160. This rate of construction matched that of prewar destroyers (one flotilla per year). Even that proved impossible, given the poor state British finances.

As of 1952, the Royal Navy counted a total of 219 actual or potential frigates, most of them relatively slow war-built types: 68 designed for ASW (19 *Loch* and 25 *River* class frigates, 24 slower *Castle* class corvettes), 94 for anti-aircraft support (25 *Black Swan*, 21 *Bay*, 48 *Hunt*), and 57 M through Z class destroyers awaiting conversion (with the first two prototypes newly completed). Of the destroyers, 27 would receive the full (Type 15) conversion, 18 a limited (Type 16) conversion, and 12 would be converted to air direction escorts (Type 62). The other two O class destroyers, generally included in

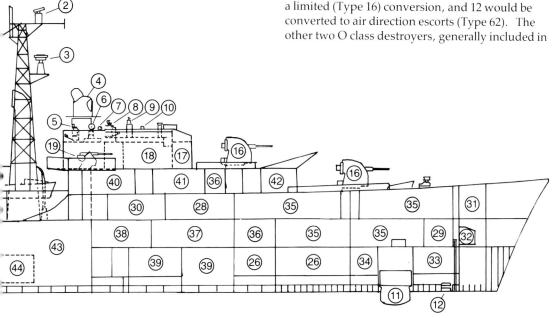

BUDGET	1950-51	1951-2	1952-3	1953-54	Total
FRIGATES	3	5	15	4	27
COASTAL MINESWEEPERS	20	12	12	12	56
INSHORE MINESWEEPERS	21	8	8	12	33
SEAWARD DEFENSE	2	0	8	8	18

TABLE 6–1: FRIGATE LEGENDS (New Construction)

	TYPE 12	TYPE 14	TYPE 61	TYPE 41
LWL (ft,in)	360,0	300,0	330,0	330,0
LOA (ft,in)	370,0	309,0	339,10½	339,10½
BEAM (ft,in)	41,0	33,0	40,0	40,0
DEEP DISPLACEMENT	2310	1290	2110	2185
DRAFT FWD/AFT (ft,in)	11,0/13,0	8,4/11,1½	9,6½/11,6½	9,10/11,10
STD DISPLACEMENT (tons)	1840	1007	1738	1835
SHP (Tropics)	30,000	15,000	14,400	14,400
SPEED (Dirty)	27	25	23	23
OIL FUEL	360	235	252	230
ENDURANCE (Dirty)	4500/12	4500/12	5000/15	4500/15
COMPLEMENT	283	143	217	220
4.5in GUNS (Twin)	1 (375)	—	2 (300)	1 (300)
STAAG 40mm	1 (1500)	1 (1510)*	1 (1200)	1 (1200)
40mm SINGLE	—	1 (288)	—	1 (1200)
LIMBO	2 (20)	2 (20)	—	—
SQUID	—	—	1 (10)	1 (10)
TORPEDO TUBES	4 (12)	4 (4)	—	—
WEIGHTS:				
GENERAL EQUIPMENT	287	119	224	224
MACHINERY	377	225	465	465
ARMAMENT	240	100	215	300
HULL	988	579	918	930
RFW	18	10	—	—
MARGIN	40	22	36	36

NOTES: * indicates a Bofors Twin Mk V rather than a STAAG mounting in Type 14. Figures in parentheses are the number of rounds per gun, the *total* number of torepdoes carried, and the number of *salvoes* of Squid and Limbo ammunition. The Type 41 and 61 figures represent a more mature stage of those designs than do the Type 12 and Type 14 figures. To see the change in postwar machinery, compare weights with those of wartime destroyers in Table 6–3.

the total of 59 available for conversion, were retained as fast minelayers. Of the frigates, the badly worn *Rivers* and the small *Hunt I* and *Hunt II* were considered the least valuable.*

Another way to view the British frigate situation was to list projected numbers of ships with ahead-throwing weapons. In the 1952 table which follows, L is Limbo, S is Squid, and numbers in parentheses represent ships not fitted with any ahead-throwing weapon. The total requirement at D plus six months was 248 ships, including 33 converted trawlers.

	1952 L S			1954 L S			1957 L S	
A/S	7	44	(56)	15	52	(40)	33	63
A/A		3	(56)	6	43			37
A/D		2	(14)	7	9			15
TOTAL		56	(126)	132		(40)		148

Successful attack against a fast submarine demanded high speed (in a seaway) to get into position to fire her relatively short-range weapon (or even a homing torpedo). That meant a larger unit size, but the Royal Navy maintained that no ship displacing as much as 3000 tons could be maneuverable enough to be a successful submarine hunter. Moreover, British finances would not support expensive escorts. As in the case of the fleet escort, the US Navy was much more willing to accept larger unit size. It designed the ASW cruiser (later frigate, which in US parlance then meant large destroyer) *Norfolk* for high sustained speed. Fleet expansion plans (see Chapter 2) show her as a prototype flagship for HUK groups composed of converted fleet destroyers.

It was generally believed that an ASW ship required a ten-knot speed advantage over a submerged submarine. Thus the 17 to 18 knots of the *Lochs* sufficed for wartime seven-knot U-boats. The fast submarine, initially credited with 15 and then with 17 knots, required a 25- to 27-knot escort – the British Types 12 and 14, and the US *Dealey*.** This was only an intermediate step en route to the

ultimate 25-knot submarine, typified by the abortive Walter-turbine Type XXVI U-boat. It, in turn, would be hunted by the ultimate escort, with a speed of 33 to 35 knots in a seaway, beyond the capabilities of even fleet destroyers then existing.***

The alternative to developing larger, faster escorts was to develop longer-range means of detection and attack, so that the escort would no longer have to maneuver relative to the submarine. That is why the ultimate escort was never built, even though modern nuclear submarines have greatly exceeded the performance of the Type XXVI. For example, a relatively slow escort could gain an effective speed advantage by operating a helicopter, itself much faster than any submarine. Optimum escort speed might then be determined by the speed of the formation being escorted, rather than by the speed of the target submarine. This is very much the case at present.

The two navies differed in one very important respect. The US Navy would be protecting shipping, on the whole, in the open ocean, out of range of mass shore-based air attacks. The Royal Navy, however, would have to run convoys within range of shore-based aircraft, just as it had around the British Isles, off northern Norway and in the Mediterranean during World War II. Its existing frigate force included many anti-aircraft ships (*Hunts*, *Black Swans*, and *Bays*) intended for just this duty. New ones would have to be built. Like the existing destroyers and cruisers, the existing anti-aircraft frigates had obsolete fire control systems and, on the whole, obsolete weapons.

Both navies naturally saw existing destroyers as a potential basis for new fast frigate conversions. The US Navy had so many new ones that it could afford to concentrate on conversions (eg, of all 140 surviving *Fletchers*, with *Gearings* converted as tactical test platforms). The Royal Navy had only 59 suitable hulls, so it had to develop new frigate designs for mass production. In 1945, then, the naval staff began to develop requirements for three designs, each to be about five knots faster than its wartime predecessor: two variants of a 1400- to 1650-ton (2300-ton deep) 25-knot sloop or frigate (anti-aircraft and anti-submarine, as in the

* In fact, 23 destroyers received Type 15 conversion, and another ten the Type 16 limited conversion, before the program terminated as a result of the Radical Review. Four Australian and two Canadian destroyers also received Type 15 conversions, and two Pakistani destroyers received Type 16 conversions. No Type 62 conversions were actually undertaken.

** As of 1955, British intelligence credited Soviet submarines with maximum underwater speeds of no more than 14 knots. However, higher speeds were clearly coming, exemplified by the sustained 20 knots of the *Nautilus* and by a similar short-term speed reportedly attained by a new Swedish diesel-electric submarine. It appeared that only a nuclear-powered surface ship would be able to sustain high speed long enough to run down a nuclear submarine.

*** Note, however, that in 1942-43, operational commanders demanded higher frigate speeds *to catch submarines escaping on the surface*. Thus a set of staff requirements prepared in March 1943 for the prospective British 1944 frigate program called for a speed 'in action condition' of 24 to 25 knots, as well as a gun capable of forcing a U-boat to dive at maximum visibility range, about 8 miles. The new mass-production *Loch* class, with its 4in gun, could meet neither requirement. These considerations explain the practice of attaching one or more destroyers to convoy escorts. It is not clear whether any high-speed frigate was designed during 1943-44. Moreover, it appears that the Allies were generally unaware of the German fast submarine program until 1944.

Ulster displays half her battery of eight fixed torpedo tubes, 1958. She, *Troubridge* and *Zest* differed from others of this type in having their bridges one level higher, with the twin 40mm gun forward of them. Both of her Limbos are visible aft. [*USN*]

wartime *Loch/Bay*) and one of a 1945 corvette.* The anti-submarine version of the frigate would be armed with one twin 4.5in mount, a STAAG twin Bofors, and a double Squid B (Limbo); and anti-aircraft version, with two twin 4.5in, one STAAG, four single 40mm, and a single Squid. An aircraft direction variant was added in February 1946, these ships ultimately becoming Types 12, 41, and 61.

As the frigate project continued, the wartime 4.5in gun was replaced by the new medium range weapon, the 3in/70, controlled by the new MRS and by a new GDS 3 (with Type 992 radar). The anti-submarine variant was to be equipped with four torpedo tubes for 12 of the new homing weapons (see Chapter 3), and with new sonars.

The air direction role continued wartime practice: five ex-US *Captain* class frigates had been converted to fighter direction ships in 1944-45, with more planned. Three more had been employed as Coastal Forces command ships. Aircraft direction frigates would control both carrier-borne and RAF aircraft. They would operate as pickets or pylon pickets for convoys and amphibious operations, an analogy with the FADE proposed for the fleet. This would include control of AS aircraft. Here the pylon was intended as a marshalling point for returning

friendly aircraft. It would identify them, helping friendly fighters pick off enemy aircraft attempting to mingle with returning friendlies. The austere frigate was limited in this role, since its 251P beacon could not direct single-seat (eg, fighter) aircraft. They required the heavier US YE system. The fleet-capable FADE would need YE to direct future single-seat strike aircraft, and the cruisers *Jamaica* and *Glasgow* were converted as interim pylons.

In coastal warfare the aircraft direction frigate would control motor torpedo or motor gun boats, a role actually performed by British frigates in wartime.

The planned trio of types would all enjoy some overlap in capability, since complete specialization would only swell the required numbers. Thus the A/S and A/D frigates would each mount one medium-calibre anti-aircraft weapon to supplement total convoy anti-aircraft defense. The A/A escorts in turn would carry 'the best possible hand-off weapon' to supplement the A/S defense of the convoy, although it appeared that the A/D escort would be able only to carry a sufficient weapon for A/S self defence (ultimately, the A/A and A/D escorts carried the same A/S weapons and sensors).

The postwar British frigate required long endurance, 4500nm at 15 knots; the existing *Loch* class was rated at 5400nm at this speed, but it did not have anything like the required maximum speed. Similarly, an orthodox steam plant might drive a 1750- to 2000-ton hull at 25 knots or more, but endurance would be limited to 3500nm at 12 to

* The 1200-ton corvette would be armed with one 4in gun, a twin Bofors, four twin 20mm, and double Squid. Although its design was not pursued, the concept of a second-rate ASW ship for mass production led to the Type 14.

HMAS *Queenborough*, an Australian version of the Type 15, was converted at Cockatoo Island Dockyard between May 1950 and December 1954. She was similar to British ships, except for the shape of the bridge. *Quadrant*, the first conversion completed had Squids but the later three had pairs of Limbos aft. [*USNI*]

The Canadian frigate *Algonquin* was a local equivalent of the British Type 15, with a twin 3in/50 forward and a twin 4in gun aft, as well as two single 40mm abeam the bridge. Her ASW armament was a pair of Squids. The ship was originally a war emergency V-class destroyer. [*USNI*]

	As designed	A/S frigate
EQUIPMENT	115	120
HULL	595	595
ARMAMENT AND RADAR	117	145
MACHINERY	295	370
FUEL (including diesel)	279	75
RFW	21	30
MARGIN	0	27
DEEP DISPLACEMENT	1422	1422

The common hull concept for the postwar British frigates was inspired by the success of the Loch/Bay class – Lochs for ASW, Bays for anti-aircraft. *Mounts Bay* is shown here off Lafsami Island, September 1952. [*CPL*]

The *Commandante Rivière* class marked the French equivalent of the British Radical Review decision to abandon specialist anti-submarine frigates in favor of general purpose ships. Substantially larger than the E50/E52 group, it carried three dual purpose 3.9in guns (each equivalent in weight to the earlier and less flexible twin 57mm), two single 30mm, six ASW torpedo tubes, and a multi-purpose muzzle-loading 305mm mortar, which fired faster than the earlier Bofors 375mm (one four-round salvo every 25 seconds, to a range of 3000 yards). More importantly, the 305 also fired a shore bombardment round. General purpose requirements also showed in the diesel powerplant, for very long range: 7600nm at 12 knots, 6200nm at 15 knots (in overload condition, with 210 rather than 170 tons of fuel, 10,000nm at 10 knots, 9400nm at 12 knots). By way of comparison, the E50/52 series was designed to steam 4200nm at 15 knots. The ship was also designed so that her after 3.9in gun could be replaced by a helicopter platform; she could carry 80 troops, and her boats could serve as their landing craft. *Commandant Bourdais* is shown here in Tokyo, 5 February 1985, her after superfiring 3.9in gun having been replaced by four Exocet launchers. [*L & L van Ginderen*]

	A. 360 x 37 x 10ft	B. 370 x 30,6 x 10,6ft,in
EQUIPMENT	205	215
HULL	900	980
ARMAMENT AND RADAR	145	145
MACHINERY	370	370
FUEL	315	470
RFW	30	30
BOARD MARGIN	35	40
DEEP DISPLACEMENT	2000	2250 tons
MAXIMUM SPEED (knots)	25	25.5
ENDURANCE	2500nm at 12 knots	3200nm at 12 knots

(speed and endurance quoted for six months out of dock in tropical waters (allowance quarter per cent per day) with Nightshirt fitted.)

The new Canadian frigate *St Laurent* illustrates an alternative approach to the frigate design problem. Built to an operational requirement much like that which produced the British Type 12, and powered by the same machinery plant, she was strikingly different. The rounded deck-edge forward was adopted to prevent ice from forming. Note the US type twin 3in/50s, and the roller top which could close off the Limbo well aft. As in the case of the Type 12, the design included provision for long-range homing torpedoes (in this case *BIDDER* or the US Mark 35). They were never fitted, however. [*USN*]

15 knots. The problem was the combination of speed and endurance. The 4500nm requirement was based on typical convoy distances: 3290nm from Liverpool to New York, 4665 to New Orleans, 5296 to Sierra Leone in west Africa. On the other hand, it was only 2089nm to St Johns, Newfoundland, and 2833nm to Quebec City. The only compromise ultimately permitted was a reduction of endurance speed from 15 to 12 knots, on the theory that the ship would have to operate with ten knot convoys. In theory, she would cross the Atlantic in eleven days, spending 80 per cent of the time at 12 to 14 knots, 15 per cent at 18 knots, and only five per cent at maximum speed.

Although required frigate speed was well below what had long been standard in destroyers, postwar machinery designs had to meet some new and exacting requirements. Wartime machinery supply had been difficult, and the new escorts were designed for mass production. That limited their level of sophistication. At least in the British case, internal hull volume would clearly be limited, and it was difficult to provide both speed and the long endurance necessary to cross the Atlantic.

At first, it appeared that the new Admiralty standard series diesels would solve this problem, and work began on a common hull and machinery plant for all three variants of what became known as the 1945 frigate. The standard hull would be suited to mass production, using prefabrication techniques proven in the late-war frigate (*Loch/Bay*) and corvette (*Castle* class) programs. The successful *Loch/Bay* program had shown that both anti-aircraft and anti-submarine roles could be accommodated as alternatives in a single hull. However, it was soon found impossible to achieve a speed of 25 knots with any existing type of machinery which could also be mass produced. As 25 knots was considered the lower limit of acceptable anti-submarine frigate speed, the anti-submarine frigate had to be separated from the two air defense versions in 1947; their speed in turn could be cut to 23 knots, which was compatible with diesel power.

The Engineer-in-Chief now promised a 25- to

30-knot diesel anti-submarine frigate, powered by the new lightweight Deltic engine designed for coastal forces craft. However, in about 1948, this estimate had to be withdrawn. The Engineer-in-Chief then hoped for an advanced steam plant by 1952, and a combined diesel-gas turbine plant (CODAG) within another five years, for 33 to 35 knots on reasonable weights.

This was too long a wait. The smallest existing type of high-speed machinery, the wartime Hunt class destroyer plant, was too heavy, as an October 1948 DNC study showed. Preliminary weight calculations assumed an austere armament: two STAAG (twin) Bofors guns, double Limbo (20 Salvoes each), four ASW torpedo tubes (eight torpedoes), the necessary Asdics, and Anti-torpedo gear (five tons allowed). Equipment weights were increased to take account of a larger complement (to fight the ASW weapons) and postwar habitability requirements. Machinery weights had to be increased to include a more powerful electric generating plant and air conditioning.

For a Hunt class hull (272 x 31ft,6in x 9ft,11in and 1422 tons deep displacement) the effect of the increase in weights, together with the introduction of a board margin, was approximately (in tons) as given in the table on page 159.

Only 75 tons would be available for fuel, and maximum speed would be only about 24.5 knots deep and dirty, ie, six months out of dock in the tropics with Nightshirt (propeller silencing) fitted. The hull could be lengthened to reduce resistance, so obtaining a better speed and greater endurance (details are given in the table opposite).

A and B were long ships with rather shallow draft. Hull weights were high and the weight available for oil fuel limited, so that neither could match the required 4500nm at 12 knots deep and dirty. Nor could either meet the staff requirement speed of 27 knots deep and dirty. Finally, neither could carry a particularly impressive armament; each would have less of a gun battery than was being fitted in the destroyer conversion *Rocket*. As much as 50 tons might be saved on hull structure by using aluminum superstructure, but this would not offset the disadvantages.

The Engineer-in-Chief was willing to investigate an interim 30,000shp plant, which became the Y100 of the first-rate ASW frigates. However, he strongly protested any commitment to a 27-knot frigate, since 23- to 25-knot submarines might soon appear. For his part, DNC argued that a large fast ship like the American *Norfolk* might be best, but that it would be far too expensive for the Royal Navy. The mixed plant ultimately became the Y102 steam-gas turbine plant of the County class missile destroyers. In the interim, it was identified with a project for a fast anti-submarine escort, a successor to the 27-knot type with a similar armament.

The difficulty was that the displacement of the postwar frigates was limited, to achieve maximum maneuverability. It was estimated that the combined weight of the new plant and its fuel would have to be 25 to 30 per cent less than that of wartime machinery; a similar reduction in the total length of machinery space was also required.

Thus, the design of the anti-submarine frigate was delayed until 1949. High speed required an unusual hull form, with fine lines forward and the center of buoyancy well aft. It might almost be imagined as a shorter ship (like the slower anti-aircraft and air direction frigates) with a long narrow bow (described as a hydrodynamic aid by Mike Eames of Canada) grafted on to provide greater waterline length for higher speed.

Maintaining high speed in a seaway required

more. The fore end of the ship (and the front of the bridge) had to be specially strengthened and the bridge rounded to resist pressure of seas breaking over the bow at high speed. The bridge was, moreover, protected by two cusp-section breakwaters. The freeboard forward was the maximum consistent with a requirement that an observer on the bridge be able to see the water over the stem one cable ahead. The new frigates belonged to a new generation of ships in which weapons and their associated electronics would take up increasing volumes. She was therefore provided with a long forecastle, her ahead-throwing weapons mounted in a recess at the after end. This configuration did add some weight, but it also added reserve buoyancy, sheltered the weapon, and made for better sea keeping. The Type 12 hull form is still well known for its superior sea keeping. The weapon arrangement avoided any trap for seas breaking over the deck, and there was no closed well to collect water, which would drain off down the sheer aft. A bulwark around the recess protected the weapon from water washing over the deck from the bow. The deck edge was rounded for strength and for easier nuclear or chemical decontamination by wash-down.

As in contemporary US destroyers and frigates, twin rudders were provided for maneuverability. Unlike most US ships, Type 12 had very large, slow-turning propellers for silencing.

The long-forecastle design had some side

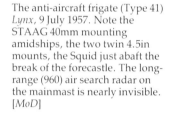

The anti-aircraft frigate (Type 41) *Lynx*, 9 July 1957. Note the STAAG 40mm mounting amidships, the two twin 4.5in mounts, the Squid just abaft the break of the forecastle. The long-range (960) air search radar on the mainmast is nearly invisible. [MoD]

effects. The main gun, on the lower portion of the forecastle, could not depress to fire upon a surfaced submarine within 30 degrees of dead ahead. This was acceptable to a staff which suspected that the weapon provided could not sink one anyway. Placing the gun on the forecastle limited the forward extension of the bridge structure, and so made it necessary to site the enclosed bridge over the operations room (CIC in US parlance). This violated the original staff requirement that the AIO be on same level as bridge.

One peculiarity of the design was that much of the planned equipment was not yet available. When the Type 12 design was submitted for Admiralty Board approval in 1950, it appeared that the ship would have to be armed with the existing twin 4.5in gun (rather than the planned 3in/70), and with double Squid rather than Limbo (20 salvoes), the latter requiring different loading arrangements. Similarly, the gun would be controlled by GDS 2 using Type 293 radar, rarther than by GDS 3 (Type 992). The new surface torpedo tubes had not yet been designed. DNC had, therefore, to provide not only space and weight reservations, but also a reserve of electrical power against future upgrade. In the case of Type 12, the electrical plant could handle the future load, but only if the domestic load (eg, heating) were reduced. DNC, therefore, allowed for an auxiliary boiler in any upgraded ship. To avoid having to fire boilers in harbor, he provided an oil-fired cooking range instead of an electric unit.

Of the Stage 2 weapons, only Limbo was available in time. Although elaborate arrangements had been made to accommodate the alternative Squid battery, they were not neeed. The prospective torpedo battery changed gradually, until, by 1951, all torpedoes were to be carried in tubes (eight single, two twin) at all times, with no reloads. In theory, this added little or no weight, it eliminated the awkwardness of reloading in a seaway, and it allowed for a new doctrine of firing three-torpedo salvoes. However, attempts to provide for similar tactics in Types 14 and 15 failed.

Sonar was also a problem. The ship was designed to take existing sets, 166 and 147F in a 100in dome, as well as 162. Stage 2 was to include the 170/172 associated with Limbo. The space reservation for future development included a second compartment which could be converted to support sonars in another (150in) dome.

Types 41 and 61 generally resembled Type 12, although both were substantially shorter. Type 41 was designed to mount two medium range guns (interim two twin 4.5), with provision for two MRS (interim Mark VI and Flyplane Predictor with AFCC); one STAAG and two or more single Bofors. It would have the best available TIU. ASW armament would be Squid with ten salvoes. Interim radars were Type 291 (air search) for gun defense and Type 293Q for surface search.

Type 61 requirements included one MR mounting, with 4.5 as interim; one STAAG or twin Bofors with simple tachymetric director; and single Squid (ten salvoes), but with provision for underway replenishment. It was to be able to control two day or one night interceptions. It would have the latest air search and height finder radars fore and aft. Interim equipment was 906P, and 277Q; in fact, the ships were completed with the postwar 982/983 combination, but there was never enough deck space for two separate installations.

In 1949, in the same paper in which he proposed the cruiser/destroyer, Admiral Edwards suggested a new type of second-rate or austere frigate. It would supplement but not replace the basic types. A/A and A/D required far too much in the way of

The aircraft direction frigate (Type 61) *Llandaff* is shown as completed. Her radars were her main battery: a Type 277Q height-finder on a stub mast forward, a 293Q short-range air search antenna (target indicator) and a 960 long-range air search antenna (with IFF antenna below it), and a 982 narrow-beam air search antenna abaft that. The fore masthead carries a VHF/DF antenna. The main masthead carries an IFF antenna. Note also the MF/DF coil abaft her foremast. Modernized in 1966, she was transferred to Bangladesh in 1976 to become that Navy's first ship (*Umar Farooq*). [*USNI*]

HMS *Malcolm* (from astern, January 1958) illustrates the designed configuration of the Type 14 frigate, with paired torpedo tubes to supplement the two Limbos. Gun armament is limited to three single 40mm: two abeam the bridge, one right aft. The bow bulwark and the breakwater were intended to protect the bridge from water coming aboard if the ship were driven hard into a sea in pursuit of a submarine. Standard submarine doctrine is to escape by steaming into a sea, so that a surface ship cannot easily follow. [*MoD*]

TABLE 6–2: THE THIRD-RATE FRIGATE, 1951

	SMALL A/S	GUNBOAT	TYPE 14
LWL (ft,in)	275,0	275,0	300,0
BEAM, EXTREME (ft,in)	31,6	31,6	33,0
DEEP DISPLACEMENT (tons)	950	1050	1290
DRAFT (ft,in)	8,9	9,3	8,4/11,1½
STD DISPLACEMENT (tons)	—	—	1007
SHP	7500	7500	15,000
SPEED (knots)	22	22	25
FUEL OIL	50	50	225
ENDURANCE (Dirty)	2000/12	2000/12	4500/12
COMPLEMENT	150	150	164
40mm TWIN Mk 5	1 (1500)	—	1 (1500)
40mm SINGLE	1 (288)	2 (1500)	1 (288)
3in/50 TWIN	—	2 (600)	—
A/S TORPEDOES	4	—	4
DOUBLE LIMBO	—	—	1 (20)
SINGLE LIMBO	1 (20)	—	—
SINGLE SQUID	—	1 (10)	—
WEIGHTS:			
GENERAL EQUIPMENT	105	115	119
MACHINERY	215	215	225
ARMAMENT	80	120	100
HULL	480	532	579
RFW	—	—	10
MARGIN	20	18	22

NOTES: This legend was prepared about October 1951, specifically to answer Prime Minister Churchill's query about the new third-rate design. They therefore represent an extremely early stage in the development of Types 17 and 42, and are probably the figures on which the DNC sketches were based.

basic equipment to make such an alternative possible. However, an austere second-rate A/S frigate was a much more attractive proposition. The only question was how austere to make it; Admiral Edwards' initial proposal was rejected as not second-rate enough. By the fall of 1949 the ship was defined as a 1200-tonner costing half as much as the earlier A/S frigate.

Admiral Edwards introduced Type numbers for these ships, the block between 10 and 40 being reserved for ASW ships; 41 to 60 were AAW ships; and 61 through 80 were air direction ships. Later, the block from 81 up was assigned to a new general purpose category. In this scheme the first-rate A/S frigate became Type 12, the second-rate, Type 14; Type 11 may have been reserved for a future diesel alternative. Types 15, 16, and 18 were destroyer conversions, and Type 17 was the even more austere third-rate frigate, described later. Type 41 was the A/A frigate, and Type 42 the air defense version of Type 17; later on this number was re-used for the *Sheffield* class missile destroyer, which only shows the close connection

between destroyer and frigate in British practice. Type 61 was the A/D frigate, and Type 62 a proposed destroyer conversion for aircraft direction.

DNC's initial request for minimum acceptable staff requirements for a second-rate A/S frigate made for a deep displacment approaching 1700 tons with one set of frigate machinery. The Controller ruled that this was still too large and expensive and directed departments to produce a vessel with half the deep displacement at half the cost of the prototype A/S frigate. Initial staff requirements were laid out in TSD 4552/49 of 29 July. The next attempt showed a deep displacement of about 1200 tons. The Engineer-in-Chief argued that the ship had to have two boilers so as to avoid the possibility of being immobilzed under ordinary steaming conditions due to a minor defect. Two boilers each of 7500shp were, therefore, provided, although this departed from standardization with the 15,000shp boiler being designed for the first-rate A/S frigate. The space requirements for the boiler room were similar, but

SENSORS
1 HF/DF
2 HDWS (RADAR 974)
3 MF/DF
4 STD DIRECTOR
5 LOOKOUT SIGHTS (PORT AND STARBOARD)
6 HULL OUTFIT 1 (SONAR)
7 TYPE 162 ASDIC
8 A/S INSTRUMENT ROOM
9 ASDIC COMPARTMENT

WEAPONS
10 TWIN 40mm BOFORS
11 2in ROCKET FLARE LAUNCHER
12 FOUR FIXED A/S TORPEDO TUBES
12A TWO FIXED A/S TORPEDO TUBES (WITH RELOADS)
13 LIMBO
14 LIMBO HANDLING ROOM, CONVEYOR, LIFTS (STOWAGE BELOW)
15 SINGLE 40mm BOFORS
16 GUN CREW SHELTER
17 SQUID
18 SQUID HANDLING AND PROJECTILE ROOM
19 DOME FOR TAS SIGHT

OTHER
20 LAMP AND PAINT ROOM AND PAINT STORE
21 CREW'S BATHROOM AND WCs
22 SEAMEN'S MESS
23 CPO MESS
24 PO MESS, A/S STABILIZER AND PLANE CONVERTER
24A PO MESS
25 BRIDGE
26 W/T OFFICE, OPERATIONS ROOM, WEAPONS CONTROL
27 GALLEY
28 CANTEEN, WARDROOM
29 DIESEL OIL TANKS
30 ENGINE ROOM
31 DIESEL GENERATOR
32 SPIRIT ROOM
33 ERA MESS, LIMBO STOWAGE
34 STEERING GEAR

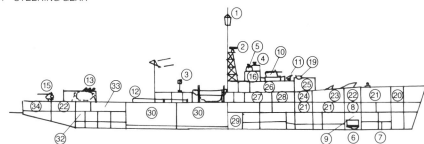

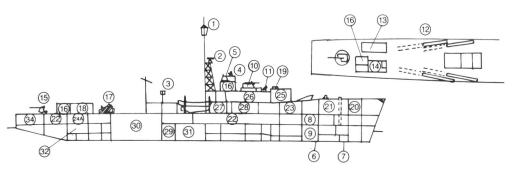

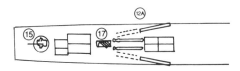

DNC approaches to a third-rate frigate, 1950.

A March 1959 official sketch of the Type 81 general purpose frigate (Tribal class) shows three of the fixed torpedo tubes originally planned, on the weather deck under the directors abeam the after uptake. Note the MRS 3 director atop the bridge, and the quadruple Seacat point-defense missile abeam the big lattice mast. The drawing clearly shows her single Limbo forward of the after deckhouse, the top of which formed part of a helicopter platform. [*USNI*]

the weight of machinery increased by about 10 tons with two boilers. The new plant was designated Y101.

The ship was made long and lean to maintain speed into a head sea, and had sufficient draft for seaworthiness and to accommodate the 12ft prop. This length also helped to achieve a speed of 25 knots deep and dirty (26 knots clean), a knot in excess of the staff requirement. Since the ship was longer than necessary for habitability, stores, etc, the spaces forward were left empty deliberately to keep the fore end light for performance in a seaway.

A World War I V and W destroyer (300 x 29,6 x 8ft,11in and 1300 tons) was taken as a basis, initially with a long forecastle. The latter, however, was found unacceptable for stability reasons and a short forecastle hull has been adopted. With a waterline length of 300ft and moulded depth of 19ft,6in to upper deck at side, initial stability was satisfactory with a beam of 31ft, but the curve of righting arms in light condition was not. The moulded depth was, therefore, reduced to 18ft,6in and the light condition ballasted to lower the center of gravity. The beam had to be increased to 33ft (with a modified form based on that of the 1937 programme patrol vessel *Guillemot*) to give a satisfactory curve.

The estimated cost was £652,000 *vs* £1,315,000 for a first-rate.

In the 1956-57 Estimates, a Type 14 was priced at £1.52 million, *Whitby* (the prototype first-rate) at £3.1 million (£2.8 milion for a later unit, *Torquay*). Type 41 and Type 61 costs were slightly lower, £2.7 and £2.9 million, respectively. In 1984 terms, the Type 14 cost would have been about £22.3 million, the Type 12 prototype £36.7 million. By way of comparison, in 1961-62 a Type 81 (*Tribal*) class frigate, *Ashanti*, was priced at £5.3 million (1984: £52.8 million) and *Leander* (1962-63) was priced at £4.6 million (£45.1 million). The missile destroyer *Hampshire* was priced at £12.6 million (£123.1 million – compared to £31.1 million equivalent for *Daring* in 1951-52). These figures are based on tables developed in 1985 by the Naval Historical Branch, based on standard deflators.

Armament consisted of one double Limbo (20 salvoes), four fixed TT (no reloads), one twin Bofors with STD director. On 200 tons of oil, endurance would be 3900nm at 12 knots deep and dirty. Adding 32 tons of emergency oil would increase this to 4500nm at 12 knots. Stores endurance, for 160 men (including 11 officers), was 45 days. In 1952, the doctrine changed to three-torpedo salvoes, and a lightweight triple tube was proposed. By that time, however, so much of the initial weight margin had been consumed (largely by the underwater fire control system) that no such addition was possible.

The more formal sketch design was modified to achieve 4500nm at 12 knots without emergency fuel. This was in the context of the North Atlantic, so no reduction for tropical conditions had to be taken into account. A catwalk was added to

	N2/184	N2/185	Second-rate
	1 Limbo	1 Squid	2 Limbo
DESIGN SPEED (knots)	22	19	25
ENDURANCE (nm at 12 knots)	2000	2000	4500
COST (£/thousands)	500–550	400–450	650–700K
MACHINERY	4 ASR I	2 ASR I	Y101 steam
EQUIVALENT	9	11	7

Mohawk, a Tribal class frigate, at Malta, June, 1964. The Helicopter platform aft is clearly visible. Compared to the 1959 sketch, she lacks torpedo tubes. Although space and weight were available for a variable-depth sonar, only two ships of the class, *Ashanti* and *Gurkha*, carried it. [*CPL*]

connect the forecastle with the deckhouse aft.

In addition, DNC was asked to work out an outline design of an alternative ASW frigate powered by two sets of Deltic (diesel) engines, on approximately the same displacement and cost. It appears not have reached the formal proposal stage, since no such ship figures in the discussions of the 1951-1955 naval programs.

Legends for these frigates are given in Table 6-1.

In May 1950, a further downward step in austerity was proposed: a third-rate frigate which might cost no more than a third as much as a first-rate. Length was limited to 275ft, approximately that of the *Hunt* class destroyer which had inspired the concept. Speed would inevitably fall, and DNC prepared two sketches of diesel powered ships with half the endurance of a first- or second-rate frigate, N2/184 and N2/185, detailed in the table opposite.

The final line indicates the numbers of ships which could be built at the same total cost. It was not particularly attractive. At best, a considerable step down in range and capability bought only one or two more ships, with little to recommend them. A single Squid was unacceptable in a special-purpose ASW ship, which left only the larger N2/184 design. It just about met the speed requirement, but not the vital endurance measure: at the least, ships had to be able to cross the Atlantic.

Alternatively, the very austere frigate could be considered a coastal design. Then, however, it would need a much better anti-aircraft battery. More generally, it was unlikely to show good sea keeping (since it was 25ft shorter than Type 14), and it had no means of killing a submarine forced to the surface, a problem in the other cut-rate frigate, Type 14.

The new design was saved (as a paper study) by two arguments. First, high speed might be somewhat overrated, since for a long time there would be relatively few very fast submarines, and even they would not always be able to go very fast. Second, the range problem could be solved: endurance could be increased (in N2/184) to 4000nm at the cost of only 50 tons of diesel fuel.

N2/184 was still less than attractive for peacetime production, but it was developed instead as part of a war emergency program which the Royal Navy would initiate upon mobilization. Initial design characteristics were: 275 x 31,6 x 17,6 (moulded) x 8ft,9in and 950 tons deep displacement; one Limbo (20 salvoes), four fixed TT (no reloads), one twin Bofors (ready use ammunition only), STD, two 2in rocket flare launchers; four ASRI diesels giving 22 knots deep and dirty and 2000nm at 12 knots. The Director of the torpedo and ASW branch considered the concept acceptable (if it could achieve 4000nm at 12 knots, with a top speed of 19 knots, like that of a wartime *River* class frigate) for war construction, when economics would be irrelevant but speed of production would be extremely important. To him it would be a 'World War III corvette'.*

* Frigate requirements were formalized several times. For example, in November 1950 the Director of Tactical and Staff (DTSD) set out minimum frigate performance standards as a more graphic alternative to staff requirements. In line with then-current practice, he divided frigates into rates, according to such features as speed, endurance, effective Asdic range, warning radar capability, gun power (for anti-aircraft and against surfaced submarines), communications, and anti-submarine weapons (ahead-throwing):

This third-rate ship would be acceptable for war over the next ten years, but it would be folly to build new ones. AA and AD frigates (such as Types 41 and 61) required ASW weapons and sensors comparable to those of the second-rate ship.

For the Royal Navy, DTSD defined rates of gun power: *First-rate:* contributes to convoy defense. One medium calibre dual purpose gun, blind fire capability, GDS capable of blind evaluation of a heavy scale of attack,

This third-rate A/S Frigate (which was ultimately designated Type 17) was soon being examined as a prototype for mass frigate production by European NATO navies such as the French, the Italians, and the Dutch. A 'gunboat' version, suitable for air and anti-MTB protection of coastal convoys would be, in effect, a modernized *Hunt*. It became the East Coast Escort, or Type 42, version of the basic design. Like Type 17, it would be built only in an emergency.

Tentative staff requirements for Type 42, developed early in 1951, called for a speed of 22 knots (deep and dirty); the ship would spend eighty per cent of her time at 12 knots, fifteen per cent at 16 knots, and five per cent at 22 knots. Any improvement over the 22-knot speed would be welcome (for the anti-MTB role), but that in turn would probably require steam power, which in turn would force up the size (and cost) of the ship. On the other hand, the short endurance of the original sketch designs, 2000nm at 12 knots, was acceptable. Displacement and length were not to exceed 1050 tons and 275ft, respectively

The ship would be armed with two (preferably three) US-supplied twin 3in/50 guns, each controlled by a US-type Mark 63 director with an on-mount Mark 34 radar, these directors being incorporated in a GDS 2* system. Each 3in/50

would have enough ammunition for ten minutes of fire. In addition, as many power-operated Bofors guns as possible would be mounted. The ASW battery would be limited to a single Squid (possibly a Limbo in later units), and sonars to Types 162 (particularly important in coastal waters) and 164. Radars would include Types 293Q and 974.

Very little work was carried out during 1950/51, so that late in 1951 the third-rate frigate and the East Coast Gunboat were described by the legends in Table 6-2. However, at that time plans called for the third-rate to be developed as a 900-ton, 26-knot steam turbine ship. As the supply of US equipment under MDAP dried up during 1953-54, the gunboat battery changed to three 4in Vickers single automatic guns, each with its own director. The two designs diverged, one being developed at Bath (Type 42) and the other (Type 17) in the DNC unit working directly with the Naval Staff in London, so that their common origin was soon lost.

Then, in about October 1953, the Ship Design Policy Committee proposed that the Type 17 and Type 42 requirements might both be met in a new common hull frigate. By this time, Type 17 was actually larger than the earlier Type 14, due to the new requirement that the crew be accommodated in bunks rather than hammocks.** The commonality requirement meant, for example, that the hull would be stressed to take a single or twin 4in gun.

The common hull would be powered by a new Y111 twin-screw steam plant sharing many features with the machinery planned for a new ocean minesweeper (see Chapter 7). Design work on the common hull frigate began in the spring of 1954. An early sketch of the A/S version showed single (later twin) Bofors fore and aft, a single Limbo, four torpedo tubes, and sonars of Types 170, 177, 174, and 162 (285 x 38ft,6in and 1662 tons with a complement of 11 officers and 187 ratings). The anti-aircraft (gun) version showed two twin 4in Mark 19, two twin 40mm L70 (CRBFD director, 3 TOM), and one Squid, with sonars of Types 147 and 162, and Type 976 radar.

Both versions grew inexorably, to 305 x 40ft and 1740 tons in the A/A version and 1812 tons in the A/S version. Such great size was unattractive, and efforts were made to develop smaller third-rate frigate and gunboat designs. An A/A frigate (285 x 38ft,6in and 1640 tons) with one twin 4in, one twin Bofors, and one Squid, with minesweeper machinery) would make about 23 knots (deep and dirty). By mid 1954, a 1500-ton version of the third-rate frigate showed gas turbine machinery, and a 1600-ton version showed COSAG machinery (10,000shp steam, 7500shp gas turbine).

---

putting armament 'on' in time to be effective. This corresponded to Type 12.
Second-rate: self defense while in company. One multiple CR mounting, visual sight, visual GDS. This corresponded to Type 14.
AA: main anti-aircraft protection for the convoy: two dual-purpose mounts, each with its own fire control.
AD: self-protection without support, by means of one medium calibre with fire control.

All were to be capable of bringing fire to bear on fast attack boats (E-boats) or surfaced submarines.

Radar requirements:
ASW: High Definition Surface Warning (HDSW) for snorkel detection and station keeping. Air search (AW or air warning, in British parlance) radar to cooperate with ASW aircraft, eg, Type 277Q.
AIO with two anti-surface plotting tables.
AA: HDWS, air search/gun direction radar such as Type 293.

	FIRST-RATE	SECOND-RATE	THIRD-RATE
SPEED (DEEP/DIRTY)	22	19	14kts
ENDURANCE	4000	3000	2000nm
ASDIC	144, 147	144, 147	128
A/S WEAPON	Squid	Squid, Hedgehog	Depth Charges

AD: long-range air search (960) and fighter control (982/983) plus aircraft control beacon (YE or equivalent); capable of controlling three intercepts simultaneously.

These requirements defined the equipment of the new Type 12/14/41/61 frigates, and also provided a basis for comparison with alternatives, such as the Type 17 proposed a few months earlier.

** The SDPC also sought to meet the Type 14 requirement in the same hull; presumably some would be built to third-rate and some to second-rate ASW characteristics.

Although both versions of the common hull frigate figured in the long-range naval construction plan of May 1954, they fell foul of the new strategy developing out of the Radical Review. Something much closer to the traditional sloop was needed, and in July 1954, the Naval Staff proposed a new common purpose frigate with second-rate capability in all three areas: two twin 4in, one twin 40mm, single Limbo,and eight ASW torpedo tubes, plus the new long-range air search radar (initially the US SPS-6C, ultimately the British Type 965). A second twin Bofors was later added so that two could be sided (centreline space was limited). The twin-screw machinery of the common hull frigate was replaced by a new single-shaft steam/gas turbine plant, this design (which became the Type 81 or *Tribal* class frigate) serving as operational prototype for such a plant.

This was much larger than the common hull frigate. The earliest sketches showed a deep displacement of 2037 tons, and final deep displacement (as built) was about 2700 tons, not far short of that of a Type 12.

The general purpose frigate (Type 81), then, was conceived during 1954 (and approved that October) as an alternative to the single purpose Type 14, replacing it in the long-term construction program. Although it had only one Limbo, that did not necessarily mean an inferior ASW performance, since Type 81 was to have eight (rather than four) ASW torpedoes, as well as the same sonars as a Type 12 or a Type 14. In wartime it would replace Type 14, supporting Type 12 in escort groups. In cold war, however, its substantial gun armament would be available for shore bombardment or for such classic naval tasks as stopping suspect ships by a shot across the bow (and, therefore, by the threat of more serious damage if they did not stop). The desired endurance, 5000nm at 12 knots, was apparently set by cold war requirements, since it exceeded the 4500nm at 12 knots of the ASW frigates. The speed initially demanded, 24 knots, was comparable to that of the Type 14 (24.5 knots).

In 1954-55, when Type 81 was being designed, however, there was some question as to whether such speeds would suffice. The response at the time was that any significantly higher speed would cost about 1000 tons, for a full load displacement of about 3300. The Royal Navy could never hope to build enough frigates in peacetime, and it would always suffer from severe fiscal and manpower limitations. A speed of 24 knots was considered sufficient in an escort (although not in a hunter-killer which would have to run down a fast submarine) facing diesel-electric or even hydrogen peroxide submarines. Moreover, the existing Type 176 and 177 sonars were effective only up to 22 and 24 knots respectively. The prospective shifts to variable depth sonar would probably buy only one to two knots. However, speed could help a ship avoid submarine-launched torpedoes, but prospective improved decoys would reduce even that advantage. In 1955, then, it was argued that only the appearance of substantial numbers of nuclear submarines (in the late 'sixties) would reverse these arguments. Then, 27 knots would not be anything like enough.

At this time, work was proceeding on the first British combined gas turbine and steam plant, which was destined first for the fleet escort and then ultimately for the County class. The Engineer-in-Chief badly wanted to get an early version to sea, and Type 81 became a natural candidate. The formal argument at the time was that the new strategy required a quick response to warning, so that ships could escape from port before nuclear weapons burst on them. Because it could start virtually instantly, a gas turbine plant could satisfy such a requirement. It could also give higher speed at a very tolerable cost in ship size and weight.

The adoption of such a plant had another major consequence. It changed the usual relationship between maximum speed and endurance, since a substantial part of the plant (the gas turbine) did not contribute to low-speed performance. The hull

Tuscan, a Type 16 limited conversion frigate, is shown in March 1954. Very little could be done to remodel her superstructure, but her forecastle could be cleared to avoid damage due to seas breaking over it. The catwalks connecting her after deckhouse to her forecastle were also seakeeping features. Her galley was in the deckhouse (note its exhaust stack), and there was no internal passage along which food (or men) could pass without risking seas breaking over her weather deck. [*MoD*]

TABLE 6–3: DESTROYER CONVERSIONS

	TYPE 15 (ROCKET)	TYPE 16 (TENACIOUS)	WAR DESTROYER
LWL (ft,in)	348,0	350,6	348,0
LOA (ft,in)	358,3	362,9	358,3
BEAM (ft,in)	35,8	35,8	35,8
DEEP DISPLACEMENT (tons)	2585	2593	—
DRAFT (ft,in)	12,10/12,6	12,11/12,5	—
STD DISPLACEMENT (tons)	1841	1866	1650
DRAFT (ft,in)	—	—	9,3
SHP	40,000	40,000	40,000
SPEED (knots)	29	29	31.5
FUEL OIL (diesel oil)	554 (75)	618 (27)	615
ENDURANCE (clean)	3350/15	3740/15	4700/20
COMPLEMENT	230	197	163
4.7 in GUN	—	—	4 (200)
4in TWIN	1 (356)	1 (310)	—
40mm TWIN	1 (1510)	1 (1488)	—
40mm SINGLE	—	5 (1488)	—
2pdr QUAD	—	—	1 (1800)
0.5in QUAD	—	—	2 (2500)
QUAD TT	—	1 (4)	2 (8)
A/S TT	4 (8)	—	—
DOUBLE LIMBO	1 (22)	—	—
DOUBLE SQUID	—	1 (20)	—
DEPTH CHARGES	—	—	20
WEIGHTS:			
GENERAL EQUIPMENT	201	162	80
MACHINERY	580	539	530
ARMAMENT	179	145	150
HULL	1003	1092	890
RFW	38	37	—
BALLAST	30	—	—
MARGIN	—	—	—

NOTE: The wartime design is the original legend of 1940. Note how much more fuel and machinery were needed to achieve a much lower endurance than that of the Type 12 in Table 6–1.

form and steam turbine could be optimized for a higher endurance speed, so that the ships were actually most economical at 18 knots, at which their endurance much exceeded the figure the staff required at 12.

There were other changes as well. From a strategic point of view, the most interesting was the substitution of low-angle 4.5in guns (ex-destroyer) for the dual purpose (largely AA) twin 4in. The 4.5in did, after all, make a much greater impression in shore bombardment. Proposals to arm the ships with such special purpose weapons as the twin 3in/70 and even the US Tartar missile were rejected, partly because of cost. Even so, it is difficult to avoid the view that they would have violated the cold war concept enshrined in the Radical Review and then in the 1957 White Paper (Defense Review).

The twin 40mm guns were replaced by Seacat missiles.

The torpedo tubes were replaced by an alternative long-range ASW weapon, a helicopter-delivered homing torpedo (MATCH); the new frigate was its first application. At about the same time, a variable-depth sonar (Type 199) was added to the design, although only two ships of the class were fitted with it.

Although described initially as a sloop (equivalent to a French colonial aviso, and intended for similar duties in the British Persian Gulf sphere of influence), the design was ultimately designated a general purpose frigate, Type 81. It was superseded in production by a general purpose version of the earlier Type 12, which became the *Leander*. Ironically, the larger *Leander* was actually less expensive, as it incorporated major elements of the existing Type 12 design. As such, it was never allocated a Type number of its own.

*   *   *

The alternative to new construction was conversion. Many British destroyers had been de-rated to AA and A/S escort status during World War II, and in April 1947, the Controller ordered the ten Intermediate (O and P) and all earlier destroyers of Tribal to N (18 ships) classes de-rated to escorts, to be converted. All emergency and later ships would be considered fleet destroyers. Within a year, the Tribal, J, K, and L classes were all gone, but the Royal Navy had many more fleet destroyers than required. All future conversion programs were based on the 59 ships of the M through Z classes, which included the ten small intermediates.

The first plan called for conversion of all 59 hulls to what became known as Type 15, or full conversion, standard. Hulls were completely stripped and armament reduced to a twin 4in Mark 19 aft and a twin Bofors Mark 5. As in the ASW frigate, the new bridge front was curved to resist the pressure of seas coming aboard, and an ahead-throwing weapon (double Limbo with 20 salvoes, double Squid as interim) placed in a recess aft. It would be controlled by Asdics 170 and 176 (interim: 174, 177, and 162). As in other British frigates of this period, the Limbo would be supplemented by homing torpedos, in this case eight with four tubes (later eight in eight single tubes). A 1952 attempt to shift to two triple lightweight (21in) tubes, for three-torpedo salvoes, on each side failed because the ships had a limited weight margin. Performance would approximate that of the first-rate frigate, but endurance would be somewhat shorter, about 3000 or 3500nm at 15 knots. The prototypes, *Relentless* and *Rocket*, were taken in hand in 1949.

On trial in home waters in November 1951, *Relentless*, the other prototype Type 15, shows her Limbos aft, and deck torpedo tubes abaft her funnel. [*CPL*]

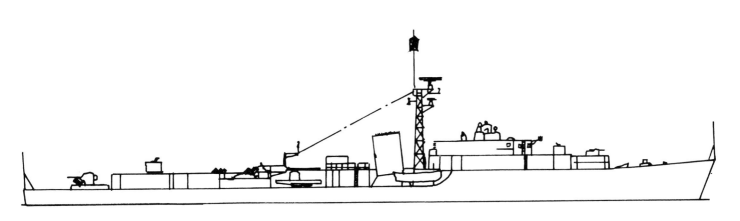

Type 18 frigate as proposed by DNC.

Legends for the destroyer conversions are shown in Table 6-3.

The Type 15 reconstruction was expensive and time-consuming, and the rest of the conversion program was spent in seeking less onerous alternatives. Initial discussions between the Naval Staff and the royal dockyard staffs developed the idea that some ships might be converted to a more austere standard, to obtain more of these valuable escorts more quickly. This limited conversion was to have been applied to the ten follow-on ships (1950/51 program). However, budget cuts delayed them a year, and money was so tight that the Naval Staff had to consider a still more austere version, lacking modern radar and fire control. The Naval Staff now rejected the simplified conversion altogether, arguing that it would be better to accept a smaller number of full conversions; the Admiralty Board agreed in May 1949, and it appeared that the limited conversion was dead.

It was, incidentally, fairly elaborate by later standards, as it cut the ship down to the 01 level and provided an entirely new bridge structure, the twin 4in gun being mounted in A position. The standard frigate air/surface search radar, 277Q, would have been installed.

Now money became tighter, and it became clear that ships would not be converted *unless* some austere version could be developed. The Naval Staff view changed to favor a combination of first- and second-rate frigates to obtain more flotillas. A prototype of this Type 16 conversion (HMS *Tenacious*) was approved for the 1950-51 program in February, 1950. DNC expected this idea to

apply to the T, N, O, and P classes, of which the appreciably smaller O and P would need a separate reduced design. The T class was chosen for the first conversion because it had the greatest endurance.

Austerity showed in several ways. The 4in gun, mounted in B position for dryness, was for self defense only; there was no money to buy a director good enough to allow the ship to contribute to convoy defense, which was normally the secondary role of the A/S frigate. An STD replaced the director on the bridge. Asdic 166Z would supersede the existing 144QZ, and the existing 147B would be modified to 147F standard. Asdic 162 would be fitted. Radar would be limited to HDWS and 293Q, converted from the original 293M.

Double Squid (20 salvoes) was mounted in X, the driest possible position. Four torpedo tubes were retained for ASW torpedoes; there were no reloads. It was later suggested that single Limbo might replace the double Squid, in which case Type 16 would have exactly half the ASW battery of Type 15, although sensors would not be comparable. Type 16 did have a heavier light anti-aircraft battery, one twin and five single 40mm.

The operational evaluation of the double Squid proved disappointing, and DNC later remarked that it seemed false economy to fit second-rate A/S equipment to these fast and valuable ships. Surely there was some alternative.

Type 18 was conceived in July 1950 as a Type 16 with a better ASW battery of double Limbo in place of double Squid. It was soon seen as a

Termagant is shown on 9 September 1953. Note the absence of torpedo tubes, which were described in 1957 as temporarily removed. The stub mast aft carried an MF/DF coil; her foremast carried the usual HF/DF 'birdcage'. The rails on the 4in shield are launchers for illuminating rockets. The 4in gun itself was controlled by an STD, equivalent to a US Mark 51 director. Two units, *Orwell* and *Paladin*, retained their minelaying rails. The last three, *Teazer*, *Terpsichore* and *Tumult*, were fitted with a higher bridge similar to that in Type 12 frigates. [*John Lambert*]

compromise conversion, a lower-cost means of achieving the military capability of a Type 15. DNC submitted a legend, based on conversion of the V class, in February 1951.

Emergency destroyers would be refitted with a new low bridge structure, one level higher than that of a Type 15 (with open wings). Like Type 16s, they would retain one set of torpedo tubes, to fire four ASW torpedoes. Double Limbo (20 salvoes) would be installed aft. Since the forward Limbo would be more exposed than in a Type 15, it would have to be fitted with a breakwater. The original destroyer-type lower superstructure level forward would be retained, and existing gun positions (A and Y) used. They would support a twin Bofors (on a raised foundation) forward, and a twin 4in aft, these relative positions having been chosen for trim. The 4in shield would carry a sextuple 2in rocket flare. Placing the 4in gun aft would also leave magazine space which could be converted into a large asdic compartment, to support the future 150in dome. Asdic 170 and 174 would be fitted in an interim 100in dome, with 162 elsewhere. The fore end of the hull would be stiffened for high speed in rough weather. Weight would limit the ship to radar 293Q (in place of the existing 293M) plus 974 (periscope detection and navigation). Unlike a Type 15, she would not have a 277Q for air and surface search.

All of these destroyer conversions required considerably more electrical power. For example, in Type 18, the two 155kW turbo generators and two 50kW emergency diesel generators of the original destroyer would have been supplemented by two 100kW diesel generators. As in Types 15 and 16, they would have to be installed within the main machinery spaces, and the 50kW generator in the gearing room would have to carry the salvage load as emergency set.

This was an extremely attractive combination. In 1951, it was estimated that a Type 18 would cost £450,000, compared to £600,000 for a Type 15 and £260,000 for a much less effective Type 16. Conversion would require 15 months, compared to 18 for Type 15 and ten for Type 16. At this time the first two Type 15 had not yet been completed, so that evaluation of alternatives was difficult at best.

Even so, the Admiralty Staff recommended in March that Type 18 replace both Type 15 and Type 16. It could, after all, carry very nearly the ASW battery planned for Type 15 (double Limbo and four rather then eight torpedoes). At this time the program called for 27 full and 18 limited conversions. The O and P classes were too small, and would still be subject to Type 16 conversion. Early planning therefore centered on the big emergency destroyers, with the five N class deferred until 1953/54.

The Director of Plans objected to having yet another design in the program. Moreover, too high a proportion of the ships would have second-class anti-aircraft batteries, and that would make for inflexibility in escort arrangements. However,

the prospective savings on each of the 27 ships were certainly attractive. Type 18 died only when the Radical Review killed virtually all further conversion projects in favor of new construction.

The other major destroyer conversion project was Type 62, the air defense frigate. Work began in 1949; staff requirements showed one twin 4in with CRBF, one twin Bofors with STD, single Squid (30 rounds), and Asdics 166, 162 (deleted by 1952) and 147F. There would be two (later three) intercept positions. Ideally, there would also be at least two full sets of intercept radars, such as Types 982/983.

Draft staff requirements of March 1952 show a required speed of 28 knots deep and dirty, with propeller silencing fitted but not working, and an endurance of about 3000nm at 15 knots. This compared with existing figures of 3095nm at 15 knots in an M, 3180nm in a late emergency (Z class), and 3650nm at 15 knots in an earlier S class destroyer. Each would require diesel fuel to run generators, and Type 62 would therefore lose some fuel stowage.

In 1950, the Admiralty planned an ultimate total of twelve conversions from two classes: all five surviving M class and seven emergency (*Myngs, Kempenfelt, Troubridge, Wager, Whelp, Savage,* and *Grenville*). Of these, the earlier Ms were slightly beamier, hence better suited to carrying heavy radars. Thus the emergencies could not support the new Type 982/983 radars, and would have to make do with only the two Type 277Q height-finders originally proposed, and only then if severe restriction of other features accepted. *Whelp* was then sold to South Africa, and *Grenville* damaged in a collision. She was therefore shifted to the Type 15 program, which in any case entailed major reconstruction, and her place in the Type 62 program was taken by *Ursa*.

It was soon clear that only the Ms, of all the pre-Battle class destroyers, were large enough for the Type 62 conversion. Even they would encounter serious stability problems. For example, the heavy Type 982 and 983 would have to be mounted on the sides of the ship at the same height (blanking each other) abaft the main mast. Alternatively, the ship could carry a lighter height-finder (Type 277Q) before her foremast overlooking the bridge and 982 or 983 on centerline aft.

In March 1952 the emergency destroyers were removed from the program. By this time only four were left in the Type 62 program. They would be more useful as 'improved limited conversion' ASW frigates (Type 18). It was best not to change the planned total number of frigates. The solution was to replace the emergencies with four more Type 61 frigates (1956/7 program), which in turn would replace two planned Type 12 and two planned Type 14 in that year. The surviving five Type 62 (ex-M class) would fill the need for fast air defense escorts for carriers, as the early postwar FADE had long since vanished.

Type 62 would need much more power and

much more internal volume. An M class destroyer already had two 200kW turbo generators in her engine room, but had to add at least three 150kW diesel generators to carry salvage and other loads. Due to the radars alone, the harbor load would be 290kW. Late versions of the design showed a 250kW turbo generator in the forward boiler room (plus one diesel generator) and two diesel generators in the after boiler room; electrical power would be more than doubled.

The ships were typical of prewar or wartime practice, hence vulnerable to a major new threat; shock. Their turbine casings, gear casings, and a considerable proportion of auxiliary machinery were made of cast iron. Anti-shock mountings (which would have been extremely expensive) would not protect them. Newer ships had cast steel. To rebuild part of the machinery plant with cast steel casings was rejected, as it would have defeated the object of destroyer reconstruction: limited cost. DNC argued that the inherent risk was acceptable because the ships would be escorting merchant ships, themselves powered by shock-vulnerable cast iron machinery. DNC justified them on the ground that a new A/D frigate would cost three to five times as much as an M class conversion.

As in many postwar warships, the Type 62 design ultimately turned on internal volume, to accommodate a large action information center (CIC in US terms) with its large radar displays. By February 1954, DNC had chosen a long-forecastle design (as in the Type 15) to add volume without excessive topweight.

Then there was the issue of main armament, which through most of the design consisted of a twin 4in aft (to save topweight). In December 1953, however, the US twin 3in/50 with Mark 63 director (as supplied under the FY 53 Mutual Defence Assistance Program) replaced the twin 4in Mk 19 with CRBF. These weapons had been allocated to Type 16 limited ASW conversions. However, the latter were dropped in the early stages of the Radical Review. At the time, four single 3in/50 originally intended to rearm four *Loch* class frigates (also deleted) were reallocated to five new ocean minesweepers (which would originally have been armed entirely with FY 54 weapons). Only *Loch Insh* had proceeded very far by this time.

Within a few months, however, the Radical Review had cut deeper, and four out of the five M class conversions had been provisionally cancelled, leaving only *Musketeer*. She, too, was soon abandoned on the grounds of shock vulnerability. After all, by this time the Type 62 was conceived, not so much as a cheap convoy escort but as part of a fast carrier task force. The Type 62 project died in April 1954. Some of the money saved was used to modernize an additional destroyer. The fleet plan prior to the Radical Review had called for modernization of the entire Ca class. That was cut down to three, then adjusted up to four (and ultimately back up to the entire class).

This did not solve the fleet air defense problem; some equivalent of Type 62 was still needed. It was supplied, first by conversion of the four Weapons and then of the 1943 Battles.

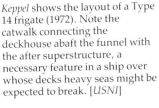

Keppel shows the layout of a Type 14 frigate (1972). Note the catwalk connecting the deckhouse abaft the funnel with the after superstructure, a necessary feature in a ship over whose decks heavy seas might be expected to break. [*USNI*]

7
MINE WARFARE

From the point of view of the two major Western navies, mine warfare was very much a double-edged sword. Given favorable Western geography, mining promised to solve a large part of the Soviet submarine problem. That was particularly important at a time when alternative ASW measures seemed unable to cope with fast submarines such as the wartime German Type XXI. Thus successive NATO war plans called for massive mining operations, both in Soviet waters and in such NATO-controlled choke points as the English Channel. In addition, the Soviets relied heavily on their inland waterways, which might be particularly susceptible to mine attack. For example, the major submarine yard at Gorky delivered its products via the Volga and lesser rivers. The Black Sea and Northern Fleets could communicate by way of a waterway system including the White Sea Canal. The US Navy could point to the lesson of Operation Starvation, in which air-dropped mines almost completely

immobilized the Japanese merchant and naval fleets during the spring and summer of 1945. For its part, the Royal Navy had used mines extensively as an ASW weapon, particularly during the coastal U-boat campaign of 1945.

At the same time, both navies were aware of their own vulnerabilities to a Soviet mining offensive. The Soviet Navy, like its Czarist forebear, was known to be an enthusiastic proponent of offensive mine warfare. All Soviet surface combatants, for example, were equipped with mine rails. British and continental ports and their approaches were all considered vulnerable to mine attack, as in World War II. After all, there would be little point in protecting ships from submarines in the open ocean, then losing them in shallow water or in ports themselves. Wartime experience showed that a very few mines could block a port for days or even weeks. However, the Soviets could expect to lay thousands of mines by airplane, fast attack boat, and submarine, since

At the end of World War II, both the US and British navies operated large numbers of steel fleet minesweepers. Magnetic mines rendered them obsolete, and no more were built. HMS *Mutine* was an *Algerine* class minesweeper, suitable for escort as well as for sweeping. In 1958, while in reserve, she had her 4in guns replaced by a single Squid forward. She retained the four single 40mm guns of her class, but did not have their depth charge tracks and throwers (with a total of 92 depth charges). *Pluto* had the prototype conversion (1950). *Hound* and *Lennox* were refitted about 1956, and similar modifications were made in 1958-59 to *Chameleon*, *Circe*, *Cockatrice*, *Espiegle*, *Melita*, *Orestes*, *Recruit*, *Rifleman*, *Wave* and *Waterwitch*. As in this case, refits were carried out while the ship was in reserve; hence the cocooned guns. Note that the projected ocean minesweeper was also to have had a single Squid forward. [MoD]

distances from their own bases were relatively short. To counter this immediate threat, the earliest US Navy program of assistance to European navies enabled them to build or buy large numbers of modern minesweepers.

The nations with direct access to the two main European choke points, the Danish Straits and the Dardanelles (Denmark, Greece and Turkey) received minelayers converted from wartime landing ships (LSM) in 1952, under the US Mutual Defense Assistance Program (MDAP). Similar logic explains why the Royal Navy retained three fast minelayers and did not convert two of her O class minelaying destroyers into frigates. Four C class destroyers were fitted as minelayers postwar.*

The US position was very different. The Soviets would probably find it difficult to mount any major mining offensive against US ports. However, mines could cancel out a major element of US offensive sea power, the amphibious assault. At Wonsan, in 1950, a combination of modern magnetic ground mines and quite primitive moored mines kept a US fleet at bay for some time.** The much more advanced types,

* Note that it took five destroyer minelayers to equal the mine outfit of one *Abdiel* class fast minelayer (156 mines), and that the destroyers could not lay so concentrated a field as fast.
** The US Navy estimated that the Soviets shipped 4000 mines, of which 3000 were laid. A total of 225 were swept to form a safe channel. The cost was four minesweepers and one fleet tug sunk and five destroyers damaged.

already in service in the West, would have presented much worse problems. Thus, the United States tended, through much of the postwar period, to lump most of its minesweepers with its amphibious assault forces. The threat to home waters (primarily small submarine-laid fields) was not discounted, and successive long-range plans did generally show a few sweepers assigned to keep US ports open. But the US Navy port clearance effort had nothing like the urgency of the contemporary British and continental programs.

Because of its concentration on amphibious assault, the US Navy ultimately needed a very different kind of minesweeper. Virtually all minesweepers were relatively small for two reasons. First, they had to be built in very large numbers because no existing sweep device could clear mines at any very great rate. Large numbers also cushioned against the inevitable heavy scale of losses. The British, for example, included over 600 sweepers in the first month of their war plan in the mid 'fifties. This was not a huge figure: in 1944, 1494 minesweepers served under Royal Navy operational control.

Second, the smaller the sweeper, the better the chance that it could avoid triggering influence (primarily magnetic, acoustic and pressure) mines. Schemes for sweeping such mines required the sweeper to tow a device which would mimic the signature of a large (hence valuable) target. the smaller the sweeper's signature, the better the

Unlike the Royal Navy, the US Navy did continue to build ocean minesweepers – using non-magnetic materials. At the time they much exceeded the formerly accepted limit on the size of modern wooden warships, and were considered a major achievement in shipbuilding technology. *Agile*, shown here, was the prototype, authorized under the FY50 program. She was designed to be able to tow two XMAP pressure countermeasures caissons, although, in fact, only one was ever built, and that proved unsuccessful. Of 93 ships built to this design, the US Navy retained 58. These ships were initially designated AM (as in World War II), then redesignated MSO (Ocean Minesweepers) in February 1955. The older steel minesweepers then became MSF. New ocean mine counter-measures ships (sweeper/hunters) coming into service in 1986 are designated MCM. Note that, unlike contemporary British minesweepers, the US postwar craft had crude minehunting sonars (UQS-1). When modernized, they were fitted with SQQ-14 variable-depth sonars. [*USN*]

chance that the mine would be triggered by the sweep rather than by the sweeper.

Small sweeper size inevitably meant limited sea speed, generally no more than 17 or 18 knots in an ocean sweeper. That was quite acceptable in World War II, when amphibious convoys rarely made as much as ten knots. After the war, however, the US Navy sought a new amphibious sustained speed standard, 20 knots, which was clearly beyond the potential of any existing craft. The US Navy therefore began to develop a minesweeping force which could be transported overseas aboard the ships of the amphibious task force. They might either be carried in the davits of the attack transports and cargo ships (which imposed a 36ft length limit) or they might be carried in the well decks of dock landing ships (in which case they could be considerably larger, but only at a cost to the task force as a whole, in terms of utility landing craft (LCU) normally carried in the same well decks). Of course, the larger the minesweeping craft, the more capable it could be. Similar considerations made minesweeping helicopters attractive. Moreover, unlike the surface sweepers, they were not vulnerable to destruction by anti-sweeper mines.

World War II began with moored contact mines, which were effective only against ships actually hitting them. They could be swept simply by cutting their mooring lines. The floating mines could then be destroyed by gunfire. Several influence mechanisms, mainly magnetic, were in production or in service.

Magnetic mines had to be laid on the sea bottom (as ground mines). Otherwise they were subject to accidental explosion as the mine rose and fell (in the earth's magnetic field) with the tide. They were, therefore, limited to relatively shallow water, since otherwise the mine would be too far from its target to cause significant damage. Magnetic mines complicated sweeper design in two ways.

First, the countermeasure, a cable loop creating a large enough magnetic field to trigger the mine far from the sweeper, absorbed considerable power. The prewar US *Raven* (AM 55) class, for example, was redesigned (as the *Auk* AM 57 class) for turbo-electric drive, so that propulsion power could be shifted to the magnetic pulse. Postwar, British inshore minesweepers were provided with three diesel engines of equal size and power, only two of which provided propulsion for the vessel. The third was dedicated to sweep pulse current generation. Sweeper design was already complicated enough, in that a relatively small hull had to accommodate sufficient power to pull a heavy sweep. This power problem would become particularly acute with the development of pressure mine sweeps such as the US XMAP. This combined requirement for relatively high power in a very small space was not too different from that imposed on fast coastal craft although, of course, there were important differences. Note that the same British high-speed diesel developed to

The US Navy built coastal minesweepers (MSC) derived directly from the wartime YMS. The design was intended specifically for transfer to foreign navies under the MDAP assistance program, and of 169 of the original *Bluebird* class built, only 20 were retained for US service. The Portuguese *Horta* is shown off New York, 22 June 1953. She is still wearing her US bow number, for AMS 61. The World War II-YMS still in service were redesignated (and re-numbered) in an AMS (minesweeper, small) series in 1947, then again redesignated MSC (Coastal Minesweeper) in February 1955. The new (1986) coastal sweeper/minehunters (MSH) are approximate equivalents. [*USN*]

Coniston shown on 11 May 1955, was the first of the very numerous Ton class British coastal minesweepers (CMS). Due in part to its sheer size, this was the most expensive single British naval program prior to the Polaris submarines. Many ships went into reserve upon completion, not because they were redundant, but because the large mine countermeasures establishment required in wartime could not be maintained in active status in peacetime. In the past, it might have been possible to convert existing trawlers. However, with improvements in mine technology, that was no longer feasible, at least on a large scale, and special ships had to be built. One alternative is to subsidize fishing companies to build craft more suitable for conversion (eg, using non-magnetic components). A CMS II minehunting version was planned but not built, as the necessary technology was not considered mature enough. *Shoulton* was converted by Vosper Thornycroft to prototype minehunter in 1957, with waterjet propulsion. Series conversions to minehunter began with *Kirkliston* in 1964, a precision sonar (Type 193) being installed beneath the bridge. Active rudders were installed, and the ship equipped with two inflatable boats for mine disposal divers. Fifteen others were later converted. Although all had their magnetic sweep gear removed, some could tow acoustic noisemakers. [*MoD*]

power British coastal craft, the novel Deltic, was also adapted (in de-rated form) to British coastal sweepers. Because it attained some of its light weight by aluminum construction, it was inherently non-magnetic.*

Second, the sweeper itself had to avoid triggering the mine. It was therefore degaussed. The magnetic field of the ship varied as the earth's field around her varied, for example as she changed heading. Full degaussing therefore involved elaborate sensors of the magnetic field remaining as the various coils were energized. Just how much degaussing was needed depended on how much magnetic material the sweeper contained.

World War II magnetic mines were insensitive enough that steel sweepers could be degaussed to avoid triggering them. Wooden hulls were chosen for some of the smaller sweepers of that period, such as the US YMS (British BYMS) and the British MMS for ease of production, rather than for any anti-magnetic virtues. Engines, for example, represented a considerable magnetic mass.

By the end of the war, however, magnetic mines were considerably more sensitive. Postwar sweeper designs took this increased sensitivity into account. All US ocean, coastal and inshore sweepers were built of non-magnetic materials. They suffered badly in service, though, because their non-magnetic engines tended to be unreliable. British coastal and inshore sweepers were originally designed with composite construction, with aluminum alloy decks, framing, and bulkheads, and double skin mahogany

planking.** However, the British did retain steel construction for a proposed new class of ocean sweepers. Magnetic mines would be much less important in deep water, due to tidal effects. Only later were moored magnetic (total field) mines developed. The steel ocean sweeper fell victim to the Radical Review (it was cancelled in January, 1955), but the Royal Navy recently built a series of modern steel hulled ocean sweepers (River class). Presumably, the argument is that they can be sufficiently well degaussed to deal with deep-water fields.

Acoustic mines, responding to the sound of a ship's propeller or engines, could be laid on the bottom or moored in deeper water. Sweepers were silenced to avoid triggering them, and the mines were generally swept by noise-making, either by means of an acoustic hammer mounted in the bows of a sweeper, or by a towed noisemaker or explosive sweep. Postwar, the Royal Navy developed a 'petrol-air-acoustic' sweep which it considered superior, as it was easier to tune over a wide range of possible acoustic mine settings.

In both the acoustic and the magnetic cases, then, sweeping consisted of presenting the mine with a triggering signature comparable to that of a ship. There were several counter-countermeasures, most notably ship counters (to allow several sweepers to pass before exploding under a valuable target) and arming delays. The latter might protect a mine against sweeps. The

---

* It seems remarkable in retrospect that gas turbines, which at one time seemed to solve the power/weight problem for small fast attack craft, were not used to power minesweepers. Note, however, that gas turbine sweep generators were installed in US 57ft minesweeping boats (MSBs). Reasons may have included the lack of a unit of suitable power, and the noise and electric signature associated with gas turbines.

** However, US experiments showed that aluminum was not acceptable because eddy currents, which induced magnetic fields, could be set up in it. The British therefore had to redesign with laminated wood frames. American estimates (1951) showed that the aluminum-framed British sweeper had about two to three times the magnetic signature of the American coastal types. The US ocean sweeper was expected to have an even smaller signature. Note, however, that the French version of the design (*Sirius* class) and the somewhat larger Canadian 'Bay' continued to use composite construction.

Cranham was typical of a numerous Ham class of inshore minesweepers (IMS). IMS Type 11 was an inshore minehunter (Ley class). She is shown on 31 May 1954. She was laid up that fall, and spent her life in Operational Reserve, being sold in 1966. [MoD]

Dingley was built as an inshore minehunter (IMS Type II). Compared to Cranham, note the absence of sweep gear and the extended deckhouse for the minehunting sonar. The Leys also had smaller engines, as they did not require towing power. The object next to the davit is an inflatable diver-support boat; note also her boat boom and the Dan buoys. Divers were an essential element of minehunting because of the failure of efforts (both US and British) to develop mine-detection sonars good enough that objects they found could be destroyed by special shipboard mortars. The mortars were precise enough, but the rate of false contacts was so high that they would soon have exhausted their ammunition. The current alternative is a small remote-control submersible equipped with underwater television. Dingley was designated for disposal in 1967, and was sold in 1968. [MoD]

swept area would be declared safe – after which the mine would arm itself to destroy ships passing through a supposedly safe channel. In 1950, US and British mine countermeasures were based on the assumption that mines could count up to 11 ships (hence had to be swept 12 times) and that arming delays of up to ten days were possible (against which war channels would have to be swept very frequently). These two considerations alone would have required extremely large sweeper fleets, and the explain the scale of postwar construction.***

The pressure (Oyster) mine was an even more difficult proposition. Devised roughly simultaneously by both Germans and Allies, it was triggered by a signature virtually impossible to simulate without using a real ship. Lying on the bottom in shallow water, it was, therefore, unsweepable, a threat so severe that the US Navy had delayed its introduction for fear that the Germans (who, it turned out, had pressure mines of their own) would copy it. Thus, the US Navy began production (for the aerial mining campaign against Japan) only after the Germans had employed pressure mines off Normandy in 1944. In addition, the RAF mined German coastal waters

with pressure mines late in the war.

The signature in question was one of the most basic of all, the drop in water pressure (due to a change in effective water depth) as a ship passed over. It would, therefore, have to be laid on the bottom in relatively shallow water, where it had only to distinguish between the pressure drop due to a ship and the pressure drop due to the shift of the tide. The difference was that the tide changed relatively slowly, whereas the pressure change due to a ship was relatively quick. A small ship, then, could hope to avoid triggering pressure mines if it moved over them slowly enough. Since the critical speed fell as ship size increased, large and valuable ships would always tend to trigger such mines. The critical combination of size and speed depended on mine technology. As in the

*** Many British coastal and inshore minesweepers were laid up as soon as they were completed. Some writers, therefore, have assumed that the minesweeper program was poorly planned, perhaps little more than an attempt to maintain small British yards in business. However, it would never have been possible for the Royal Navy to man a wartime-scale mine countermeasures force in peacetime while also carrying out its essential cold-war duties. The sweepers were held in reserve because they could not have been extemporized fast enough in an emergency. They became an embarassment only after the Radical Review, and then the Admiralty did argue that to cut the program too abruptly would cause serious economic problems. It is not clear whether this argument was really advanced because some within the Navy suspected that the Radical Review strategy might represent too sanguine an assumption.

SENSORS
1 ASDIC TYPE 164
2 IFF TRANSPONDER
3 HDWS RADAR (974)
4 VHF RADIO ANTENNA
5 HF WHIPS
6 UHF RADIO ANTENNA

WEAPONS
7 SQUID
8 40mm BOFORS GUN
9 3in/50 GUN
10 MK 63 DIRECTOR
11 2in ROCKET FLARE LAUNCHER
12 ROCKET FLARES FOR LAUNCHER
13 3in MAGAZINE AND DIESEL OIL TANKS
14 BOFORS MAGAZINES
15 SQUID PROJECTILE STOWAGE
16 ASDIC INSTRUMENT ROOM AND SQUID METADYNE
17 MAGNETIC SWEEP CABLE DRUM
18 MINESWEEPING WINCH
19 DAN BUOY STOWAGE
20 MINESWEEPING DAVIT
21 OTTER
22 MINESWEEPING FLOATS (PORT AND STARBOARD)
23 MINESWEEPING STOWAGE
23A EXPLOSIVE SWEEP MAGAZINE

OTHER
24 AUXILIARY MACHINERY
25 SEAMENS' MESS
26 COLD AND COOL STOWAGE
27 WINDLASS
28 CABLE LOCKER
29 ENCLOSED COMPASS PLATFORM
30 WHEELHOUSE
31 CAPTAIN'S ACCOMMODATION
32 OPERATIONS ROOM (CIC), ASDIC CONTROL ROOM
33 MESSES
34 FUEL OIL
35 COFFERDAM
36 RESERVE FEED WATER
37 BOILER ROOM
38 CONTROL ROOM
39 TURBINE
40 DOMESTIC BOILERS IN THIS SPACE (STARBOARD)
41 CANTEEN
42 OFFICERS
43 POTATO AND VEGETABLE LOCKERS
44 27ft WHALEBOAT, 14ft SAILING DINGHY; CABINS
45 GEARING ROOM
46 SEAMENS' MESS
47 PO MESS
48 SICK BAY
49 STEERING GEAR

The proposed fleet minesweeper, October 1954

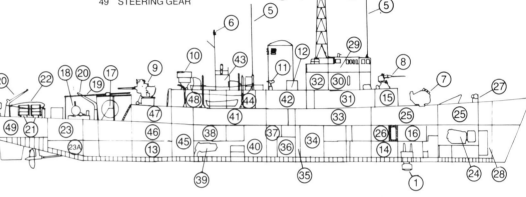

The US Navy first produced underwater object locators or minehunters (AMCU) during World War II: six LCT(6) were reclassified AMCU 1-6, and five infantry landing craft (LCIL) became AMCU 7-11 on 10 March 1945. Further conversions followed in 1951-3: AMCU 12-14 and 44-50 were former wooden coastal minesweepers (YMS or their PCS patrol craft counterparts) and AMCU 15-42 were former infantry landing ships (LSIL, formerly designated LCIL). Seven of the latter were not converted as planned. Nine of the LSIL were not recommissioned. In addition, one ship, *Bittern*, was specially built as a minehunter (AMCU 43, later MHC 43). AMCU 13, *James M Gillis*, had been converted to a surveying ship in 1945, and then converted to AMCU at New York Naval Shipyard. She was recommissioned on 5 September 1951, and is shown on 18 June 1952. Her most visible minehunting features are the prominent Dan buoys (to mark safe channels) around her funnel and the diver support boat on her quarterdeck. [*USN*]

case of wartime magnetic mines, early pressure mines were relatively coarsely set, and fairly large ships could evade them by moving slowly enough. Postwar improvements made that more and more difficult, so that ultimately only a ship as small as a minesweeper or minehunter could be considered immune.*

The earliest pressure mines responded entirely to changes in water pressure, and so could cometimes be triggered by heavy waves or even by the turn of the tide. Off Normandy, for example, waves triggered the few German oysters. However, it was relatively simple to combine a pressure sensor with a magnetic or acoustic sensor which would protect the mine against such natural phenomena. Then it became, in effect, unsweepable.

Conventional sweeping techniques either cut mine cables or simulated the signatures which triggered mines. The pressure mine was immune to both. Since it always lay on the bottom, it had no tethering cable to cut. The natural approach was signature simulation. Unfortunately, that required something approaching the size of a valuable ship. To be cost-effective, it would have to be explosion-proof, since it would suffer mining each time it triggered. The Germans actually ran converted merchant ships (*Sperrbrechers***) through minefields to clear them. The Allied navies developed several towed ship-simulators. Examples included the British stirling craft and the US egg crate.

Several similar devices were tried postwar. The

Most of the US minehunters were converted landing craft (LCIL/LSIL). Externally, they were little modified, as this photograph of *Cockatoo* (AMCU-21, from astern, 1954) shows.

* An alternative concept, in which a ship might travel over the mine so fast that the mine would respond only after it had passed, was tried several times both during and after World War II.

** Note, however, that the *Sperrbrechers* preceded the Allied pressure mining campaign. They were initially intended to detonate magnetic mines, which is why they had large coils wrapped around their hulls.

At the end of World War II, the US Navy built four small minesweeping boats (MSB). Although too large to be carried in standard amphibious ship davits, they could be transported aboard landing ship docks (LSDs). This is the first of a new series begun in the early 'fifties: *MSB5*, newly completed by John Trumpy Boat Works, 21 January 1953. The prominent uptakes abaft the bridge lead from her gas turbine magnetic sweep generator, the first use of such a powerplant in an operational US ship. [*USN*]

US Navy devised a 2500-ton armored cylinder, XMAP, which a sweeper could tow. It was abandoned as too expensive, too unwieldy – and too vulnerable to the explosion of a mine. The Royal Navy continued to experiment with two wartime ideas, the fabric sweep (a fabric cone or tube) and the barge. Fabric could not be towed in water less than six fathoms deep or it would touch bottom, hence the need for the barge as well. Both

were described as difficult to handle, sweeping only a narrow path, and vulnerable to mine explosion. By 1952, it seemed fundamental that displacement sweeps such as these could not sweep pressure mines set to greater tonnages. They could, therefore, protect only ships of less than about 2000 tons.

Both navies also tried the simulation approach already in use in the cases of magnetic and acoustic mines, in forms such as long-pulse acoustic generators and even hydrogen peroxide driven pulsers. None was effective. Nor did the US Navy ultimately adopt an alternative, proposed in the late 'forties, which it had developed: a large bottom-clearing net loaded with explosives, which two small minesweepers could tow. Pressure mines are still essentially unsweepable four decades later.

That left a much more painful and tedious alternative, to seek and destroy mines one by one by minehunting, which was already in use in rudimentary form in 1945. Note, however, that the pressure mine was not so dominant as to make earlier types, even the moored contact mine, obsolete. thus quite conventional minesweepers continued to be built in large numbers after World War II.

Perhaps worst of all, in 1945 further 'unsweepable' mine mechanisms were in prospect. The Germans had devised at least two: the cosmic-ray mine and the gravity mine. The

Inshore mine warfare, as in Korea, required very small minesweepers, which could be transported to the area aboard larger ships. The US Navy converted many of its standard motor launches for his role, often transferring them to friendly governments. This 40ft minesweeping launch was photographed at Long Beach Naval Shipyard on 26 September 1952. [*USN*]

cosmic ray mine measured the increase in radiation as a ship passing overhead effectively reduced the depth of water, and therefore the amount of shielding against cosmic rays. The gravitational mine responded to the subtle change in the earth's gravitational field due to the reduced density of water overhead, as a ship passed. In 1945, the US Naval Technical Mission to Europe dismissed both as somewhat fanciful attempts by their inventors to avoid service on the eastern front. Three years later, however, the US Bureau of Ordnance was actively pursuing both, and a technical intelligence report on Soviet naval capabilities considered them significant enough to note that the Soviets had not captured German work on either mechanism.

Although nothing seems to have come of these ideas, they are a good illustration of just how far mine developers were prepared to go, even in 1945.

Both in the United States and in Britain, minehunting supplanted attempts to sweep pressure mines. In theory, the minehunter would locate and identify mines one by one, using such instruments as a high-definition sonar and perhaps a metal detector (like that of a land mine locator). It would then have to destroy them one by one, perhaps recovering a few of them for examination (to develop new countermeasures). High-definition sonars already existed; the US Navy fitted one to its submarines to assist them in evading buoyant mines while entering Japanese

home waters. The obvious complementary weapon was a mine-destroying mortar, similar, perhaps, to Squid. Weapons of this type were developed independently by both navies, but they were never successful, and therefore they were never brought into service.

Instead, the minehunter of the 'fifties supported divers, who would examine and destroy mines one by one, using hand-held sonars and small explosive charges. The next step, in the early 'sixties, was a remote-controlled underwater vehicle. The US Navy devised Sea Nettle, a small wire-guided torpedo with its own small sonar. It was guided by the ship's minehunting sonar. Sea Nettle never entered service, however. Current systems, such as the French PAP-104 and the US mine neutralization system, employ small recoverable submersibles, also guided on the basis of shipborne sonar data, but depositing explosive charges on the mine rather than exploding themselves atop it. These submersibles have onboard cameras, and, at least in the case of the US Mine Neutralization System, an onboard high-definition sonar for what amounts to terminal guidance.

None of this evolving technology could solve the basic problems of minehunting. The basic sensor, a high-frequency (for high definition) sonar, could have only a very short range. That in turn made a low search rate inevitable. Even so, it might miss mines in hollows on the bottom, or even buried in the silt of the bottom. The false

For the US Navy, minesweeping often meant *assault sweeping*, in which case the minesweeping force had to be as mobile as the assault force. The solution was to carry what amounted to miniature sweepers. Conversions of former amphibious ships were planned as early as 1955, but they were not carried out for a decade. This is USS *Ozark* (MCS2), newly converted, on 31 August 1966. Her davits carry 20 specially-bulit minesweeping launches (MSLs), the successors to Korean War motor launches and converted landing craft. Note also the helicopter pad and hangar aft, for two minesweeping helicopters. This was a transitional phase for US mine countermeasures. Within a few years the launches would be eliminated altogether in favor of larger numbers of helicopters carried aboard amphibious carriers (LPH). [*USN*]

Given the naval geography of the Soviet Union, offensive minelaying was a natural NATO strategy. Minelayers would include submarines, surface ships – and carrier and land-based aircraft. As Appendix III shows, the US Navy had several squadrons of specialized minelayers. However, all of its attack aircraft could lay aerial mines, of the type which had paralyzed Japan in 1945. This is a Skyraider loaded with three Mark 25 Mod 2 2000-pound pressure mines, 21 June 1949. No one has yet found a simple countermeasure to such weapons: Mark 25 was still in use three decades later. [USN]

alarm rate would inevitably be high. Mines could, moreover, be camouflaged, shaped, for example, like rocks. A metal detector could not solve these problems, since mines did not have to be metallic. In 1952, for example, a British analysis of the prospects for minehunting suggested that clearance divers (not divers directed by minehunters) might have to be used to clear water less then three fathoms deep.

Worst of all, unlike minesweeping, minehunting could not guarantee that any given area was clear. It was so expensive, moreover, in terms of time and effort, that it was inconceivable to run a flotilla of hunters through an area which might or might not be mined. Even if an anti-mine mortar were perfected, quick clearance would require lavish expenditure of its ammunition on all contacts, confirmed or not. The usual solution was to run a special 'guinea pig' over a swept area to check the efficacy of the sweep. At least from 1948 onwards, for example, the US Navy formalized this procedure with instruction for the conversion of surplus merchant ships (eg, with all engine controls led to the bridge, furthest from any explosion, and special anti-shock seats for the limited number of personnel aboard).

The US Navy acquired five Liberty ships in 1952-53, converting them to 'guinea pigs' (YAG 36-40) at Yokosuka, with remote engine room controls on their bridges. One of them, YAG 37 (ex *John L Sullivan*), was reactivated in 1957 and converted from conventional propulsion (which would be vulnerable to mine explosion) to power by four deck-mounted T34 turbo props. She was tested against underwater explosions in Chesapeake Bay, then broken up in 1958. A sixth Liberty ship, the former *Harry L Glucksman*, was converted to a 'special' minesweeper under the FY66 program (completed August, 1969), with over-the-side (in effect, outboard motor) propulsion and shock-mounted control positions

and auxiliary machinery. Her hull was filled with plastic foam.

This was the technical base against which the Western navies had to contemplate a Soviet mining offensive. The Royal Navy expected Soviet bombers, submarines, and perhaps coastal craft (the equivalent of the German E-boats) to lay 4500 to 6000 mines per month in British coastal waters. In 1950, it was estimated that, given aggressive minesweeping by the forces which would be in place within two years, 25-30 mines would be required to sink one merchant ship. If, then, the acceptable loss rate was 50 merchant ships per month, Britain could tolerate 1500 to 2000 mines per month.

Such figures were based on World War II practice. The war channel had to be swept *frequently* (against arming delay), separately for different types (moored, magnetic, acoustic, pressure), and 12 times to overcome ship counters. It would need thousands of sweepers; even to sweep essential channels for only one actuation daily, or with one wire sweep (against moored mines) would need three times the total peacetime force.

Some alternative concept of mine counter-measures was needed. It had to take into account active measures against the minelayers, as well as what amounted to cover and deception. Unfortunately, it had to be accepted that fighters would generally concentrate on bombers attacking British cities, and therefore that the most efficient minelayers, the bombers, would be able to operate almost unhindered. Surely, however, offensive mining would make it more difficult for Soviet submarines and fast surface craft to enter British waters.

First, mine hunting efficiency could be maximized if the initial locations of the mines was known. Visual minewatching (to locate aircraft-laid mines) had been effective in World War II. Now a special minewatching radar was devised. Experiments in underwater minewatching (presumably through the use of harbor defense sonars) also began.

Second, once a channel had been cleared, it had to be concealed, to make re-mining difficult. The narrower the cleared channel, moreover, the more difficult to plant mines precisely in it. In 1950, as in World War II, the standard means of marking a clear channel had been the dan buoy, visible to enemy as well as to friend. Now, however, the British introduced a Leader Cable, to be laid on the bottom in water less than 30 fathoms deep. In deeper water, ships could navigate much more precisely, using the Decca electronic system. In neither case could a bomber pilot easily locate the clear channel, in order to replenish it with mines. Moreover, as long as the new 'invisible' techniques could be kept secret, dan buoys could be laid to deceive an enemy and so cause him to waste mines, replenishing unswept channels. Leader was particularly attractive because it made for very narrow paths which would be difficult to

re-mine even if they were located.

In August 1952, the British Director of Torpedo, Mine, and ASW Division (DTASW) credited Leader and minewatching with increasing the number of mines per ship loss to 45-50, so that existing or programed British resources could deal with the accepted threat.

This did not mean that the problem had been solved, only that it had been reduced to the point where is was solvable. DTASW emphasized that:

— The fact that the British could not yet sweep pressure mines must be kept secret;

— the British intention to use leader cable must be kept secret. Britain might well be able to deceive the enemy into thinking she was still using buoyed channels;

— the British plan to employ Decca or super-Decca for navigation in deeper waters must be concealed;

— minehunting progress and techniques had to be kept secret.

Beyond these concerns, however, was the greater problem that many outside the Royal Navy had no idea of the extent to which Britain depended on waterborne trade, and hence of her vulnerability to a future coastal mining campaign. For example, London depended for her power on coal brought by sea into the Thames. In this sense British Government decisions quite outside the scope of the Navy, such as stockpiling or changes in the British rail network, might have profound effects on British naval vulnerability. By 1953,

DTASW could say only that he had succeeded in bringing most British naval officers to some understanding of how important mine countermeasures would be.

As of 1949, the Royal Navy had 60 ocean sweepers, 77 coastal MMS (34 on loan), 32 minesweeping motor launches, and 92 earmarked trawlers (only 68 of which could be used in coastal waters because of safe depth limitations). Despite severe fiscal problems, the Royal Navy planned to build three new classes: an ocean-going steel sweeper, an improved version of the wartime *Algerine* (five ships), a 300-ton coastal sweeper (73 ships), and a 100-ton inshore sweeper (62 ships). In addition, there would be 36 minehunters, based on the coastal and inshore sweeper hulls. At the end of the war the modern British minesweeping force had amounted to 161 ocean sweepers and 424 coastal sweepers (140 BYMS, 284 MMS), exclusive of converted motor launches. The minimal 1949 figures grew through the pre-Radical Review fleet plans. Thus a 1950 estimate of British forces required to meet NATO and overseas commitments showed a total of 125 ocean sweepers (61 available in 1954 according to current planning), and 148 inshore sweepers (118 available in 1954). By May 1954 the new construction plan showed five ocean sweepers, 167 coastal sweepers, and 115 inshore sweepers, plus coastal and inshore mine hunters. In fact, only 118 coastal sweepers, 37 inshore sweepers, and ten inshore mine hunters were completed.

The United States converted nine medium landing ships to coastal minelayers in 1952-54; this is the Danish *Beskytteren* shortly after her transfer at the New York Navy Yard, 10 June 1954. The landing ship well deck was converted to a mine deck, with two mine rails, and the ship was armed with four twin 40mm and six 20mm guns. She could carry 100 to 300 mines. Two others were transferred to Greece in 1953, two to Norway, and three to Turkey. The Norwegian ships were retransferred to Turkey in 1960. A further coastal minelayer was built in Denmark for Turkey under the US Military Assistance Program in 1962. In 1971, the United States transferred the destroyer minelayer *Robert H Smith*, which became the Turkish *Muavenet*. The survivor of a class of twelve such ships, she retained her minelaying rails, and can carry 80 mines. In addition, four war-built *Auk*-class fleet minesweepers were converted into coastal minelayers for Norway in 1960-62, one in a Norwegian yard. Additional large minelayers were built or converted by the other NATO countries and by Japan, which also faces strategic straits leading from Soviet naval operating areas. [*USN*]

The steel ocean sweeper, which was not built, was an improved and somewhat enlarged version of the wartime *Algerine,* the most obvious difference being its armament: a single Squid (with 34 rounds) forward (with Types 164 and 147 Asdic) and a US-supplied single 3in/50 aft, plus two single 40mm guns and two 2in rocket flare launchers. Thus, like the *Algerine,* it would have served as a coastal ASW escort. Its legend was approved by the Board in January 1953 for the 1953-54 program, based on staff requirements dated June 1952. However, in January 1955, it was deleted from the 1953-54 program as a result of the Radical Review.

Displacement would have been 1522 tons deeply loaded (237ft LOA x 38ft 6in x 10ft 6½in fwd, 11ft 4¾in aft; 5000shp geared double reduction turbines would have driven it all 11.5 knots while towing a sweep or at 17.5 knots when free. The design included an improved degaussing system with automatic course correction and silenced propellers. The proposed electrical generating plant suggests the extent of magnetic sweeping requirements: one 350kW turbo generator for ship services, but one of 375kW for sweeping. Two 150kW diesels were provided for salvage and harbor loads.

The more urgently needed coastal and inshore designs had been developed earlier, and improved by the Board as early as 1949. The coastal sweeper (Ton class) staff requirement demanded a higher sweep speed, 12 knots rather than the eight knots of the past. To provide, simultaneously, full engine towing (with a nine ton pull) and full magnetic pulse power required five times the power to drive the ship herself at 12 knots, which in turn made the development of the new lightweight Deltic crucial to the success of the design. Non-magnetic construction and improved degaussing were expected to halve the current safe depth of eight fathoms.

The Deltic was not yet in production, and alternative commercial Mirrlees and EEC the latter not, in the event, used) diesels would reduce sweeping speed to 11 or 11.5 knots (1920 or 2300 rather than 2500bhp). Deep displacement would be 336 tons (152ft LOA x 28ft x 6ft 6in fwd, 7ft 7in aft); endurance would be 3000nm at 10 knots.

The smaller inshore sweeper (Ham class) began as 80ft but the design finally submitted for Board approval was 100ft long on the waterline (106ft 4½in LOA x 20ft 6in x 4ft 6½in fwd, 6ft ¼in aft, 114 tons fully loaded). Like the coastal sweeper, its success depended upon a new lightweight diesel, in this case the Paxman YHX 12 (350 BHP on each of two shafts). A minehunting version (Ley class) would have a Type 144 sonar, large for so small a hull, as well as a Triple Echo Sounder, Contact Indicator System, and an Underwater Ordnance Locator, a US magnetic metal detector. It would support divers, and would have a one and a half ton derrick to lift recovered mines for examination.

A parallel US program was intended mainly for MDAP. It began with the AMS (later MSC), an adaptation of the wartime YMS design, but larger in order to recapture depleted weight margins, and to obtain better sweeping capabilities. It had greater magnetic sweeping current, a smaller magnetic signature, better stability and better seaworthiness. A new large sweeper was designed, not so much for ocean service, as to tow the big pressure sweep (XMAP) and the new large sweep cable, which was expected to increase the width of a swept path from 124 to 175 yards. Thus it was, in effect, a large coastal sweeper, and had to be non-magnetic.

The AMS was smaller than the British 'Ton', but it had a more powerful generator (for a 5000 ampere current, compared to 3000 in the British ship, in each case using .04 ohm cable) and hence could be expected to sweep a wider path, estimated at 116 to 124 rather than 64 yards.

Canada, France, the Netherlands, Portugal, and Yugoslavia built the British 'Ton' class in modified form, and France and Italy the British 'Ham'. Most of the US AMS/MSC were built in the United States, but a number were built in Europe in Belgian, Italian, and Norwegian yards.

Most of the US minehunters were converted surplus infantry landing ships (LSIL); only one ship, USS *Bittern,* was specially built as a hunter (MHC). Others were former coastal sweepers (YMS).

Meanwhile, in Korea, the US Navy was developing its alternative approach to minesweeping, using minesweeping boats (MSB) and helicopters for mine-spotting (not yet for sweeping; that was first tried in the late 'fifties). The wooden MSB could sweep to 3 fathoms but needed a carrier, usually a Landing Ship Dock (LSD), since it was too large to swing from attack transport davits. The war-built 220 ft steel AM was used to plot and control the MSBs, and as the area element command ship for wooden AMS – which could sweep influence mines inside the 30 fathom curve. It had good endurance, was independent of logistic support, and was liked for its high speed when streaming sweep gear over long coastal areas. Its magnetic signature was not considered a problem, as the AMS was available for influence minesweeping. Compared to the larger ship, the AMS had insufficient self-support. Topweight problems caused the removal of all ASW equipment, the 3in/50 gun, the CW radio, and much else. The wooden AMS, built in World War II, also experienced increasing maintenance problems.

The MSB concept was a direct descendent of World War II practice, when motor launches and small landing craft had been converted for limited minesweeping. According to a US report of the time, it 'has largely come into its own during the Korean War ... A comparison of results obtained by these boats with the scores attained by vessels of many times their acquisition cost would indicate the advisability of completely re-evaluating mine force types'. However, the MSB sweep could not be accepted as 100 per cent clearance of moored mines.

Helicopters proved valuable for locating moored mines ahead of MSBs and AMSs; they could spot floating mines in low surface vision, greatly reducing the hazard to the lead echelon in sweeping for moored mines. An LSD fitted with a mezzanine deck could carry both MSB's and helicopters. It was, however, quite valuable in its original amphibious role. By 1955, the US Navy had developed a future sweeping concept in which a specialized mother ship (the MCS) would carry both boats and helicopters to the amphibious objective area. The MSB was too large for a davit, so a smaller Minesweeping Launch (MSL) was developed. The wartime vehicle cargo ships (LSVs, originally laid down as fast minelayers) were earmarked for future conversion, and two of them actually converted in 1963-67, each operating 20 MSL and two minesweeping helicopters. One LSD and one LST also served as mine countermeasures support ships. From the early 'seventies on, all of these ships were superseded by minesweeping helicopters based aboard amphibious assault carriers.

NATO requirements for minelaying are typified by those assigned by SACLANT to the UK in 1952:
— Baltic exits, Elbe and approaches (by *Opportune* class destroyer minelayers);
— Dover Barrage. (In World War II 3000 mines were laid there beginning eight days after war was declared. Future plans called for mining to start on D-Day);
— Black Sea exits;
— the Danube;
— defensive fields around the UK;
— Soviet submarine bases and training areas.

Postwar, the Royal Navy did not manufacture new mines, although it continued some research, and tested a new mine shape suitable for laying by the new fast carrier aircraft. The US Navy continued both production and stockpiling, emphasizing both ASW and weapons suitable to disrupt Soviet inland waterways. In 1948, as US rearmament began, the stockpile goal was 25,000 to 50,000 mines on M-day, a goal which the US Navy expected to reach by 1953. Its long-range mine development program was to have been completed by 1957. By 1952 there were to have been 500-, 1000-, and 2000-pound aircraft-laid ground mines; aircraft laid moored-sweeping obstructors, and aircraft-laid moored 500- and 2000-pound mines; and general purpose surface-ship laid mines with 300 or 500 pounds of explosives. The rest of the program comprised submarine-laid ground, moored, and torpedo mines (like the current US Mark 67, a converted torpedo which can be fired into position from a safe distance); aircraft-laid 4000-pound ground mines; ASW or anti-invasion and beach mines to be laid by surface ships; 25- to 50-pound drifting mines to be laid in clusters by aircraft; and moored homing mines to be laid by aircraft, surface ships, or submarines. There would be maximum component standardization, for faster production.

The US equivalents of global strategy and then of the Radical Review much reduced this program; the waterway and anti-invasion mine projects survived, but with very limited funding. The big air-laid mines were actually used in the Hanoi-Haiphong operation in 1972. In addition, the United States developed a series of 'destructors', bombs with mine triggering mechanisms, that were quite effective in Vietnamese waterways and presumably would have fulfilled the requirements set out in 1948.

As in the case of ASW, all of these ideas are probably more important now than they have been for the past 20 or 30 years, since, like submarine warfare, mining becomes more and more productive (or destructive) as a war continues. Thus the very small number of minecraft now serving in NATO navies is probably more unpleasant to contemplate now than it has been for several decades. After all, the fundamental problem of countering the pressure mine still has not been solved.

The destroyer minelayer *Opportune* acting as escort to the *Vanguard*, February 1947. Her sisters *Obdurate* and *Obedient* were retained postwar as active minelayers, and consequently survived longer than any of their sisters that were not converted to Type 16 frigates. [CPL]

8

SUBMARINES

Western submarine development during the decade after 1945 was a combination of a new operational concept, the fast snorkel-equipped submarine, and a combination of new submarine roles, particularly in the US Navy. The great irony was that the US submarine force, which had sunk much of the Japanese naval and merchant fleets, would find many fewer targets in any future war against the Soviets, who had almost no merchant fleet. Postwar development effort was justified partly by the need to explore the implications of the new propulsion technology (which the Soviets would surely use against the West). It was generally agreed that ASW forces would be unable to develop appropriate counters unless they could operate against submarine forces, themselves aggressively developing both technology and tactics.

In 1948, the Admiralty made ASW the primary British submarine mission. As in contemporary US thinking, attention was concentrated on the need for long-range passive sonars coupled with high-performance ASW homing torpedoes. On the other hand, the Royal Navy did not then go so far as to develop a specialized mass production ASW submarine such as the US K class.

Both Britain and the United States exploited the new technology in two ways. First, they converted

substantial numbers of existing submarines to incorporate as much as possible of the new technology represented by the German Type XXI U-Boat. This class, the prototype of postwar fast submarines, had four main features: it could dive more deeply than its predecessors, it had a much greater battery capacity (which required increased hull volume), it was highly streamlined and had more powerful electric motors (for higher underwater speed), and it had a snorkel.

The earliest intelligence of Type XXI was obtained in 1944, from intercepted and de-crypted reports by the Japanese Naval Attaché to Berlin. Since the new submarine represented a new underwater problem, the Royal Navy converted the submarine *Seraph* for high underwater speed. Battery volume was obtained by removing engines, so that she could run at very high speed for a short time, but had to spend considerable time after that recharging. *Scotsman* was similarly modified postwar to allow her to achieve 17 knots for 40 minutes.

Postwar, then, US fleet submarines and British T class submarines were converted for high sustained underwater speed. There were also more limited conversions. Most British submarines were fitted with snorkels but otherwise largely unaltered. The parallel US 'fleet

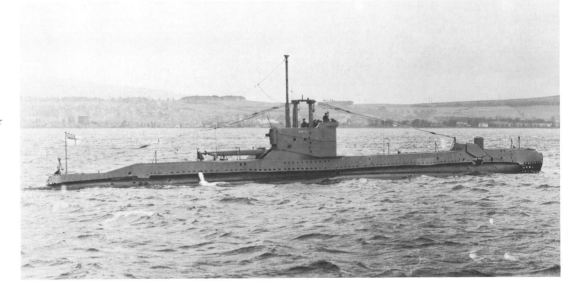

After World War II, the Royal Navy installed snorkels on most of its submarines, removing their deck guns as a minimum streamlining measure. A German-type snorkel was tried successfully in *Truant* in 1945, and similar modifications ordered for the new A class and for most other British submarines. *Subtle* is shown in 1953, with her snorkel folded down on deck abaft her fairwater. Aside from the removal of her gun, she is in wartime condition. [*MoD*]

snorkel' conversion entailed streamlining of the bridge structure. In most cases deck guns were removed, as the submarine was expected to spend most of its time submerged.

SUBMARINE CHARACTERISTICS

	T CLASS	T CLASS (Converted)	A CLASS	PORPOISE (B Class)
L (PRESSURE HULL) (ft)	244	258	—	—
LWL (ft,in)	268,6	271,1½	272,9	281,6
LOA (ft,in)	273,6	285,4	277,9	285,3
BEAM (ft,in)	26,6	26,6¾	22,3	26,6
SURFACE DISPLACEMENT	1325	1565	1360	1942
STANDARD DISPLACEMENT	1090	1260	1120	1526
SUBMERGED DISPLACEMENT	1575	1680	1590	2260
DIVING DEPTH (feet)	300	350	500	625
SURFACE SHP	2500	2500	4300	3680
SURFACE SPEED (knots)	15.75	15	19	15
OIL FUEL (tons)	134	210	224	221.5
ENDURANCE (nm/knots)	10,100/10	11,500/12	12,200/10	11,500/10
CELLS	336	448	224	448
MOTORS	4	8	4	4
SUBMERGED SHP	1150	6000	1250	6000
SUBMERGED SPEED (knots)	9	17	8	17
SPEED (1 HOUR) (knots)	9	14.5	8	15.5
ENDURANCE (8 knots)	—	11	—	—
ENDURANCE (4 knots)	21	—	20	38
SNORT SPEED (knots)	—	10	9	11
SNORT ENDURANCE (nm/knots)	—	4700	4130/8	5870/10
FWD TT (torpedoes)	8 (17 TOTAL)	6	6 (10)	6 (8)
AFT TT (torpedoes)	3	1	4 (10)	2 (3)
COMPLEMENT	60	—	60	70
WEIGHTS (tons):				
TORPEDOES	70	—	73	84
GUNS	10	—	10	1.5
MACHINERY	105	—	142	77
BATTERY	146	—	116	231.5
MOTORS	36	—	36	52
GENERATORS	—	—	—	18
W/T, RADAR, A/S	—	—	7	19
STORES, PROVISIONS	—	—	10	17.5
CREW, EFFECTS	—	—	6	10
EQUIPMENT, FITTINGS	32	—	6	10
FRESH WATER	56	—	24	35.5
TRIM, COMP. WATER	56	—	34	77.5
HULL	718	—	415	638
FIXED BALLAST	718	—	14	16.5

NOTE: In the *Porpoise* class, the three after torpedoes are half length, eg, US Mark 37s.

Faced with reports of fast (16 knots submerged) German submarines early in 1944, the Royal Navy converted HMS *Seraph* as a high-speed target. She was drastically streamlined and fitted with T class propellers, which had a greater pitch. As a result, she achieved 12.52 knots underwater, compared to 8.82 knots in an unconverted S class submarine. *Seraph* was completed in August 1944, and *Satyr, Statesman, Selene, Solent* and *Sleuth* were converted to similar fast targets. *Seraph* was ultimately used as a live torpedo target, heavily padded (as here) to avoid damage. She is shown on 1 April 1958. [*MoD*]

Compared to a Type XXI, a full conversion was about as fast and might even handle better underwater. Its primary drawback was that it could dive only about half as deep. Thus a Type XXI could hide beneath the 'layer depth' in the North Atlantic, about 600ft down. A full conversion British or US submarine could not.

Both navies also began to develop postwar submarines more closely comparable to the wartime Type XXI, several examples of which they had tested. They became the US *Tang* and the British *Porpoise*. The US design was completed first, and for a time the British considered duplicating it in order to get new submarines into service fast enough. From a technical point of view, the greatest problem in these designs was internal volume, to accommodate the combination of more batteries and powerful diesels. The US Navy hoped to solve it by using radial 'pancake' engines. The Royal Navy, which lacked a sufficient base of domestic diesel production,

developed its own Admiralty standard range engine (which was also installed in frigates). In the design stage the ASR I seemed distinctly inferior to the more compact 'Pancake'. However, the latter apparently pressed the state of the art too far, and proved unreliable. Boats which had been fitted with it had to be lengthened so that they could be refitted with conventional replacement diesels.

Even so, the postwar fast submarines were substantially larger then their wartime predecessors. In 1952, the British Director of Plans remarked that the existing (and projected) fleet of 53 British submarines could not suffice even for peacetime fleet ASW training. A small submarine might be easier to produce, and might even be better for some purposes. After all, the Royal Navy had followed just such a two-tier policy (large S/T and small U/V classes) during the war. It seemed to him that the *Porpoise*s owed too much to Type XXI ideas. Surely the Royal Navy did not plan to fight convoy battles in the open ocean. Did it really need high speed, which (in the Director's view) had been adopted to overhaul convoys? Long-range homing torpedoes might even reduce the speed requirement.

At this time the building plan called for 18 *Porpoise*s by 1958. In wartime British yards might build as many as 18 per year (each taking two years to build). However, they would have to make up for a high wastage rate. War experience showed that a submarine typically became mechanically unreliable, hence unfit for war service, after three years. It might, then, be wise to look at an alternative smaller submarine for the 1954-55 and later programs.

Long endurance, full speed when snorkelling and on main engines, many torpedoes, rapid reload gear, deep diving depth, sea search radar (when a low frequently passive sonar was available), air search radar, and a high frequency radio mast were all *Porpoise* characteristics associated with the wartime Atlantic convoy role. However, the Royal Navy planned to operate in quite different areas: off the Norwegian coast (on anti-submarine patrol), in the Arctic (where a few

Scotsman was rebuilt postwar as a 'super *Seraph*' high-speed target, with higher motor power, 3600hp as compared to 1300 in unmodified units. However, her hull had only limited volume, so the new motors cost her most of her diesel powerplant; its power was reduced to a mere 307hp, which could recharge her batteries only very slowly. Thus she could make her high burst speed only at the cost of a lengthy period of recharging. She achieved 16.33 knots on trials. [*Wright & Logan*]

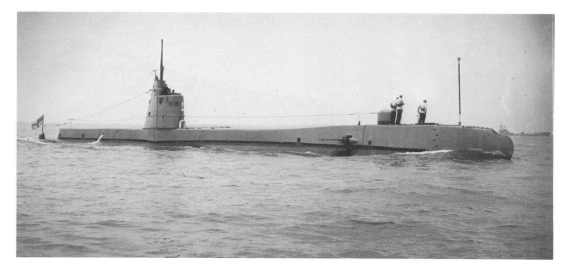

submarines would severely disrupt Soviet traffic, and where few US submarines were fitted to go), in the Baltic, the Black Sea, and in the Mediterranean.

Ideal characteristics for each role could be combined to define the ideal small British submarine. For ASW patrol off the Norwegian coast the submarine would need a 300ft diving depth (compared to 750ft desired for the *Porpoise*, and 625ft attained), 28 days' provisions, a maximum snorkel speed of eight knots (5000nm at six on snorkel, at least five knots silent speed). Note that 300ft was considered the greatest depth from which torpedoes could be fired by air ejection. For anything deeper, a heavier and more elaborate firing system would be needed. Three torpedo tubes (six torpedoes) would suffice. Principal sensors would be a low frequency passive sonar, a Super High Frequency Radio Detection-Finder SHFDF (against radar emissions), and a torpedo detection hydrophone. This was not far from the US mass-production SSK idea. However, the Royal Navy could not afford a specialized ASW submarine. The same design would have to meet other requirements.

For the Arctic, a modern version of the wartime German Type VIIC seemed ideal. It would correspond to the submarine intended for Norwegian coastal operations, except for more torpedoes and tubes (ten torpedoes, four tubes) and a gun for use against small targets.* It would also be strengthened against ice. The Baltic and the Black Sea were both iced part of the year, and were very shallow, so much so that a shallow

* The gun was needed to deal with enemy coastal traffic which might be heavy when supporting army operations; 750 small craft were sunk by submarine gunfire in World War II. It was also feared that BIDDER, the homing torpedo, might be ineffective in shallow water. Moreover, being a passive homer, it would be ineffective against any craft which anchored inshore. Against this, the gun would not contribute to the submarine's primary role, ASW. The HTP torpedo (FANCY) was considered as economical against small craft as gunfire (submarines in World War II averaged 70 rounds per small craft). The air threat would probably limit opportunities to use a gun, and it would be wrong in principle for a submarine commander not to try to remain unobserved.

periscope depth would be a considerable asset. The targets would be unescorted ships and small convoys. Ideal requirements would include four torpedo tubes (ten torpedoes) as well as one countermeasure torpedo tube (with two countermeasures or anti-escort torpedoes). The submarine would require 48 hours' endurance at slow speed on main motors. Shallow water would invite ASW mining, so she would require a mine detection sonar. Similarly, it would limit the value of any passive sonar, so the Baltic or Black Sea submarine would require a radar periscope.

Staff requirements showed one 4in Mark 23 gun and four twin 0.303 Lewis guns. The 4in gun would not be mounted when the submarine was employed in her primary ASW role. Its cost was estimated at 2ft in overall submarine length, 15 tons surface and 18 tons submerged displacement, plus 23 tons reserve buoyancy to provide an acceptable gun platform, ie, an increase of about 40 tons or three per cent of submerged displacement. That cost about three per cent in submerged speed and about six per cent in endurance. Resistance would be somewhat lower with the gun landed, so submerged speed would be somewhat higher. The gun would have been fitted in the after part of the sail.

The US response to the new submarine technology included both a new-design attack submarine (*Tang*) and a large program to convert existing fleet submarines. The newly converted Guppy II *Catfish* is shown off Mare Island, April 1949. The Guppy conversion entailed installation of new batteries and modified motors; underwater speed increased from about 10 to as much as 16 knots. Some fleet submarines received a much less ambitious conversion in which a snorkel was installed and the bridge fairwater streamlined; although the staff requirements (characteristics) specified a 5in deck gun, it was rarely fitted. This 'fleet snorkel' was designed for further conversion into a Guppy, although no such conversions were undertaken. The name Guppy was taken from the program designation: Greater Underwater Propulsive Power. [*USN*]

The converted units of the welded T class were British equivalents of the US Guppy. They were drastically streamlined (external torpedo tubes removed), cut amidships, and a new section containing two more electric motors and a fourth section of batteries added. Underwater speed was nearly doubled. *Turpin* (shown here in September 1951) and two sisters (*Thermopylae* and *Titan*) of the first such group were lengthened by 12ft; the prototype, *Taciturn*, was lengthened by 14ft. These conversions were occasioned by delays in the design and construction of the new British fast battery drive submarine, the *Porpoise*. [*CPL*]

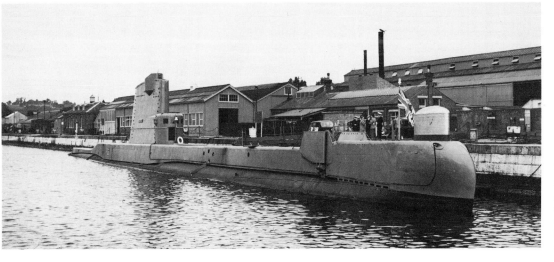

The second group of converted
Ts were lengthened by 20ft:
Tabard (shown here on 27 June
1955), *Tiptoe, Trump* and
Truncheon. Trump was externally
similar to *Tabard*, but the other
two had a stepped sail. [*MoD*]

Five rivetted T were streamlined,
the result being roughly
equivalent to the US 'fleet
snorkel': *Talent, Token, Tireless*
(*shown here in 1956*), *Tapir* and
Tiredo. Higher capacity batteries
(6560 amp/hr *vs* 5350 amp/hr)
were installed. The effect of
streamlining was to add 1.4 knots
in underwater speed. However,
streamlining was considered
more important as a means of
eliminating flow noise. In their
postwar ASW role, US and
British submarines found high
underwater speed less valuable
than had been supposed, and
both the 'fleet snorkels' and the
streamlines remained in service
for many years. Note the space
for a 4in gun forward of the sail.
[*MoD*]

The most modern of the war-
built British submarines, the A
class, were streamlined, with
higher-capacity batteries and
new bows, sterns, an bridge
fairwaters. However, larger
motors were not fitted, so speed
did not materially increase.
Amphion is shown at Cape Town,
30 September 1961. [*CPL*]

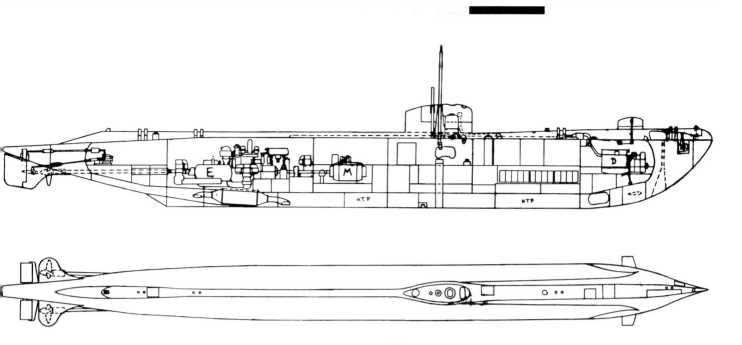

Inboard profile of *Explorer*.

If Soviet land forces reached the Mediterranean, the Soviets would have to use coastal shipping, and, as in World War II, British submarines would have to attack it. Characteristics of the ideal submarine to operate there would have to include a limited displacement (less than a thousand tons) and a removable gun, to deal with small ships. Small size would have the advantage of reducing enemy sonar detection range.

Staff requirements were dated December 1952 (and revised in April, 1953). By this time the small general purpose submarine (most of whose missions were anti-ship) was intended primarily for ASW. The original concept survived in a requirement that the submarine be of minimum size for fast production and to present a minimum sonar target. Special consideration was to be given to operation in the Arctic, with special reference to reserve bouyancy and surface stability.

For better concealment, the snorkel would discharge above or below water, at will, and the design was to have included arrangements for cooling the exhaust. The submarine was also to have been designed for rapid depth change, with up angles as great as 30 degrees. It would have had automatic control for both forward and after planes, and would have been able to hover at any depth.

Submerged speed was to be ten knots, and surfaced speed at least 11 knots. The ship would have snorkelled at eight knots, and minimum speed would have been two knots. The prime requirement was a high silent speed, not a high maximum submerged speed. Surfaced endurance was to be 3500nm at 10 knots, three months out of dock. Battery endurance would be not less than 120nm at four knots (30 hours), and snorkelling endurance 3500nm at five knots. In an emergency, the main ballast tanks could be filled with fuel for a total endurance of 5000nm at ten knots.

Armament would have consisted of four internal bow tubes for 21in full length weapons (eight to ten torpedoes forward); and two swimout (25in) stern countermeasure tubes for BIDDER homing torpedoes (4 of which would be carried). The forward tubes would fire from as much as 300ft depth, and they would accommodate both anti-ship and anti-submarine torpedoes (Mark 8, BIDDER, FANCY) with at least four reloads. Buoyant ground mines would be carried as alternatives to torpedoes. Unlike the *Porpoise*, the small submarine would not need rapid-reload and power loading.

The result displaced about 1100 tons. This was a great deal for a severely compromised submarine. Yet attempts to keep down size, show the cost of her limited features. Engine and battery sizes were fixed by standardization, so any increase in size had to reduce speed and endurance. Larger submarines would also take longer to build, would be more expensive, and would be larger sonar targets. All of these considerations argued against using stern tubes, gun, or certain sonars.

Stern tubes had several advantages. In larger submarines, they were typically loaded with anti-escort homing torpedoes, so that the submarine could fire at a pursuing escort. Alternatively, they could fire decoys. But their cost was their size (two tons in direct weight, 27 tons in surface displacement, 4ft 6in in length). Moreover, it could be argued that stern tubes would be less valuable given future torpedo angling devices (BIDDER could angle 145 degrees, others 180).

The sonars in question were Types 171 (attack and depth finder), 718 (long-range passive detection array), and 719 (passive torpedo warning). Type 171 would also be used for mine detection and for underwater communications. It would be useful in setting the safety 'sandwich' (maximum and minimum depths, outside which the firing submarine would be safe) of the BIDDER homing torpedo at short range. However, its

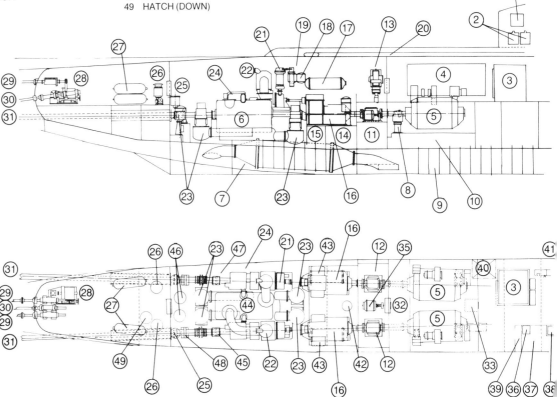

1   INDICATOR BUOY
2   HTP EXPANSION CHAMBER
3   W/T OFFICE
4   SWITCHBOARD
5   MAIN MOTOR
6   TURBINE
7   EXTERNAL COOLER
8   CIRCULATING WATER PUMP
9   AFT HTP TANKS
10   COMPENSATING TANKS
11   RESERVE FEED WATER
12   THRUST BLOCK
13   TRIPLE FEED PUMP
14   RESERVE LUBRICATING OIL TANK
15   LUBRICATING OIL DRAIN TANK
16   EPICYCLIC GEAR AND CLUTCH
17   LUBRICATING OIL COOLER
18   DIRT SEPARATOR
19   CATALYST CHAMBER
20   DIESEL EXHAUST (FROM ENGINE FORWARD)
21   COMBUSTION CHAMBER
22   PRIMARY JET CONDENSER
23   CONDENSATE PUMPS
24   EXHAUST CO_2 GAS COMPRESSOR
25   STERN GLAND MOTOR

26   SEAWATER CIRCULATING PUMPS
27   AIR BOTTLE
28   HYDROPLANE AND STEERING GEAR
29   TO RUDDER
30   TO STERN PLANES
31   PROPELLER SHAFT
32   HTP EVACUATION PUMP
33   CO_2 ABSORPTION UNIT
34   GYRO PANEL
35   TRIM PUMP STARTER
36   TORPEDO DIRECTOR
37   CHART TABLE
38   AUTOMATIC PLOT
39   E/S GEAR
40   W/T MACHINERY SPACE
41   HP PANEL
42   LUBRICATING OIL PUMP
43   MAIN GEAR WHEELCASE
44   COMBINED CONTACT CONDENSER AND GAS
     SEPARATOR
45   TORSIONMETER
46   SURPLUS CONDENSATE PUMPS
47   PLUMMER BLOCK
48   BRAKE
49   HATCH (DOWN)

HMS *Explorer*. HTP powerplant.

active transmissions might give away the position
of the submarine, and it had a large heat output.
Type 719 was fitted in the keel and was therefore
the only set available when the boat was surfaced.
It was considered valuable during an enemy
surface counter attack. Type 718 was a long-range
passive detection array. Ships would initially be
completed with Types 168 and 169.

Planned radars were 973 (periscope ranging
only, interim until 1956) and 1002 (combined air
and surface search and periscope ranging).
Together, the Asdics and radar would cost 37 tons
surfaced, 44 tons submerged. They would also
require operators and maintenance personnel,
adding 17 and 20 tons respectively.

Eliminating stern tubes, guns, sonars, and

radars in an 1130-ton (surfaced) submarine would
save 96 tons in surfaced, and 137 in submerged
displacement, and 16ft,6in in length.

The final version of the design showed an
Albacore hull and re-cycle diesel (Kreislauf) power
(if it should become available in time), with six
21in torpedo tubes (all of which would have to be
forward) and 18 torpedoes. It fell victim to the
Radical Review. Within a few years the Royal
Navy was working towards its first nuclear attack
submarine, and there was little point in a further
diesel design.

Beyond these diesel submarines, capable of 15
to 17 knots for up to one hour underwater, lay the
very fast or 'true' submarine, typified by the
wartime German Type XXVI project. Powered by

closed-cycle engine, such a submarine would maintain about 25 knots for ten hours. The German craft was to have been powered by a hydrogen peroxide (High Test Peroxide, or HTP, in British parlance) turbine, and the Royal Navy recommissioned a smaller HTP submarine (U 1407, *Meteorite*, after the war). HTP seemed so clearly the submarine propulsive plant of the future that the British 1945 program included two unarmed HTP submarines, which became *Explorer* and *Excalibur*, to help develop ASW tactics. A series of six HTP submarines was to have followed the six British 'fast battery drive' (FBD) submarines of the *Porpoise* class.

By mid 1952, with the two HTP target submarines well along the way, the Royal Navy began once more to consider building operational HTP craft. This time, however, HTP was evaluated in the context of the ASW (underwater picket) mission. Existing low-frequency passive sonars already promised in the near term ranges of about 70nm (two convergence zones) against snorkelling or surfaced submarines, with a long-term goal of 40nm in deep water under ideal conditions. The effective exploitation of such great ranges would require a combination of prolonged submergence in areas nominally controlled by enemy forces and high silent speed (so that the ASW submarine could close to within firing

The US SSK, a specialized anti-aircraft anti-submarine submarine, typified postwar US concerns. Writing late in 1948, the British DNC was impressed by the large numbers needed for the intended tactic of lying in ambush in picket lines off enemy bases to detect and attack snorkelling or surfaced submarines transiting to their patrol areas. He doubted whether the British shipbuilding industry had the necessary capacity, and assumed that the British naval staff would much prefer a dual purpose (anti-ship/anti-submarine) design, even though that would be larger than the specialist SSK. DNC was particularly impressed by the planned 'packaged' or unit type powerplant, designed for total replacement rather than in-ship repair at a forward base. Provision for submerged anchoring was another new feature: by this time US submarines had anchored submerged (using a small positive buoyancy) with about 500ft of cable out, to listen with their motors off. USS *K3* is shown here in April 1954. [CPL]

From 1945 on, the Royal Navy considered the HTP submarine the weapon of the future. It consistently referred to fast battery-driven submarines as intermediate, and did not design an operational unit of that type (the *Porpoise*) until it had become clear that HTP would be relatively difficult to employ. Hence it lacked such craft through the period of this book. The less optimistic US Navy designed its *Tang* class in 1945-46, and had units in service by 1952. The Royal Navy built two HTP-powered submarines, *Explorer* and *Excalibur*, to gain experience with the powerplant and also to develop ASW tactics suited to countering fast submarines. By the time they had been completed the Royal Navy had begun to develop its own nuclear submarines. *Explorer* is shown here on 26 March 1956. [*MoD*]

range). ASW submarines would be disposed in depth to assure interception of Soviet submarines transiting towards their patrol areas. That would require large numbers of relatively inexpensive submarines.

Ideally, these requirements could only be met by a small, relatively quiet, nuclear submarine, which the US Navy tried to build as the *Tullibee*. In 1952, with many operational problems as yet unencountered, HTP seemed an attractive solution. Its price was falling (it was expected that it would soon reach about a fifth of the current price, and then fall even further). Moreover, an HTP plant was already running at Vickers (Barrow). A team which had developed an alternative closed cycle ('direct oxygen steam') plant (cancelled in 1951) was available to devise a new HTP plant. It even appeared that, counting the cost of replacing batteries, an HTP submarine might be competitive with a conventional one. Batteries had to be replaced annually (after six patrols) at a cost of about £120,000, or £20,000 per patrol. Each HTP patrol would cost about £15,000, for 300 tons. These calculations excluded the nuclear solution altogether because that seemed so distant.

HTP would be used, not to achieve very high speed (as in the German Type XXVI), but rather to achieve long underwater endurance. Maximum speed would be set by the requirements of long-range interceptions based on low frequency sonar contacts. It was assumed that human factors would limit any one war patrol (in a small submarine) to about 20 days, which at four knots equated to about 1350nm. The submarine would have to achieve up to about eight knots, and she would be designed for maximum efficiency at an intercept speed of about five knots. She would snorkel on passage to her patrol area, so as not to consume too much of her crew's endurance. Some

minimum battery power (one section, 112 cells) would be required as back-up, and also to provide power when the submarine was shifting from diesel-electric to HTP power.

Sketch staff requirements for this slow HTP submarine were written in 1952, and it appears to have been considered an alternative to the battery-powered 1953 submarine described above. However, as a very specialized hot war system it fell foul of the Radical Review. By 1957, the Royal Navy was able to begin construction of much more flexible nuclear attack submarines, and the specialist slow ASW submarine was abandoned. Note, however, that current British diesel patrol submarines (most notably the new Type 2400 or *Upholder* class) are designed for just the ambush role conceived for the HTP submarine. One difference is that instead of accelerating to intercept the submarines they detect, they may find it much easier to call in martime patrol aircraft. This, too, is a concept first tested in the 'fifties.

The US Navy pursued new propulsion systems on a broader front. It sought a two-shaft plant which could develop 15,000shp (for 25 knots in a *Tang* hull) for ten hours; by 1948 it expected to begin prototype construction under the FY52 program. The engine would have to use air when snorkelling, but at depth (1000ft) it would use a stored oxidant. This dual requirement was considered extremely stringent. When running on the oxidant, the main motors would act as generators. The future submarine would creep silently at up to six knots (for 48 hours), and it would be able to run on battery power at 15 to 20 knots for one hour. It would be able to cruise on the surface at 18 knots while charging batteries, and to snorkel at 10 knots while charging at the full rate.

Quieting was also considered important. Although new sonar equipment was in prospect, it appeared that full advantage had not been taken of existing sets due to self-noise. For example, a fully silenced submarine with wartime sonars was able to detect destroyers at multiple convergence zone range off Florida as early as 1947.

These specifications applied to four projects: Alton (Walter cycle), Ellis (pressure-fired steam), Wolverine (gas turbine), and Gentry (gas turbine). A closed-cycle diesel, considered too bulky for a combat submarine, was also developed, as Project Gumbo. Similar size and power (though not snorkelling or battery-charging) requirements applied to an atomic powerplant, which was the only one of the postwar projects carried to fruition. The closed-cycle submarine was designed, but it was never built. Instead, the FY52 program included the prototypes *Nautilus* and *Seawolf*, powered by alternative types of reactor. The *Nautilus* proved successful, and her plant formed the basis for all subsequent US submarine reactors. However, she was about twice as large as the earlier *Tang*. The next class of nuclear attack submarine (*Skate*) therefore deliberately sacrificed

The shape of the future: the experimental missile-firing submarine *Cusk* at Mare Island Naval Shipyard, December 1950. The perceived threat of Soviet equivalents began to draw American ASW forces back towards the continental United States from about 1953 onwards. [*USN*]

reactor power (hence speed) for reduced size and, presumably, cost.

The realization of the other great postwar submarine development, the *Albacore* hull, falls outside the period this book covers. Indeed, except for the *Tangs*, the *Nautilus* and the *Albacore* herself, truly modern US submarines date from 1956 and later.

At the same time, several submarine functions, which had been more or less subsidiary during World War II, fitted the new strategic situation particularly well.

They fell into four categories: support for carrier strike forces, direct strike against enemy territory, special operations, and anti-submarine warfare. In each case, the submarine had the unique advantages of being able to operate in forward areas nominally controlled by an enemy. Strike aircraft would have to overfly those areas, and enemy submarines moving to their patrol areas would have to pass through them.

Wartime submarines had scouted for amphibious landings and for carrier strikes. They had also saved many pilots. In 1945, moreover, as the surface radar pickets were decimated off Okinawa, the submarine seemed to be a useful replacement. It could not possibly carry anything like the radar or directing CIC of a destroyer, but it could submerge under air attack; too many destroyer pickets had submerged involuntarily. Twenty-four fleet submarines were to have been converted for the invasion of Japan, but only two, *Grouper* and *Finback*, were actually done. Conversion amounted to little more than an improvised CIC and radios to communicate with

aircraft. Even so, the concept was so important that a new project, Migraine, was set up postwar for a more complete conversion. The first two, *Requin* and *Spinax*, were completed in the fall of 1946, followed by Migraine I (*Tigrone* and *Burrfish*), Migraine II (reconstruction of the first two boats), and then Migraine III (six fleet submarines, FY51-53). Two new pickets, *Sailfish* and *Salmon*, were built as such, although their hull design was based on that of the 'fleet boat', and the huge nuclear submarine *Triton* was built as a fleet radar picket.

All of these submarines suffered from limited surface or submerged speed; except for the *Triton*, they could not keep up with a carrier task force. However, they could proceed independently to an objective area. In theory, they might take up station 50nm offshore, the carriers launching aircraft from a greater distance. Each would have its own assigned Combat Air Patrol (CAP). She would direct strike aircraft towards the target, and her CAP would prevent enemy aircraft from following the returning strike. The submarine would also provide early warning – as, reportedly, did British submarines during the Falklands War. Note that such early warning required only a good air search radar (such as many US submarines of this period possessed), not the elaborate height-finder of the full picket conversion. In an amphibious force, submarines could form an unnoticed advanced picket line 50-200nm ahead of the force, to provide early warning and to control interceptions. Once the landing had been made, they could form a semi-circle 30-50 miles from the beach. In one exercise, they patrolled the other side of an island to detect enemy forces seeking to

SENSORS
1 BOW ACTIVE SONAR
2 BOW PASSIVE SONAR
3 REARWARD-LOOKING ACTIVE SONAR
4 ATTACK PERISCOPE
5 ECM PERISCOPE AND SEARCH PERISCOPE (SIDE BY
   SIDE)
6 RADAR (SEARCH) PERISCOPE
7 PASSIVE SONAR INTERCEPT RECEIVER (DUUG-1)

WEAPONS
8 TORPEDO TUBE SHUTTERS
9 TORPEDO TUBES
10 TORPEDO STOWAGE

OTHER
11 BATTERIES
12 DIESEL ENGINE
13 ELECTRIC MOTOR (*NOT* DIRECTLY CONNECTED TO
   DIESEL)
14 SWITCHBOARD

15 MUFFLER
16 SNORKEL EXHAUST
17 SNORKEL INTAKE
18 NAVIGATING BRIDGE
19 ACCESS TRUNK
20 CONTROL ROOM
21 BOW PLANES (TO DIVE)
22 BOW PLANES (TO SURFACE)
23 ESCAPE AND TORPEDO LOADING HATCH
24 ESCAPE HATCH

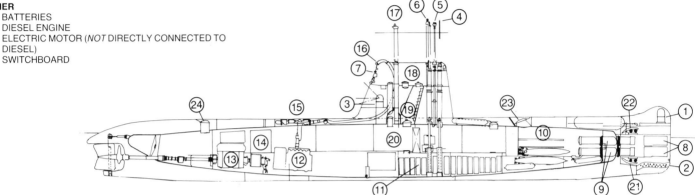

Inboard profile of a French *Arethuse* class ASW submarine. Like the US Navy, the French Navy invested in specialized ASW submarines. Its choke point was the neck of the Mediterranean East of France, between the toe of Italy and Tunisia. The Straits of Gibraltar were considered primarily a British responsibility. Four ships of this type were built. They were the first French diesel-electric submarines.

counter attack.

Pickets could direct aircraft towards distant enemy targets, improving their navigational accuracy. Similarly, they (as well as less elaborately converted submarines) could provide missile guidance.

US interest in direct strike appears to have originated with German wartime projects. In January 1945, there were intelligence reports (subsequently shown to have been false) that U-boats approaching the US coast were carrying or towing missiles. Although the Germans did not actually fire heavy missiles from their submarines, they were, in 1945, developing a submersible barge in which to tow V-2 rockets. Postwar, the US Navy attempted unsuccessfully to complete this project. At the same time it mounted cruise missiles, first Loon (an adapted V-1 'buzz bomb') and then the Chance-Vought Regulus, aboard converted fleet submarines. They were the direct predecessors of the current fleet ballistic missiles.

The original V-1 was entirely unguided, depending on a timer to cut off its engine at a pre-determined moment. As a result, it had a CEP* of eight nm, too poor a performance even with a nuclear weapon. The next step was command guidance, limited in range to line of sight. The solution, both in Loon and then in Regulus, was to provide a second or even a third guidance source, closer to the target, aboard a submarine or submarines. In the case of Loon, the terminal guidance submarine applied a signal which caused wings and tail to blow off, so that the missile fell in a predictable trajectory. CEP fell to half a mile, presumably helped by better quality control. Regulus was more sophisticated, and the guidance submarines could supply steering

commands. Beside two fleet submarine conversions, one nuclear and two diesel submarines were built to launch Regulus missiles. A much larger planned program was stopped in favor of the more efficient Polaris, which required no terminal guidance.

From a strategic point of view, the impact of these missile submarines was matched by their effect on the US Navy itself. As soon as Regulus was ready for service, in about 1954, the submarine service began to emphasize the threat of similar Soviet craft – after all, the Soviets had surely captured at least some of the wartime German data. The result was the reformulation of American ASW strategy described in Chapter 2. By 1957, the US government was deeply concerned with the threat of a Soviet surprise strategic attack. The Gaither Committee, which sought solutions, described SOSUS as a means of tracking Soviet strategic submarines, rather than as a means of defending the Atlantic convoy routes.

Special or clandestine operations formed a natural postwar category. British and American submarines had been the only available links to guerilla forces operating in occupied territory. Submarines also transported raiding parties to enemy-held islands in the Pacific. In the late 'forties it must have seemed quite possible that very similar operations would be required in the future, and both governments raised special forces for future penetrations of occupied territory. By 1949, the US Navy was experimenting with submarine-launched swimmers, using a British submersible canoe, Sleeping Beauty. The submarines Perch and Sealion were refitted as troop carriers in 1948. The designer of the postwar Dutch triple-hulled submarines proposed something more ambitious: a submarine which could land enough troops to turn the flanks of

* Circular Error Probable, the radius within which 50 per cent of all shots would fall.

enemy positions, but the US Navy rejected it. In 1955, BuShips included a submersible LST in a list of advanced ship concepts, but it was far too expensive to be practicable.

Then there was the ASW mission, which both navies advanced. Several submarines had torpedoed enemy submarines during the war, including a unique British engagement in which a submerged submarine sank a submerged U-boat in 1945. Although such submarine-to-submarine attacks had been relatively rare in wartime, the concept gained attractiveness as technical developments made more conventional forms of ASW more difficult. In the case of the US Navy, a new low-frequency passive sonar, adapted from German sets, made the ASW submarine particularly attractive. In theory, it could be mass-produced to lie off Soviet ports. Mass production in turn would be practicable because high overall system performance would be attained by using long-range homing torpedoes, rather than by giving the submarine itself high speed or deep diving depth.*

A description of British work of this period will give some idea of early postwar capabilities. Experiments began in 1947. The Soviets, whose submarines were then limited to a diving depth of 250ft, were expected to be able to duplicate the *Porpoise* by 1956-57, when advanced homing torpedoes would be available. Performance would include 17 knots for 20 minutes submerged; maximum speed 11 knots when snorkelling (normally eight knots); surface speed 15 knots. Maximum silent speed underwater would be eight knots. Normal maximum diving depth would be 750ft.

The enemy would usually proceed submerged, so that sighting of a snorkel or periscope would be fortuitous. Active sonar range would be only about 2500 yards, and the sonar ping would alert the enemy. Passive sonar would be much more effective. British exercises in coastal waters showed that a snorkelling submarine at six to eight knots could be detected at 6000-7000 yards. There was no means of measuring target depth using existing equipment, and target range and course had to be obtained by plotting. Typical accuracy was 15 degrees in bearing and one knot in speed (it was not always easy to distinguish between the noise of a fast submarine at long range and a quiet one at short range). Existing listening equipment was limited in accuracy (two degrees) and in frequency range (it operated at ten kc/s). At this time, the US Navy was achieving ranges of about 30,000 yards using lower-frequency equipment.

The existing silent speed, two knots, was too low to allow a submarine with so short a detection range to reach a good firing position in time.

Clearly, then, a large longer-range passive sonar array was needed, to achieve better ranges. Passive ranging (by comparing the inputs of several arrays, as in the US PUFFS system developed somewhat later) would provide an accurate plot without alerting an enemy (by the noise of maneuvering). A similar system would, in theory, provide passive target depth estimation. As in the US Navy, the early experiments convinced the British that it was essential to minimize self-noise by silent mounting of all machinery, silencing of propulsion and hull, and careful streamlining. The attacking submarine would have to hover silently, or operate at very low speed yet retain good depth control. In 1950, it appeared that all of these goals, except perhaps passive ranging and passive depth prediction, could be achieved. If the latter two problems could not be solved in the submarine, they would have to be solved in its weapon, in the form of homing. If, on the other hand, the submarine could achieve good enough target data, it could direct a wire-guided torpedo (MACKLE) all the way to its target.

For the present, there was really no alternative. The existing Mark 8 stream torpedo was adjusted to run at greater depth by changing its depth gear ratio to 5:1, so its maximum of 44ft became 220ft. Typically, torpedoes were spread across the target's path by firing them over a time interval, dependent on enemy speed and length. For a 250ft long target submarine, snorkelling just below the surface (hence well defined in depth) at seven knots and using a 45-knot torpedo, the interval could be as much as ten seconds. If estimates of enemy course and speed were correct, the first two would pass ahead, and the noise they made would give an undesirably long warning before the arrival of those which should hit.

Trials showed that a Mark 8 running at 45 knots would be detected at 1200 yards. The torpedo would take 48 seconds to cover this distance. It would probably take 15 seconds for the submarine to classify the sound as a torpedo, and 15 seconds for her sonar operator to warn the officer of the watch, and for the latter to start taking action. He in turn would still have 18 seconds to react. He might increase speed, alter course, change depth, or do all three simultaneously. In this time an A class submarine could maneuver at six knots (snorkel speed) so that less than 30 per cent of her would remain in the original predicted area when the torpedo arrived. A fast battery submarine snorkelling at ten knots could clear the area entirely by the time the 45-knot torpedo arrived.

The conclusion was that existing preset impact torpedoes would have little chance of success, unless the range was short and the depth too shallow for evasive diving. Results would be improved if spreading were replaced by interval firing. In this method, the torpedo aimed to hit

---

* Ironically, even though the SSK as built was quite austere, it could not be mass-produced, as planned, by non-submarine yards. Nor was it large enough to operate effectively in rough Northern waters. The numbers cited in Chapter 2 would have been attained largely by re-converting existing fleet submarines. for example, the Guppy conversion was designed to be compatible with further conversion to SSK. A few submarines, such as *Grouper*, were converted initially as SSKs.

was fired first, after which the others were fired at three-second intervals so that gratuitous warning time was eliminated. Other possibilities included higher torpedo speed, to keep warning time within the minimum reaction time of about 30 seconds (70 knots would suffice, but was considered impractical) or a major reduction in torpedo noise, using the same Nightshirt silencing as was then being applied to British surface ships.

Another possibility was a pattern runner with an influence pistol: the pattern would deal with evasion in the horizontal plane, the influence pistol evasion in depth. One salvo would be fired in layers separated in depth of 50ft (pistol range plus submarine pressure hull diameter). The maximum salvo was six torpedoes, so a compromise between one layer and up to six layers (down to 300ft) had to be made. Analysis showed that coverage would be good in relatively shallow water (18 fathoms). In 18-27 fathoms, the torpedo could deal with depth evasion coupled with alteration of course or speed (dependent on the pattern selected); or with alteration of course and speed, but then it would give only 50 per cent coverage for depth. At greater depth, however, coverage would fall as low as 10-20 per cent.

In 1950, these limits were still offset by limited Soviet diving depth, 250ft (42 fathoms).

Within three years, an interim ASW torpedo, the HTP-powered FANCY (a converted Mark 8) would be available. It would pattern-run with a range of 20,000 yards at 45 knots. Maximum depth would be 200ft, and its magnetic influence pistol would be effective at 15ft against a degaussed submarine. It would also be easier to interval-fire, because it would be able to accept large gyro angles.

Only some Mark 8 would be converted, since existing stocks would form the bulk of the available torpedo inventory in any near-term war. All Mark 8 not converted to FANCY, however, were to have been converted as deep runners. Torpedo tubes would be modified for large-angle spreads, which would also be useful against surface ships. With the failure of the FANCY project, however, Mark 8 had to be retained as a standard anti-ship torpedo.

At this time it was expected that the ultimate ASW weapons would be BIDDER (Mark 20) and a wire-guided homing torpedo, MACKLE. BIDDER, which could be fired by both submarines and surface ships, was the first British homing torpedo to enter service, about 1957. MACKLE ultimately appeared as GROG (Mark 23). Trials began in 1955, and it entered service in 1966. Both were specialized ASW weapons, and so had to be carried alongside Mark 8 anti-ship torpedoes.*

Note that, as the situation was understood in the early 'fifties, BIDDER, a passive homer, would not necessarily make FANCY obsolete. It could be countered by an increase in the silent speed of Soviet submarines, in which case FANCY would still retain some value, if an effective depth-finding sonar was available.

---

* This was still true of the original Mark 24 (TIGERFISH), which was why *Conqueror* sank the Argentine cruiser *Belgrano* with Mark 8. Note that the *Porpoise* class was originally designed to carry three US Mark 37 aft, as anti-escort weapons, leaving one of two countermeasures tubes open for other devices. These stern tubes were large-diameter for swim-out launching. A *Porpoise* carried 18 torpedoes forward, typically eight Mark 20 and ten Mark 8. The latter, being unguided, had a much reduced lower single shot kill probability and therefore had to be fired in salvo.

Scotsman in 1955. This boat went through a series of modifications (see also the photograph on page 190), this being the final and most advanced form. [*MoD*]

9
INSHORE WARFARE

For the purposes of this chapter, inshore warfare has two quite distinct aspects. One is coastal surface warfare, the domain of the motor torpedo and motor gun boat, and now of the fast missile boat. The other is shallow water ASW. A third aspect, inshore mine countermeasures, has already been treated. All three generally involve small craft, and all three had to be virtually extemporized for World War II. At the end of the war, then, the question was to what extent specialist inshore forces would be retained by the two major Western navies.

By their nature, individual inshore units had little weight: coastal forces were effective only insofar as they could operate in substantial numbers. Nor were these small wooden craft

particularly durable. The US Navy, for example, found that PT boats in the South Pacific had to be replaced within two years, as their hulls absorbed water and gained weight. Thus a commitment to maintaining effective coastal forces carried with it a continuing expensive building program. Manning and maintenance would also be costly.

Nor, in British terms, could coastal craft of any type contribute to cold war strength. They were, indeed, the epitome of the specialized hot war forces. The Royal Navy retained them (in very small numbers) as a hot war mobilization base after World War II, and then began to produce new craft as it rearmed for what many expected would be World War III. Coastal forces, then, were the natural victims of the Radical Review and

Completed in August 1948, the Vosper-built *MTB538* served as prototype for the Gay class.
[*Vosper Thornycroft*]

SGB 2009, the first gas turbine warship, running in the Solent. Gas turbine intake air was ducted from a protected position abaft the bridge. Even so, it was subject to spray, as is clear from the photograph. [*MoD*]

HMS *Grey Goose*, February 1956. She was the world's first solely gas turbine-propelled warship. [*MoD*]

then of the 1957 Defense White Paper which followed it. A cold war Navy might well encounter hostile coastal craft, but it would not really expect to operate any of its own. That is why the only fast attack boats the Royal Navy ordered after 1957 were the unarmed *Scimitar*, *Cutlass*, and *Sabre*, designed to simulate hostile missile attack boats.

Matters seemed very different in 1945. Both navies had very recently experienced the effects of unpreparedness. The United States, for example, had suffered very severe losses to its coastal shipping in 1942, due to an absence of small (coastal) escorts. Many yachts had been brought into service, but they had not been particularly satisfactory. In Britain, there was an uncomfortable awareness of the scale of the late war German midget submarine (small battle unit) program. It seemed likely that the Soviets would

build midgets of their own, and by 1949 numerous intelligence reports (erroneously, as it turned out) confirmed this. The original rationale for the British postwar midget submarine (X-craft) program was to develop tactics for harbor defense against such small battle units, although within a few years the X-craft had taken on a much more offensive character, the new submarines being designed to tow them into attack position.

As for coastal surface attack forces, both Britain and the United States ended World War II with large numbers of motor torpedo and motor gun boats. However, they performed quite different tasks. Many of the British craft were required to fight similar German coastal craft for control of the English Channel and the North Sea. Others fought abroad, along the Mediterranean coast and in the Far East. For the US Navy, coastal craft were exclusively for overseas operations, primarily in the southwest Pacific.

Thus the end of the war seemed virtually to end US concern with inshore warfare. Postwar, it would influence events abroad primarily by means of carrier air strikes, or by trans-oceanic amphibious landings. In either case, only ocean-going ships, or craft which could easily be transported across oceans in operational conditions, seemed worthwhile. Motor torpedo boats had achieved some useful results, but they were expensive to maintain and operate. All but four were, therefore, scrapped, sold, or converted to subsidiary uses. Four new ones, *PT 809 – 812*, were built as experimental prototypes for possible future production. Some argued that Korean War experience clearly demonstrated their continued value, but in 1953 the US government still considered that war a unique anomaly, not a portent to future experience.

The British position was very different. Nothing could change British geography. Any Soviet advance along the European coast would re-establish the conditions which, in 1940, had led to

The two Bolds were intended as prototype convertible motor torpedo or gun boats. However, none of the projected 'long' boats was ever built, as they were considered too expensive. *Bold Pathfinder* is shown in 1953 in her MGB configuration, with two wartime-type 4.5in (8cwt) guns and one Bofors gun. The operational limitations of the 4.5 led to (abortive) postwar efforts to develop a fully stabilized version, as CFS 1. Note the prominent uptakes characteristic of her gas turbine boost powerplant. [*MoD*]

all of those Channel battles. This possibility shows in the staff requirements for the postwar air direction frigate (with its secondary coastal forces direction role), and in the interest in a heavily gun-armed Type 42 frigate for wartime production. Offensively, British coastal craft could help to block a major choke point, the Danish Straits leading from the Baltic.

From a technical point of view, there were four outstanding issues in 1945: hull form, power plant, hull material, and armament. Most wartime US and British fast coastal craft had hard chine or planing hulls, which achieved their maximum speeds by riding the surface of the water. As a result, they pounded badly in rough water, when they would glide off a wave top into a trough. By way of contrast, the German S-boat had a conventional displacement-type hull better adapted to rough water, but ultimately slower. Both the British and US navies built comparative prototypes after the war. In the British case, *Bold Pioneer* had a conventional hard-chine hull, *Bold Pathfinder* a German-type round bottom. The US *PT 812* was the displacement-hull test ship. She was about five knots slower than her hard-chine contemporaries, but was said to ride much better in rough water. Both navies also experimented with hydrofoils, which promised high speeds and better sea keeping in moderately rough waves. In the British case, the experiments were conducted primarily in Canada; after British Coastal Forces were disbanded, the Canadians drew on their experience to build the large ASW hydrofoil *Bras d'Or*. The US experiments led to an ASW hydrofoil (*High Point*) and then to a series of hydrofoil gun and missile boats (in the 'seventies and later); the US Navy also experimented with hydrofoils as a means of achieving much higher speed in a landing craft.

Fast coastal craft performance depended as much on power plant as on hull form. Indeed, these craft had first been invented as a

Bold Pioneer shows the experimental 3.3in CFS 2 coastal forces gun, developed from the wartime 17-pounder tank weapon. Lighter than the CFS 1, it was, nonetheless, too heavy for smaller coastal craft. [*Wright & Logan*]

consequence of the rise of high-speed (aircraft type) gasoline engines. The prewar and wartime British aero engine industry was too hard pressed to supply aircraft engines for naval use. The earliest British MTBs were therefore powered by imported Italian Isotta/Fraschini engines. In both navies, wartime craft were generally powered by US-built Packards. All burned aviation gasoline, which was hazard enough without coming into contact with highly flammable wooden hulls. Only the Germans powered their boats with high-speed Mercedes-Benz diesels, burning a much less dangerous fuel.

The Royal Navy planned to install captured Mercedes-Benz diesels in its two experimental boats. However, they were redesigned to take a combination of Metrovick G2 gas turbines and diesels. Norway, Denmark, and West Germany all began their postwar fast attack fleets with Mercedes-Benz powered war-built S-boats, partly because of the attractiveness of the diesel; Denmark actually built a modified S-boat as the postwar *Flyvefisken* class.*

Postwar, the Royal Navy tried two alternative forms of propulsion. One was to use the new gas turbine. It was far more compact than a steam plant, and provided more power per unit volume or weight than did conventional gasoline engines. In the two experimental boats, the shift from diesel to gas turbine/diesel was credited with adding about five knots, a speed improvement required to meet the original 45-knot staff requirement.

The other alternative was a new lightweight diesel, the Deltic. It was particularly attractive because, according to a contemporary account, 'it will enable us to meet staff requirements which [otherwise] could only be met by the gas turbine of the future'. Work began in 1943, a committee

*The modern German Lurssen boats are all derivatives of the wartime S-boat designs. The argument between planing and displacement hulls is by no means over.

being set up under Sir Roy Fodden. A contract with English Electric (Napier) was signed in August 1946, and work began in the spring of 1947. The Deltic weighed about a fifth as much as the next lightest British diesel, the Admiralty standard range I, itself about 10 per cent lighter than any commercial diesel of equivalent output and reliability. It had three banks of cylinders, each containing a series of opposed pistons. The banks were arranged as the sides of a triangle (ie, a Delta), so that adjacent pairs of pistons drove three crankshafts which were geared to a single power shaft. The result, described as about the size of the First Lord's desk, could deliver 2500bhp. It was built of aluminium, for light weight. Deltics powered the major postwar British fast attack boat, the *Dark* class. The next step was to have been a compound Deltic, in which the diesel exhaust drove a gas turbine, to give a total of 6000bhp.

However, as implied above, the British always expected gas turbines, with their excellent power-to-weight ratio, to be the ultimate small attack craft powerplant. They were, moveover, the natural successors to the wartime gasoline MTB engines,

Gay Bruiser, a unit of the first postwar (interim) short MTB class, is shown as a gunboat, on 12 November 1953, with the standard battery of one 4.5in forward and one 40mm aft. Note also the depth charge abeam the 40mm gun, the smoke generator on the port side aft, and the 2in rocket flare launcher abeam the bridge. Note the tracks on deck which would otherwise have supported torpedo tubes. [*MoD*]

which were marinized versions of contemporary aircraft engines. Discussions between the Engineer-in-Chief and Metropolitan Vickers began in July, 1942, and a contract for a marinized version of an aircraft jet engine was signed in August, 1943. Trials in the Camper and Nicholson-built *MGB 2009* began in July 1947. One of three gasoline engines (Packards) was replaced by a Gatric gas turbine derived from the wartime F 2, which had powered the prototype of the Gloster Meteor fighter. A follow-on Metrovick gas turbine, the G 2 (4500shp) combined with Mercedes-Benz diesels in the two experimental *Bold* class craft. The US Navy later installed a pair of modified G 2 in *PT 812*.

Meanwhile (in 1946) Admiralty contracts had been let for two marine gas turbines designed as such from the beginning, the English Electric EL60A (6500shp) and the Rolls-Royce RM60A (5400shp). The latter was intended specifically for Coastal Forces, and it was installed in the steam gunboat *Grey Goose* in 1953; the gunboat thus became the world's first entirely gas turbine-propelled warship. The next step was an operational installation: three Bristol Proteus

engines (3500shp each) powered each of the two *Brave* class, the last British Coastal Forces craft.

Since it assigned coastal craft a relatively low priority, the US Navy did not follow up its wartime lead in engines with a new lightweight diesel. Although it did test gas turbines in one of its experimental torpedo boats, it had to import Deltics to power its Vietnam-era fast coastal craft (PTFs).

As for hull material, the existing wooden hulls were difficult to maintain, and could become waterlogged. The most obvious alternative was aluminum, of which all four experimental US craft were built. Aluminum structural marine engineering was still in its infancy, and the boats experienced much corrosion. They were useful, then, as a means of gaining experience with the material, which was later successfully applied. The Royal Navy completed two boats essentially of wartime design, the Vosper *MTB 538* (later redesignated *FPB 1601*) and the Saunders *MTB 539* (*FPB 1602*) as comparative experiments, the former with a plywood hull and the latter of aluminum. The later *Dark Scout* was also built of aluminum, but all other postwar British fast attack craft had

Gay Bruiser as a minelayer, 2 November 1953, carrying six cylindrical ground mines. Coastal minelaying had been an important wartime role for the German S-boats (MTBs), and in World War I the large British Coastal Motor Boats (which were actually MTBs) were designed specifically to lay magnetic mines in areas U-boats would have to pass through. [*MoD*]

Dark Antagonist as a motor torpedo boat, July 1957. Eight similar boats were built for foreign navies: five for Burma (with aluminum skins), two for Finland, and one for Japan (*PT 9*). Although externally similar to the earlier Gays, the Darks were powered by diesel (Deltic) rather than gasoline engines. The Deltic was first tested aboard *FPB 5212*, a former German S-boat. The new hull, built of wood planking on aluminum alloy frames, was derived from that of the experimental Saunders *MTB 539* completed in 1951. She was lost soon afterwards; her silencer exploded and her engine room flooded, in September 1951. She parted her tow and disappeared on 30 January 1952. The last unit of the class, *Dark Scout*, was built entirely of aluminum. [*MoD*]

Dark Hussar is shown as a motor gunboat, November 1957. In constrast to the Gays, her pole mast is surmounted by the 'candlestick' of a UHF radio. The big dipole is a VHF antenna, and the whips are HF. [*MoD*]

wooden hulls (generally on aluminum alloy frames).

Finally, there was the issue of armament. No fast attack boat could perform well as a high-speed gun platform because the movement was too great. Both navies therefore attempted, after the war, to develop special stabilized guns suited to small craft. The US Navy soon abandoned this project, but British work on a new Coastal Forces' gun continued to the end.* The problem was weight. The mounting had to incorporate both gyro/stabilization *and* enough gun power to be useful, without overly straining a light hull. The original CFS 1 (Coastal Forces Ssytem Mark 1) gun was an adaption of the wartime '8 cwt' 4.5in weapon. Stabilization made it too heavy to be usable. The alternative CFS 2, a modified 20-pounder (3.3in) tank gun, was under development in 1957, having been tested aboard the experimental *Bold Pioneer*.

As for complete designs, in 1949 the Royal Navy planned to retain some of its existing craft and to operate a few captured S-boats. Many served in experimental roles. The only new craft were the two small hull-material prototypes (which were not expected to lead to production orders) and the two large experimental units (*Bold* class). As an indication of projects then in hand or contemplated, the Trident exhibition (a display of the future of the Royal Navy for British officers) included models of (a) a prototype A/S boat (medium speed); (b) conversion of a D-Type Fairmile as a prototype for emergency conversion; and (c) a prototype convertible Coastal Forces craft, the latest attempt to meet staff requirements.

* This is still a problem. The current standard US small craft gun is the unstabilized M242 25mm Chain gun. A fully-stabilized Gatling gun has been proposed, and trials began in August 1986. The US Navy currently has a stabilized 40mm gun, but it has not been entirely successful in service.

Brave Borderer was one of two medium convertible fast patrol craft, the ultimate British postwar development in this field. She and her sisters were powered by gas turbines, and were credited with speeds as great as 50 knots. Their beam was unusually great to accommodate the three engines, and they had a hydraulic trim flap in the transom. The bridge structure was located unusually far aft, so that a CFS2 3.3in gun (as tested aboard *Bold Pioneer* could be mounted forward. That in turn pushed the engines aft, and they had to employ V-drives, exhausting through the transom rather than through conventional uptakes as in earlier gas turbine craft. The CFS2 was never fitted (at 8.5 tons it was too heavy for a boat with a total payload of only 10 tons), and the boats carried two 40mm guns (as here) and two 21in torpedoes (in side-launching cradles) as gunboats. Alternatively, they could land the forward 40mm gun and carry four torpedoes. The objects abeam the bridge are long-range self-sealing fuel tanks; only the after one was carried in the MGB and MTB configurations. *Brave Swordsman* differed in detail. A similar but unarmed craft was built as the yacht *Mercury* for Stavros Niarchos, and Vosper further developed this design in the privately-built *Ferocity*. Foreign sales were: two to Germany, six to Denmark, four to Malaysia, one to Brunei and three to Libya. The *Scimitar*, an unarmed target for the Royal Navy, was a further development of the same concept. [USN]

The Coastal Forces model showed the hard chine hull design alternative.**

By 1949, the Royal Navy had decided to build only large (long) MTBs, because only they could easily accommodate a wide range of alternative armaments. They would, moreover, enjoy much superior sea keeping. since all small craft would be expensive, the main justification for building any one type would be the ability to carry a worthwhile and effective armament. Moreover, if either the Deltic engine or the gas turbine succeeded as expected, the short boat would lose its only existing advantage, higher speed. Thus, given limited funds, it seemed unwise to continue the line of short MTB development in parallel with the long MTB line.

This view was not universally accepted. The chief operational small attack craft commander argued that there was still a major cost (3:1) and manning (5:2) difference. Short boats enjoyed a small silhouette and presented a small radar target. They were also relatively easy to ship overseas. Although DCAM (Director Craft and Amphibious Matériel) disagreed (he suspected that these views were based entirely on wartime experience, most of it in short MTBs), the Director of Plans included two (later cut to one) short (less than 75ft) convertible MTB/MGB in the 1950-51 program. They became the Deltic-powered *Dark* class. Operational experience would later confirm DCAM's suspicion that they were just too small to be flexible.

** The 1948 fleet plan had shown a total of 12 MTBs (built three per year) and 24 seaward defense craft (12 per year over two years). However, these programs suffered when money became tighter in 1949, and, apart from the two prototypes, no new coastal craft were ordered until the outbreak of war in Korea.

Thus, when Britain began to mobilize in 1950, the Deltic was not yet available. Instead of the new *Dark*, the wartime Packard-powered 1944 Vosper MTB was virtually reproduced as the *Gay* class. Further 'short' boats (to a quite different hull design) powered by the new Deltic became the *Dark* class. None was entirely satisfactory. All were designed to be convertible between torpedo boat and gunboat roles, but by the fall of 1951 it was clear that they would be suitable only as torpedo boats. They could only carry a locally-controlled 4.5in gun, which could not compare to the CFS 2 – which, unfortunately, could not fit aboard. The short MTB program was, therefore, ordered stopped after 31 boats. For the future, the Royal Navy would employ a truly convertible medium fast patrol boat. An even larger (long) boat would be more desirable, but too expensive for peacetime construction.***

*** Short MTB characteristics (designed to a 1950 staff requirement): A: *Gay* class (12 boats, all wood), B: *Dark* type (19 boats, composite construction). Alternative batteries: (a) MGB, (b) MTB, (c) both, (d) minelayer.

	A	B
DISPLACEMENT (tons)	65 (MGB)	51
DIMENSIONS (ft,in)	71,4 x 19,5 x 2,7 forward/7,2 aft	75,4½ x 19,8 x 2,½ forward/6,1 aft
POWERPLANT	3 Packard W 14	2 Deltic T 18 diesel
BHP	4050	5000shp at 40 knots
MGB	1 4.5 Mk 1 (8 cwt) or 1 Bofors Mk 8, 2 2in RFL forward 1 Bofors Mk 8 or 2 2in RFL, 2 DC Mk VII aft	
MTB	1 twin Oerlikon Mk 12A, 2 2in RFL, 2 DC Mk VII 4 21in TT	2 21in TT

Conversion: A only: 2 21in, 1 4.5in (8 cwt) or Bofors Mk 8, 2 2in rocket flare launchers, 2 DC Mk VII, Asdic 712A.
Minelayer: 6 ground mines, 1 Bofors or twin Oerlikon (A); 1 twin Oerlikon (B), 2 2in RFL, 2 DC Mk VII.

The French 'coastal patrol boat' *L'Etourdi* is representative of a type which was very numerous in the US and Royal Navies during World War II, but virtually abandoned postwar. The design was derived from that of the US wartime 173ft PC, but considerably modified. Note the 120mm anti-submarine mortar forward of the bridge, which (like other French ASW mortars) fires both anti-submarine and shore-bombardment rounds. France built 14 (three funded by MDAP, five under her 1955 naval program, and six under her 1956 naval program) for her own Navy. MDAP funded the construction of six more units, three for Portugal (which built five more in local yards), two for West Germany (one serving as an ASW trials ship, later transferred to Tunisia; the other was delivered instead to Ethiopia, then transferred to Italy) and one for Yugoslavia. The US Navy also devised its own modified version of the 173ft vessel, with a trainable Hedgehog forward, for the Turkish Navy. Others were built in Chile. [DTCN]

Due to delays in the completion of the two experimental long MTBs, the *Bolds*, no long hull design was completed. Instead, a compromise medium boat was developed, based on a 1952 SDPC proposal. It appeared that a prototype might be ready in 1955, but in January 1953 that date was advanced to 1957. Sketch staff requirements were issued in October 1953.

As of August 1951, the planned program showed the 31 short boats and eight long boats

(1953-54). A new medium design was planned for the 1954-55 program. Under the Radical Review all eight long boats were cancelled. However, eight medium boats were retained for the time being. Ultimately, only two medium craft, the *Braves*, were built.

Captain, Coastal Forces argued in 1951 that long boats (comparable to the two *Bolds*) were far too expensive. Short boats could not take the CFS 2, partly because of trim and partly because the fore

HMS *Shalford*, the prototype seaward defense boat, is shown here on 6 May 1954. She was the only one of her class equipped with an ahead-throwing weapon, the full Squid on her quarterdeck. A single-barrel version of this weapon, the intended armament of the class, never materialized. Nor were any of them fitted with the higher-powered engined intended for such craft. The class was limited to a speed of 13 knots. [MoD]

part of the boat could not be sufficiently strengthened without an unacceptable loss in maximum speed. To fit a third engine, however, would require an increase in the size of the boat to take it, and the fuel and extra weight involved might well offset the extra power provided.

He proposed that any future motor gunboat have: CFS 2 or 4 21in torpedoes, reasonable gun platform, good sea keeping, a speed of 46 knots, and an easy and cheap construction.

Probably, this could be achieved on 80-90ft with diesels compounded with a gas turbine, ie, two compounded Deltics. Without some very high-powered engine, such as the compound, the Royal Navy would be forced to build expensive long boats as gunboats and therefore with limited resources it could not have enough torpedo boats. A truly convertible FPB would have great advantages in building cost, maintenance, supply, and time.

Staff requirements prepared in 1953 showed a vessel of 98ft x 25ft,4in x 7ft,3in ans 120 tons; with three Proteus gas turbines, 10,500shp giving 46 knots for one hour, 40 knots continuously and 400nm at 40 knots. The FPB would be convertible as MGB, MGB/MTB, MTB, Minelayer; for joint/combined (ie, amphibious) operations. Alternative armaments were specified as:

— 1 CFS 2, single Bofors L60
— 2 torpedoes and tubes, as above
— 4 torpedoes and tubes, 1 Bofors
— 10 ground mines, 1 Bofors
— 1 Bofors
— 2 Mark XIII DC chutes could be carried in all four standard conditions.

Due to the run-down of Coastal Forces, only two *Brave* class convertible medium FPBs were built to this specification. They were the last of a series which could be traced back about two decades. CFS 2 itself was built in prototype form, but does not appear ever to have been mounted aboard a *Brave*.

Seaward defense was a matter of considerable controversy. A 1948 study suggested that harbors might best be defended, not by local patrol craft, but rather by fixed obstructions, seabed sonars and long-range weapons either ashore or aboard large anchored hulks. One argument was that the delay between detection of a small submarine and reaction by a distant motor launch might be far too long. Better to develop a long-range Limbo and emplace it on a nearby breakwater, with a direct connection to a harbor defense headquarters.

The main drawback to total reliance on fixed defenses was short sonar detection range, particularly against very small craft. Fixed defenses would have to be provided in substantial numbers to cover any of the important ports. The program actually adopted in 1949 called for a combination of patrol craft with fixed defenses and harbor obstructions. The patrol craft became the seaward defense craft of the 'fifties, the *Ford* class.

As in the case of the fast attack craft, the two principal problems in their design were propulsion (for relatively high speed) and suitable weaponry. Studies conducted in 1949 showed that a speed of 15 knots was desirable, if not essential. The staff requirements called for at least 20 knots in the final design. The chosen weapon was a single-barrel version of Squid. Hedgehog showed too small a probability of success. Depth charges were better. As for torpedoes, homing weapons probably would not succeed in shallow water. Only a command-guided (wire-guided) torpedo held much promise.

Speed was a major problem. Only the Deltic promised anything like the required 20 knots, and the program stalled at least once because the only alternative, the Paxman diesel, could drive a boat at only 13 knots. All were, however, completed with the lower-powered plant, two Paxman 12YHAXM 550bhp diesels on the wing shafts, and a 100bhp Foden FD6 on the center shaft for loiter, with a range of 2000nm at 12 knots and a maximum speed of 13 knots. Armament consisted of one Bofors Mark 8, two 2in rocket flare launchers, and ten depth charges in chutes, with Type 163A sonar. One boat, *Shalford*, was completed with a triple Squid and ten Mk 12 depth charges.

Four war-built Fairmile 'D' type MTBs were converted as prototypes for mobilization; they were redesignated MASB in 1953, and later SDB, or Seaward Defense Boats. Two were used for prototype trials, and two for training. The two trials craft (*SDB 3050* and *SDB 3053*) had Hedgehog and two rocket flare projectors forward, and a 40mm Bofors and depth charges aft.

These craft would operate under the control of a Seaward Defense Headquarters, provided with data from harbor-bottom sonar and from magnetic loops. Detection and classification of small targets was, in fact, the most difficult aspect of the problem. Of the two available methods, acoustic was considered more effective than magnetic. Even so, the existing Type 131 HDA (Harbor Defense Asdic) and the Port Entrance Asdic (Type 135) were expected to detect and locate pygmies at ranges of only 200 yards, so large numbers would be needed. Standard magnetic loops could detect SBUs of 50 tons or more in depths of 30 fathoms and MILL loops could detect midgets in depths of eight fathoms. Such loops were useful primarily as a warning system, but they had to be backed up by HDAs and patrol craft.

Radar would be used primarily to assist in classification (eg, by detecting periscopes), and to con SD craft on to contacts obtained by fixed locators. The plot in the seaward defense headquarters would assist in classification. Contacts appearing to move in unnatural fashion (eg, at very high speeds) could be discarded as false.

Both measures could be assisted by harbor obstructions, such as booms, which would reduce the area to be covered. Fixed obstructions were best, with nets and booms – and mines – as the

Sprat: the other side of inshore ASW. Originally designed to test British defenses against imagined Soviet midgets, the four postwar British midget submarines (X-craft) were ultimately built to attack Soviet harbors. She is shown on the Thames, June 1957. [CPL]

Cutaway of *Stickleback* as completed. [*John Lambert*]

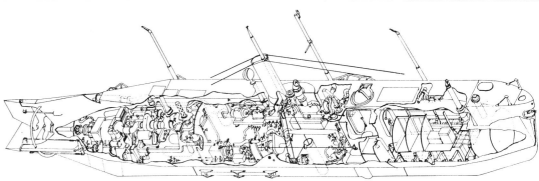

next best alternatives. However, nets and booms were clearly not impassible, and hence had to be defended by patrol craft, or by boom vessels armed with effective ASW weapons such as Squids. Small size might well protect midgets and other small battle units from mines.

Weapons would be mounted both on shore and on the patrol vessels. Existing coast defense guns and mortars were considered ineffective, although small calibre guns on forts and breakwaters might be useful against pygmies and midgets that had to break surface. Depth charge throwers and squids aboard Gate vessels and on breakwaters would be useful, but they were limited to a fixed danger zone. Limbo was much more attractive, because it could be aimed over a wide area, both in train and in range.

Extensive fixed defenses were emplaced between 1949 and 1954. Harbor entrances were reduced by fixed steel obstructions and preparations made to narrow them further by booms in wartime. Although the booms themselves would not be emplaced in peacetime, their moorings were laid and swamped. The building program included new boom defense vessels to tend them in wartime. The narrowed entrances were to be monitored by a combination of outer guard magnetic-detection loops, harbor defense Asdics, and inner guard loops, all laid on the bottom. Commercial radars were installed as an interim seaward defence measure, and a special shore-based seaward defense radar developed.

Efforts were also made to counter the other

major threat to the harbors, air-laid mines. A Royal Naval minewatching service was formed in 1952. It was to number 30,000, but recruiting was slow and this goal was never reached. A special minewatching radar was developed.

The defended ports were:

Portsmouth Command:	Flag Officer Scotland:
Portsmouth*	Firth of Forth*
Plymouth Command:	Clyde
Devonport	Loch Ewe
Milford Haven	Tyne
Belfast	Scapa Flow*
Nore Command:	Mediterranean:
Thames*	Malta (radar only)
Sheerness (radar only)	
Humber*•	
Dover*	
Harwich	

Asterisks indicate planned fixed obstructions. In some cases there were local problems. For example, loops and Asdics could not be laid on the floor of the Firth of Forth in peacetime as they would disturb the local fishing industry.

Seaward defense was clearly a hot war program, and to do it correctly would be quite expensive. It was therefore a candidate for reduction or elimination under the Radical Review. As of July 1954, a total of 18 Fords were planned, 16 of which were complete (of which 13 would be held in reserve in peacetime), and two were built to replace two sold to South Africa. One seaward defense motor launch was in commission. The British mobilization plan called for a build-up to adequate defense of all 27 Group I ports within about six months. A total of 104 ex-Naval motor launches would be taken over, 29 of which would be pressed into service as emergency patrol craft. Another ten would be fitted out (with sonars) each month; this was the maximum possible, given other mobilization programs. There were also five seaward defense trawlers, and another 50 earmarked for emergency service.

This concept had two great defects. First, none of the ports would be defended much before the six-month build-up had been completed. The emergency patrol craft, for example, would be much too thinly spread. An alternative might be to concentrate the sonar-equipped craft in three ports, and the non-sonar craft in five more. British ports were rated according to their importance to the overall Allied war effort. The three Bristol Channel ports were omitted as they were not suited to non-sonar craft. The Thames Estuary might be omitted because small battle units would find it difficult to negotiate. A sample list, then, in order of importance, would be:

1 Tyne (or Loch Ewe) 5 Portsmouth
2 Clyde   6 Milford Haven
3 Mersey   7 Humber
4 Forth   8 Portsmouth

Even this reduced list would consume 68 per cent of existing British boom defense vessels plus converted trawlers, or nearly all of the boom defense vessels alone.

The second defect was strategic in character. The existing policy could, at best, protect eight ports if given 30 days' notice. Surely they would be the prime nuclear targets in a hot thermonuclear war. After the strike, if food could be imported at all, it would have to come in through small ports and anchorages. No existing force could defend them all, given existing concepts. Moreover, the main threat would surely be submarine-launched torpedoes and mines. Small battle units would be a negligible threat unless the war became protracted.

Worst of all, seaward defense contributed nothing to cold war, and therefore, acording to the new policy, it could receive no priority over the next four to five years. It therefore was allowed to die off.

HMS *Greatford* illustrates the standard configuration of the Ford class seaward defense boats: note the two long and two short depth charge tracks aft. She is shown here in 1954. [*USN*]

10
EPILOGUE

Thirty years after the end of the period described in this book, the critical naval issues have not really changed. The great problem is still how to balance global (hot war) and cold war naval capabilities and requirements. Nuclear deterrence increasingly seems limited in its application, so that the choices made in 1955 (eg the Radical Review) seems less attractive now. Remarkably, the two major new naval weapon systems developed over the last thirty years were already included in British and US projections made at that time: ballistic missile submarines and vertical take-off aircraft.

They did not have quite the effects foreseen at the time, however. The advent of the ballistic missile submarine did overthrow the primacy of

the RAF in the British deterrent force. However, the Royal Navy was not able to maintain its other important role, tactical strike. Its VSTOL Sea Harrier fighters and their carriers became almost a sop to make up for the elimination of the British large-deck carrier force. In the US case, the advent of submarine-launched strategic missiles detached the carriers – and the fleet as a whole – from the hot war mission.

Nor was it ever possible for either major Western navy to limit hot war investment to the deterrent: NATO saw to that, since its members could never agree to base their survival entirely on a US or Anglo-American nuclear threat. Thus the simple choice of the Radical Review, to limit expenditure to deterrence and cold war (global

The shape of the future, *circa* 1955: a US carrier-based nuclear bomber (a modified North American AJ Savage) fuels a nuclear-capable fighter-bomber (North American Fury). Note that the large Savage (and the larger Douglas A3D) were built around the dimensions and weight of the 1945-era atomic bomb; the Fury could carry a more powerful weapon externally, albeit not to the same range. [*USN*]

peacekeeping) forces, always had to be stretched to include NATO forces which could contribute to the early stages of a hot war, before nuclear escalation set in. The assumption that any European war would end quickly due to the threat of nuclear escalation tended in turn to discount the value of naval forces required to maintain the Alliance over the course of a lengthy conflict. In the case of Britain, the NATO calculation was complicated by the need to maintain a sufficient contribution to justify British national prestige within the Alliance. Similarly the British contribution to the Alliance deterrent continues to be predicated, in part, on the need to maintain a say in overall Alliance nuclear strike policy.

The logic of the Radical Review was inescapable. Money could be spent either on hot war or on cold war naval forces. In 1955, Britain still saw herself primarily as a global power, and the choice was simple: cold war or presence or global peacekeeping forces had to be preserved. They were used the following year, at Suez. The disaster, in which the United States was able to abort the Anglo-French operation, had profound effects. British global power was clearly limited. Although the cold war choice survived the 1957 Defense White Paper (which, like the Radical Review, was intended to cut defense costs to a tolerable level), Britain began to retreat from her overseas commitments. Finally, she officially gave them up altogether by withdrawing from 'east of Suez' in 1971. In theory, that ended the cold war mission altogether, although in practice the Royal Navy continued to provide global naval presence. Ironically, the major postwar British cold war operation, the Falklands War, occurred eleven years later.*

The naval development described in this book has been brought up to about 1955, when national (and naval) strategies, at least in the United States and Britain, were changing radically, based on increasing faith in nuclear deterrence. The conclusions of the British Radical Review were the strongest example of this shift, as evidenced by the rapid demise of the British reserve fleet (particularly its ASW elements) and of the postwar British minesweeper program. The wealthier US Navy never went quite so far, but operations in Vietnam wore out its surviving war-built destroyers, and ships in reserve had to be scrapped as new ASW equipment (particularly sonars) was much too massive to be included in any worthwhile modernization program. Perhaps more importantly, the US Navy was unable to replace the ships it lost. Its strength was approximately halved in a few years, from a high of 960 in 1967 down to 682 in 1971, and to 468 in 1978.

Worse, the choice of the 'fifties, hot war (ASW, mine countermeasures, strike carrier) *vs* cold war

(gun ships, amphibious craft, more austere strike carriers), has been further complicated by the emergence of the ballistic missile submarine. Unlike the strike carrier, it has no role in either a hot (non-holocaust) or a warm war. Nor is the deterrent as inexpensive as some imagined, particularly for a relatively small navy. Thus, although the choice was not explicit, it appears that the British choice of Polaris as the future deterrent doomed the British fixed-wing carrier force. Costs were roughly equivalent. Moreover, the adoption of Polaris withdrew a major mission from the RAF, leaving tactical air strike. Because there could not be enough money to support both the new tactical aircraft the RAF wanted (such as a British version of the US F-111) and new carriers designed to mount deep tactical strikes, the RAF treated the fight over the future of the British carrier force (in 1964/65) as a fight for its effective existence. It won.

The United States did not have to make so stark a choice, partly because ballistic missile submarines represented a smaller fraction of its much larger budget. However, as Defense money became tighter under the Carter administration, the US Air Force began to claim that, using air to air refuelling, it could mount strikes anywhere in the world from US territory. Large expensive carriers would not be replaced as they wore out. Instead, the US Navy would concentrate on the deterrent (in the form of Trident submarines) and on sea control forces for global war (frigates and, perhaps, mine craft). This argument also had its proponents inside the US Navy itself. Under the Reagan Administration, the global war-fighting forces are once again being emphasized, and the rate of Trident authorizations is considerably below that planned by the Carter Administration.

In the face of a massive Soviet nuclear arsenal, deterrence is two-sided. It seems more and more difficult for the West to rely entirely on its own nuclear weapons to prevent a Soviet non-nuclear attack, or even swiftly to end a war begun with such an attack. Two-sided nuclear deterrence probably precludes even the tactical use of nuclear weapons at sea, as in anti-submarine warfare. The implication would seem to be that, should a major war ever begin, it would be protracted, like the wars envisaged soon after 1945. Hence the revived US interest in hot war naval forces.

That is not to say that general war, even general non-nuclear war, is particularly likely. No one is likely to risk escalation to nuclear warfare, however unlikely. However, wars sometimes begin through incidents which in turn force both sides into relatively gradual escalation. In a time of crushing nuclear superiority, NATO might have been able to stop such escalation by a timely nuclear threat. That is no longer possible, at least with current types of forces. Even so, the risk of escalation is likely to limit Soviet adventures to the Third World.

As the logic of the Radical Review shows, to accept this implication is also to accept

* It has often been argued that Argentina was encouraged by the scrapping of what amounted to cold war ships, which seemed to them to show a lack of British resolve.

One lesson of the postwar period is that sheer numbers in a fleet guarantee a substantial degree of flexibility, as ships can be spared for experiments and modifications. *Epperson* was one of two *Gearing* class destroyers completed as experimental escorts. Note her Weapon Alfa forward, her fixed Hedgehog (on the superstructure deck just abaft it), and her array of K-guns and depth charges aft. She also had four fixed torpedo tubes, the muzzles of which are visible in the deckhouse just forward of her second funnel. This photograph probably dates from about 1958. [*USN*]

considerably more expensive naval forces. The West must be prepared to deal with the threats of both central global war and local limited conflict. Worse, with the rise of many relatively wealthy Third World countries, conflict not involving the Soviets (hence not deterrable in the usual ways) is more likely. Thus the choice made during the Radical Review, to depend upon the least expensive form of deterrence to avoid hot global war, while concentrating on cold war forces, seems less and less supportable. However, the logical basis of the Radical Review, that it was virtually impossible (at least for Britain) to afford both specialized global war and cold war naval forces while maintaining a healthy economy, still seems to apply.

In the case of the United States, which has most fully accepted the possibility of protracted non-nuclear war, the proposed solution, the current Maritime Strategy, has been to recast the global war strategy, so that cold and hot war requirements more nearly match. This in turn is possible largely because the strategic context, in Soviet terms, has changed since the 'fifties, providing the West with a point of leverage in the

shape of Soviet ballistic missile submarines. Given this leverage, a hot sea-control war may no longer require very large numbers of more and more expensive escorts – which NATO as a whole seems unable to provide in the requisite numbers.

Moreover, the context of sea control has changed. In the early postwar period, the NATO area could be divided into zones. In the Mediterranean, Soviet bombers would be the primary threat, particularly if Soviet armies advanced along the northern coast. Soviet submarines would find it difficult to penetrate either the Dardanelles or the Straits of Gibraltar. Conversely, the major threat in the Central Atlantic would be Soviet submarines. Bombers lacked the requisite range. Only in the North were both threats present. Therefore only in the North did successful NATO sea control require a combination of carrier-based fighters and ASW ships with highly effective anti-aircraft weapons.

However, as they have evolved, Sovet naval bombers have gained range, to the point where they can indeed threaten the open Atlantic. The most expensive existing escorts may be able to cope with their missiles, but they cannot be

expected to destroy the bombers themselves, which can therefore adopt a strategy of exhaustion. The actual destruction of the bombers, then, becomes a prerequisiste not merely for free use of the Norwegian Sea, but even for free use of the North Atlantic. This task can only become more important as Soviet naval aviation replaces the obsolete Badger with the newer Backfire and then Blackjack bombers and new, longer-range anti-ship missiles.

The bomber threat, then, makes an earlier NATO policy emphasizing single-role ASW escorts obsolescent. As in the immediate postwar period, attack at source becomes much more attractive. It in turn requires a combination of offensive weapons, probably primarily large strike carriers. Given the threat the carriers represent, moreover, the Soviet naval bombers can be expected to attack them before they can strike. It therefore becomes very important for them to be able to destroy the Soviet Naval Air Force in the air, in what is now called the outer air battle. These strategic and tactical ideas in turn are being expressed in new weapon systems. Their roots go all the way back to the immediate postwar period.

As for ASW, current US thinking is based on two aspects of known Soviet doctrine. One is that the Soviet Navy is very much a junior service, with three major wartime roles: protection of Soviet territory from assault from the sea (eg, by carrier aircraft); direct support of the Soviet army (eg, by staging amphibious assaults on the seaward flanks of the army); and contribution to the Soviet national deterrent through its ballistic missile submarines and their numerous supporting ships. At the outset, then, attacks on Allied sea lanes of communication would not be a primary Soviet naval role. The Allied strategy, then, should be to ensure that this role is not adopted (presumably at the behest of an army-dominated General Staff) after fighting has begun, perhaps after a relative stalemate has developed. The second point is the primacy of nuclear weapons, and hence of Soviet ballistic missile submarines, in overall Soviet thinking.

From a Soviet point of view, nuclear weapons, whether or not they are actually employed, have a very special place in war. Since the end of World War II, the Soviets have asserted that they cannot be defeated by conventional weapons. This was

Kent, a County class destroyer, displays her Third World gun battery, forward. It was symbolic of the retreat from East of Suez that the Royal Navy replaced one of the two 4.5in guns with four Exocet anti-ship launchers – weapons perhaps useful in the North Atlantic against Soviet warships, but not in the old Commonwealth role. The long unbroken space amidships covers her missile magazine. Note the big helicopter aft, the first British approach to removing helicopters from carriers. The ship is shown here at Chatham, October, 1963. [*CPL*]

Stalin's way of saying that not having been fully prepared for Hitler's invasion in 1941 had not been a potentially fatal error. That in turn was necessary to Stalin's political position within the Soviet Union. His successors thought otherwise. Part of the posthumous rejection of Stalin was the adoption of a new doctrine, the Revolution in Military Affairs, which held that, unlike conventional weapons, nuclear weapons could be decisive, even against the largest country. Had Hitler had the atomic bomb, Stalin's error would have been fatal. This issue was particularly important because standard Soviet ideology assumed that a major war would occur when the Western powers, sinking under the weight of historical force, tried desperately to save themselves by destroying the center of the world revolution engulfing them, the Soviet Union.*

Ever since 1955, then, nuclear weapons have had a central place in Soviet thinking. The ultimate goal has been to neutralize the Western strategic arsenals, since, given Soviet doctrine, they are the most threatening Western weapons. At the very least, the Soviets assume that the primary Western war aim is to destroy their own nuclear weapons. They assume that the nuclear balance is the primary determinant of the peace settlement at the end of a war. Thus, even if a war never escalates to nuclear exchange, they assume that the nuclear balance will determine which concessions either side must make.

Khrushchev, who practically invented the Revolution in Military Affairs, was willing to reduce radically his non-nuclear programs in order to buy small numbers of strategic weapons, to achieve what might be called minimum deterrence. In that sense his military ideas came quite close to those of the British Radical Review and the 1957 Defense White Paper. They raised much the same sort of uproar (albeit within a much more secretive establishment).**

The failure of Soviet deterrence in Cuba may

have been the equivalent of the failure of Western deterrence in Korea: in each case it became painfully obvious that the nuclear threat had its limits. Khrushchev's military opponents helped depose him, and then to introduce a more broadly-based program. It still included a heavy emphasis on nuclear weapons, but also less futuristic systems such as bombers and tactical aircraft.

The Soviet Navy, which had been the first to build ballistic missile submarines in 1955, had been shunted out of the strategic arsenal in favor of the land-based strategic rocket forces. About 1963-64 (Khrushchev fell in 1964) it resumed the development of sea-based strategic missiles. In line with the fundamental requirement to eliminate Western nuclear weapons, it had already assumed the mission of finding and destroying Western ballistic missile submarines. Unlike the Western powers, the Soviets never really accepted the idea that ballistic missile submarines were somehow immune from detection and attack. That in turn led to what, for them, was a new naval mission: control of the sea areas in which their missile submarines would operate in wartime. This mission largely explains the construction of such ships as the VSTOL carrier *Kiev*.

As the Soviet strategic arsenal grew in proportion to that of the West, it bacame possible to imagine that its deterrent force was such that it could keep the Western powers from using nuclear weapons even after the outbreak of war. The Soviets began to imagine fighting a war without actually using their nuclear weapons at all — a protracted non-nuclear conflict. Note that, in their view, ultimate success in such a conflict requires them to draw down the Western nuclear arsenal while at the same time preserving their own — including their ballistic missile submarines.

Ultimately, such a conventional war emphasis may lead to increased Soviet naval interest in attacks on Western sea lanes of communication, such as the transatlantic trade route. After all, NATO cannot keep fighting if it cannot be resupplied. However, the past exerts an enormous pressure, in terms of actual ships and equipment, and also in terms of doctrine. In 1986, the large Soviet submarine fleet is still designed primarily for two tasks: to attack Western naval strike forces, particularly carriers and amphibious ships; and to protect the Soviet ballistic missile submarines from Western attack.

This current emphasis represents an unusual opportunity for the West. Continued pressure on the Soviet ballistic submarine 'bastions' or holding areas will tend to tie down the Soviet attack submarines which might otherwise be available for attacks on trade. Similarly, the presence of US carrier and NATO amphibious forces in the north, near the Soviet land mass, must attract many submarines not well suited to anti-submarine warfare. Certainly the joint requirement to maintain this sort of protection and also to keep

---

* This doctrine did not preclude a Soviet pre-emptive attack, which might look suspiciously like aggression to its Western victims. Similarly, the Soviets might categorize Western defense of the status quo as aggression against the natural force of history. The point here is how the Soviets view themselves, not how some future scenario might unfold.

** Examples included the cancellation of much of Stalin's cruiser and submarine programs. Khrushchev was once heard to say that he had no use for any submarine which could not fire nuclear missiles. Like the British government of 1954-57, moreover, Khrushchev decided that he could best spend his limited resources on future rather than on current technology. If war could be avoided by near-term bluff (Khrushchev being an expert), then there was little point in spending vast sums on systems which, like bombers, would soon be outdated. Khrushchev's memoirs show that he generally suspected that professional military advice was motivated more by the careerist desires of his officers than by any rational consideration. Colonel Oleg Penkovskiy claimed that he became a traitor to avenge Khrushchev's unacceptable treatment of the Soviet General Staff.

Western strike forces out of attack range of the Soviet Union has been translated into a demand to control the sea (and the contiguous land) out to increasing distances, and probably ultimately to beyond the Greenland-Iceland-United Kingdom-Norway line.

Thus it is possible to envisage an ASW strategy based on two elements. Western nuclear submarines penetrate the 'bastions' mainly in order to hold down as many Soviet submarines as possible. They try to reduce the size of the Soviet submarine fleet, but their overall holding-down effect is probably much greater than the level of losses they can inflict. Second, the NATO Strike Fleet operates in the Norwegian Sea, where it attracts attacks by both submarines and Soviet naval aircraft: Its strong escort, like the convoy escorts of the past, tends to destroy these submarines which attack it. Its aircraft destroy the Soviet Naval Air Force either at its bases or in the air. A few submarines do leak into the Atlantic, where they must face SOSUS-directed aircraft and HUK groups. Convoy escorts are available, but only in very limited numbers.

One of the major advantages of this strategy is that most of the forces it requires, the carrier battle groups, are also needed to fight limited wars. Another is that it is effective even though the newest Soviet submarines are very quiet, and hence very difficult to detect in the open ocean. It is a strategy solution to a severe technological problem. That alone is a major departure from recent practice. To some extent it may reflect a feeling that much of the material – but not the tactical potential of the post-1945 technological revolution has already been realized. A new generation is coming, but it is some time away.

Between 1945 and about 1960 it seemed that the rate of new technological development was accelerating very rapidly. However, many systems were introduced before the technology they incorporated was mature for general service use. Surface-to-air missiles were the major case in point. The first Terriers entered service in 1955, yet seven years later they (and their successors) were considered quite useless tactically, because only very rarely could they meet anything like their designed performance. Meanwhile, a rapidly developing radar and electronics technology promised better and better performance. It took some years for the Navy to discover that 'better and better' meant better and better maximum performance but, because of unreliability, not necessarily better average performance, as often the missile and guidance systems did not work at all. The 1955 missiles were not really reliable – operationally mature – until about a decade later, after an expensive 'get well' program. The more complex the system, the lengthier the development process, so that the effective rate of innovation has not been nearly so headlong as it seemed to be in the early postwar period. Another formulation would be that the simpler manifestations of the new postwar technology came first, and that more sophisticated ones came much more slowly.

Perhaps as importantly, once the new post-1945 technology had been widely distributed, mass replacement could occur only relatively slowly. It is one thing to introduce the first dozen Sparrow air-to-air missiles, but quite another to replace the first five thousand, or ten thousand Standard missiles, when production is running less than a thousand per year. Similarly, there is a great difference between the introduction of the first three or four missile ships, and the introduction of a major block upgrade to, say, fifty operational ships.

The advent of really reliable electronic equipment is probably a far more radical technological advance than the invention of any particular weapon system. In many cases the rated performance of current systems does not much exceed that of systems entering service in 1955-1960. The difference is that they can make their rated performance most of the time, whereas the 1955-60 systems could not. For example, the US '3-T' (Terrier, Talos, Tartar) missile system 'get well' program of the 'sixties explicitly avoided any improvement in maximum performance. Reliability was what counted, and it was achieved. It was very nearly enough, at least at the time, because airplanes were not achieving the futuristic levels of performance which had been expected when the missiles were being developed.

Reliable solid-state electronics is much more compact than its vacuum-tube predecessors, and it required far less power. The result is that missile-ship functions can be packaged in far smaller, and far less expensive, hulls. The US Aegis system is the primary case in point. It achieves substantially higher performance in a destroyer hull than the much more expensive Typhon system (planned in about 1960-62) would have achieved in a large cruiser hull. At the same time it is substantially more reliable than even the 'cured' versions of the earlier missile systems. Its SPY-1 fire control radar provides such a good tactical picture of the surrounding air space that force commanders sometimes choose to exercise their commands from the cramped spaces of an Aegis cruiser rather than from carriers.

Much the same might be said of sonars. In 1955, the US Navy was shifting from the 5,000-yard SQS-4 towards the larger 10,000-yard SQS-23. An even lower-frequency sonar, SQS-26, was in prospect. It was credited with 20,000-yard direct-path performance, and also with the ability to detect targets as distant as 70,000 yards using convergence-zone propagation. From about 1958 onwards, then, SQS-26 was the standard sonar in all new US surface designs. Although early models entered service within a few years, the sonar did not reliably attain anything like its design performance until the mid 'seventies, when it had been redesigned with solid-state components, rubber-window domes and with a new power supply. Now, as SQS-53, it is considered fully reliable.

All of this history suggests where current technological developments may lead. Just as offensive nuclear weapons shaped postwar strategy and technology, the prospective development of defensive strategic weapons may dominate future strategy. For example, if both the United States and the Sovier Union should shift to a defensive nuclear strategic emphasis (as seems entirely possible at present), then the current shift towards forces designed for non-nuclear protracted conflict should strengthen. However, the kind of fiscal choice exemplified by the Radical Review will still remain: how will the cost of expensive war-fighting forces be balanced off against that of strategic defense? Given their past concerns, the Soviets will have to continue to develop strategic defenses of their own, whatever their arms control posture. They too, will encounter budget problems, just as Khrushchev did in the 'fifties. However, unlike offensive weapons, defensive ones do not contribute to deterrence or to non-nuclear war-fighting capability. How will the Soviets balance the cost of their expensive new blue-water navy against that challenge? That is quite aside from the cost of modernizing the Soviet economy. After all, the Navy is the junior Soviet service.

Then there is the new tactical technology. At the most fundamental level, computing power is becoming cheaper and more reliable. That should greatly increase the intelligence inherent in future missiles, both defensive and offensive. Increased computing power should also improve the performance of passive sonars (through better signal processing), although it is clearly an open question whether submarines can become quieter faster than sonars can improve their signal processing.

There is also the new technology of stealthy aircraft (and, ultimately, missiles). Presumably, both sides will eventually adopt it. Stealth should greatly increase carrier strike power – but also the effectiveness of anti-carrier attacks. Very little has been said about its mechanism, but it is often suggested that longer-wavelength radars should be more effective than shorter-wavelength ones in detecting stealthy objects. If that is indeed the case, then warships, with their large dimensions adaptable to long-wavelength radars, should find themselves at an advantage. If new technology makes ballistic missiles very nearly obsolete, then carrier-based stealthy attack aircraft may well be the most effective remaining means of strategic attack.

Stealth ideas can, of course, be applied to warships as well as to aircraft. Several recent ships have been designed specifically for reduced radar cross section. Properly supplied with data from external sources (such as RPVs), such a ship might operate passively until a target appeared, and only then turn on fire-control radars. More intelligent missiles might be able to function with less and less shipboard support. For example, the current SM-2 (Aegis) requires a series of discrete commands, and then a few seconds of terminal illumination. The next step might be to replace the missile's semi-active seeker with an active radar, so that not even a brief period of continuous illumination would be required.

The smaller AIM-120 Advanced Medium Range Air-to-Air Missile (AMRAAM) already incorporates an active radar for autonomous homing. However, it is still (1986) experiencing some development problems.

Beyond all of these developments are the promise and the threat of the ocean reconnaissance satellite. The ultimate threat would be continuous surveillance of the entire surface of the ocean, so that no surface ship would be immune from detection and missile-borne attack. However, most ships at sea at any one time are not targets. Moreover, the more that the inherent signature of any one target ship can be reduced, the more that it can be altered to resemble those of the non-targets. Missiles and their carriers will probably always be expensive, and therefore it will not be attractive to risk wasting them. Moreover, as at present, a missile attack will tend to reveal the attacker, and so to make it vulnerable.

These considerations suggest that increased levels of ocean surveillance will tend to change the shape of surface navies (mainly in the directions of stealth, cover, and deception) but not to abolish them. World trade must still move over the surface of the sea, because the laws of nature which make that movement efficient are unlikely to be repealed. Navies will move with it, to protect it in peace and in (probably non-nuclear) war.

APPENDIX I: STAFF REQUIREMENTS FOR MODERNIZATION OF THE FLEET, 1948

In 1948, the British Naval Staff developed sketch requirements for fleet modernization, based on the 1948 long-range fleet plan (PD 06/48). As the starting point for much of the modernization described in this book, they are outlined here. The Staff could not list requirements in order of priority, but did avoid cases in which improvements would be either minor or of low priority. Perhaps the most interesting aspect of the 1948 document was the extent to which modernization was needed.

Requirements of major importance by class:

(a) Conversion of carriers to operate modern aircraft and modernization of AAFCS. [Anti-Aircraft Fire Control System]

(b) Establishment of modern AA FC equipment in DIDO class,

(c) Rearmament of 6in cruisers with DP main armament guns, AA FC, and close range armament,

NOTE: It may be possible to fit guided weapons at some stage.

(d) Fleet destroyers to be brought up to single Squid standard and AA armament modernized,

(e) Conversion of all T-class submarines to fast battery drive,

(f) Improvement of all S class submarines by fitting SNORT [snorkel] and seaguard radar,

NOTE: S-class submarines are shown in PD 06/48 as replaceable by new construction, but we do not consider this is firm enough to abandon the S-class.

(g) Conversion of older destroyers to Convoy A/S escort (frigates),

(h) Fitting of existing A/S frigates and Weapon class destroyers with the best available A/S and A/A equipment,

(i) Fitting of depot ships as W/T transmitting ships,

(j) Fitting of all mine sweepers with new type magnetic and acoustic sweeps and, when available, pressure mine sweeps or location and destruction equipment [pressure mine gear was outside the terms of reference of the study, but was considered so important that it was mentioned even though still in the R&D stage].

Class by class:

[In the following notes, A/T is anti-torpedo gear, a major project at the time.]

CARRIERS

Illustrious Class

Present gunnery	Proposed
8 twin 4.5Mk II	8 twin 3in/70 (8 MRS III)
4 HACS	
1 TIU (1 293)	2 TIU 3 (1 992)

(1) These proposals apply only to the three ships which are to be altered to operate more modern aircraft.

(2) The stowage and supply of 3in ammunition presents difficult problems.

To fit A/T countermeasures equipment.

To fit most modern equipment for self protection against mines.

Radar:

Type 960P (A)

2 x 982/983 (A)

992 (C)

MRS 3

Carrier Controlled Approach (B)

To modernize AIO.

Communications:

A 100 per cent (approx) increase in the number of V-UHF sets fitted.

Fitting of modern radio warfare equipment.

An additional 35ft required for RCM [Radar Counter Measures] transmitters.

Radio briefing equipment is to be fitted.

NOTE: This appendix does not attempt to list the alterations necessray to carry modern aircraft. [These were then under discussion in the case of *Formidable* as draft staff requirements.]

CRUISERS

6in Town Class

Present gunnery	Proposed
3 triple 6in Mk XXIII	2 twin 6in Mk XXVI
(barrage directors)	(1 Flyplane, 1 MRS 3)
4 twin 4in Mk XIX	
(2 HACS)	4 MRS 3 instead of HACS to control 4in
1 TIU (1 293)	1 TIU 3 (1 992)

NOTES: (1) 4.5in Mk VI, 5.25in Mk II, GWS or fighter direction facilities may replace some or all 6in turrets in some ships.

(2) The 3in/70 cannot be fitted in the Towns.

Torpedo and A/S:

(1) To fit A/T countermeasures equipment.

(2) To fit most modern equipment for self protection against mines.

(3) To be supplied with the improved anti-ship torpedo

(4) To fit the latest self protection Asdic set (149)

Radar:

(a) A/A or surface radar, etc	(B) 960P
	(C) 1 277Q
	(A) 993
	(A) MRS 275 III
(b) AD/FD picket role	(B) 960P
	(A) 2 982/983

To modernize AIO.

NOTES: (1) To fit 982/983 in cruisers, some proportion of the armament must be surrendered and there would be restrictions on arcs of fire.

(2) The fitting of a second pair aft would involve a major reconstruction.

Communications:

A 200 per cent (approx) increase in V-UHF sets.

Fitting of modern radio warfare equipment for which an extra 70 sq ft is required.

Fiji Class

Present gunnery	Proposed
3 triple 6in Mk XXIII	2 twin 6in Mk XXVI
(barrage directors)	(1 Flyplane, 1 MRS 3)
4 twin 4in Mk XIX	3 twin 3in/70
(2 HACS)	(3 MRS 3)
1 TIU (1 293)	1 TIU 3 (1 992)

NOTES: (1) 4.5in Mk VI, 5.25in Mk II, GWS or fighter direction facilities may replace some or all 6in turrets in some ships.

(2) It is difficult to provide adequate stowage for 3in ammunition. Bulk stowage for 1/2 outfit is acceptable.

Torpedo and A/S:

(1) To fit A/T countermeasures equipment.

(2) To fit most modern equipment for self protection against mines.

(3) To be supplied with the improved type anti-ship torpedo.

(4) To fit the latest self protection Asdic set (Type 149).

Radar:

(a) A/A or surface escort role	(B) 960P
	(C) 1 277Q
	(A) 992
	(A) MRS 275 III
(b) AD/FD picket role	(B) 960B
	(A) 2 982/983

To modernize AIO.

NOTES: (1) To fit 982/983 in cruisers, some proportion of the armament must be surrendered and there would be restrictions on arcs of fire.

(2) The fitting of a second pair aft would involve a major reconstruction.

Communications:

A 200 per cent (approx) increase in V-UHF sets together with an up to date re-arrangement of communication offices.

Modernization of MF- HF transmitters (certain ships only).

Modern radio warfare equipment for which an extra 70ft^2 is required.

Improved secret cryptographic office (20ft^2)

Swiftsure Class

Present gunnery	Proposed
3 triple 6in Mk XXIII	2 twin 6in Mk XXVI
(barrage directors)	(2 Flyplane)
4/5 twin 4in Mk XIX	3 twin 3in/70
(3 HACS/FKC)	(3 MRS 3)
1 TIU (1 293)	1 TIU 3 (1 992)

NOTES: (1) 4.5in Mk VI, 5.25in Mk II, GWS, or fighter direction facilities may replace some or all 6in turrets in some ships.

(2) It is difficult to provide adequate stowage for 3in ammunition. Bulk stowage for ½ outfit is acceptable.

Torpedo and A/S:

(a) To fit A/T countermeasures equipment.

(b) To fit most modern equipment for self protection against mines.

(c) To be supplied with the improved type anti-ship torpedo.

(d) To fit the latest self-protection Asdic set (Type 149 – Tigers to be fitted with improved dome).

Radar and Communications:

Fitting of Type 960P.

Fitting of Type 277Q.

Fitting of Type 992.

Fitting of Type 275.

To modernize AIO

Modern radio warfare equipment for which an extra 70ft^2 is required.

A 200 per cent (approx) increase in V-UHF sets.

Dido Class

Present gunnery	Proposed
4 twin 5.25 (2 HACS)	Substitute 2 Flyplane for 5.25 control
1 TIU 2 (1 293)	1 TIU 3 (1 992)

NOTE: If the AA characteristics of these cruisers are to be improved at the expense of their surface characteristics, it should be done by substituting 4.5in guns, not 3in/70. The 3in/70 is not a feasible weapon for these ships because there is only magazine space for three minutes worth of 3in ammunition.

Torpedo and A/S:

(1) To fit A/T countermeasures equipment.

(2) To fit most modern equipment for self protection against mines.

(3) To be supplied with the improved type anti-ship torpedo.

(4) To fit the latest self-protection Asdic set (Type 149).

Radar:

(a) A/A or surface escort role	(B) 960P	
	(C) 1 277Q	
	(A) 992	
	(A) MRS 275 III	
(b) AD/FD picket role	(B) 960P	
	(A) 2 982/983	

NOTES: (1) To fit 982/983 in cruisers, some proportion of the armament must be surrendered and there would be restrictions on arcs of fire.

(2) The fitting of a second pair aft would involve a major reconstruction.

Communications:

The communications equipment of these ships is insufficient, and in many cases, obsolete.

Several ships require modernization of MF-HF equipment. All require a 200-250 per cent (approx) increase in V-UHF sets. Up to date layout of offices is desirable by all ships. An additional 70ft^2 is required for modern RW equipment and 20ft^2 for a secret cryptographic office. It will be very difficult to find this amount of space in these ships.

DESTROYERS – Z class and earlier, earmarked for conversion to A/S frigates.

Present gunnery	Proposed
4, 4.7, 4.5in guns with	1 twin 4in Mk XIX
varying control systems	(CRBFD) and
	1 twin Bofors Mk V
	for early conversions
	1 twin 3in/70 (MRS 3) and
	1 twin Bofors Mk V
	for later conversions

NOTE: AA modernization is an integral part of the conversion to A/S frigate.

Torpedo and A/S:

(1) Fit A/T countermeasures equipment.

(2) Equip with A/S homing torpedoes.

(3) Install or modify torpedo tubes for discharge of A/S torpedoes, and provide stowage for reloads.

(4) Fit four square location and attack Asdic set (Type 166) with high speed dome.

(5) Fit PPI detection set.

(6) Fit Cockchafer [Type 162].

(7) Fit double variable range throwing weapon [Limbo].

(8) Fit Nightshirt [silencing].

(9) Fit A/S torpedo control system.

(10) Fit the most modern equipment for self protection against mines.

Radar:

(a) Fit (i)   maneuvering and pilotage radar [HDWS]

     (ii) radar beacon

     (iii) 293Q

(b) Fit set such as 291 with improved aerial giving ranges of some 40 miles.

To modernize AIO.

Low cover – Type 992

Communications:

Drawings for this conversion include the space for up to date layout of communication offices. Increased amounts of V-UHF and radio warfare equipment (above those now installed) will be required.

C Class

Present gunnery	Proposed
4 single 4.5 Mk V (55 deg)	1 Flyplane to control 4.5
(1 FKC)	
1 TIU 2 (1 293)	1 TIU 2 (1 293)
(not in all ships)	*CAs only:* replace K tower
	by Mk VIM and fit auto-follow
	mountings

NOTE: although the 4.5in single mountings are not satisfactory it is doubtful whether effort can be spared to replace them; but the 4in Mk XIX should be considered.

Torpedo and A/S:

(1) Fit A/T countermeasures equipment.

(2) Fit the most up to date equipment for self protection against mines.

(3) Modernize existing Asdic sets (Type 164, 147F).

(4) Fit single Squid aft.

(5) Fit Nightshirt.

(7) Supply improved type of anti-ship torpedo.

Radar:

Fit maneuvering and pilotage radar sets [HDWS].

Fit set such as 291 with large aerial giving ranges of some 40 miles.

Type 293 (Type 992 to be fitted as a replacement)

To modernize AIO.

Communications:

A 100 per cent (approx) increase in V-UHF sets.

Modern radio warfare equipment for which an extra 50ft^2 will be required.

Battle Class (*Armada* and *Trafalgars*)

Present gunnery	Proposed
2 twin 4.5 Mk IV	1 Flyplane to control 4.5
(1 FKC)	
1 TIU 2 (1 293)	

NOTE: Desirable to substitute 4.5 Mk VI for Mk IV, but probably beyond our resources.

Torpedo and A/S:

(1) Fit A/T countermeasures equipment.

(2) Fit the most modern equipment for self-protection against mines.

(3) Fit single squid (vessels of 1942 program only).

(4) Fit Nightshirt.

(6) Supply improved type of anti-ship torpedo.

Radar:

Fit maneuvering and pilotage radar sets [HDWS].

Fit set such as 291 with large aerial giving ranges of some 40 miles.

Low cover – Type 293 (Type 992 to be fitted as a replacement).

To modernize AIO.

Communications:

A 75 per cent (approx) increase in V-UHF sets. Modern radio warfare equipment for which an extra 50ft^2 is required.

Battles (*Agincourt*s)

Present gunnery	*Proposed*
2 twin 4.5 Mk IV; 1 US Mk 37	No change
1 single 4.5 Mk V (55 deg)	
1 TIU (1 293)	

NOTE: Desirable to substitute 4.5 Mk VI for 4.5 Mk IV, but probably beyond our resources.

Torpedo and A/S:

(1) Fit A/T countermeasures equipment.

(2) Fit the most modern equipment for self-protection against mines.

(3) Fit single squid (vessels of 1942 program only).

(4) Fit Nightshirt.

(7) Supply improved type of anti-ship torpedo.

Radar:

Fit maneuvering and pilotage radar sets [HDWS].

Fit set such as 291 with large aerial giving ranges of some 40 miles.

Low cover – Type 293 (Type 992 to be fitted as a replacement).

To modernize AIO.

Communications:

A 75 per cent (approx) increase in V-UHF sets. Modern radio warfare equipment for which an extra 50ft^2 is required.

Weapons Class

Present gunnery	*Proposed*
2 twin 4in Mk XIX	1 Flyplane to control 4in
(1 FKC)	
1 TIU 2 (1 293)	

Torpedo and A/S:

(1) To fit A/T countermeasures equipment.

(2) To fit the most up to date equipment for self protection against mines.

(3) To fit four square location and attack set (Type 166) with high speed dome.

(4) To fit Limbo.

(5) To fit Nightshirt.

(6) Equip with A/S homing torpedoes.

(7) Modify or replace existing torpedo tubes as necessary for discharge of A/S torpedoes.

(8) Install A/S torpedo control system.

Radar:

To Modernize AIO.

(1) Fit set such as Type 291 with a larger aerial giving ranges of some 40 miles.

(2) Low cover provided by Type 293 (Type 992 to be fitted as replacement).

(3) To fit maneuvering and pilotage radar set [HDWS].

Communications:

A small increase in V-UHF sets.

Space is available for all the radio warfare equipment required, but some of the D/F sets are not yet available.

Daring Class

Present gunnery	*Proposed*
3 twin 4.5 Mk VI	No change
(1 Flyplane)	
1 TIU (1 293)	

NOTE: Desirable but probably impossible to substitute TIU 3/992 for TIU 2/293.

Torpedo and A/S:

(1) Supply improved type anti-ship torpedo.

(2) Fit A/T countermeasures equipment.

(3) Fit Type 164 or 165 Asdic.

(4) Fit single Squid.

(5) Fit Nightshirt.

(7) Fit the most modern equipment for self-protection against mines.

Radar:

To modernize AIO.

Fit radar.

(1) Maneuvering and pilotage set [HDWS].

(2) Seaguard.

(3) IFF.

(4) Radar beacon.

Communications:

The ships will be completed to the 1947 communications staff requirements except that certain items of radio warfare equipment will not be available for fitting.

FRIGATES

Loch Class A/S frigates

Present gunnery	*Proposed*
2 single 4in Mk XXIII	1 twin 4in Mk XIX
(no control)	(1 CRBFD)

NOTES: (1) Not investigated and may not be possible. (2) The present equipment has virtually no AA value.

Torpedo and A/S:

(1) Fit A/T countermeasures equipment.

(2) Equip with A/S homing torpedoes.

(3) Install tubes for discharge of A/S torpedoes, provide stowage for reloads.

(4) Install A/S torpedo control system.

(5) Fit Nightshirt.

(6) Fit with the most up to date equipment for self-protection against mines.

(7) Modernize existing Asdic sets (to Type 165 and 147F).

Radar:

Fit radar.

(1) Maneuvering and pilotage sets.

(2) 293Q

(3) IFF.

(4) Radar beacons.

To modernize AIO.

Communications:

To accommodate the communications staff requirements, separated offices (receiving forward, transmitting aft) will be required. Fitting of modern radio warfare equipment, particularly D/F sets will require an additional 95ft^2. A 100 per cent (approx) increase in V-UHF sets is required.

Castle Class A/S frigates

Present gunnery	*Proposed*
2 single 4in Mk XXIII	1 twin 4in Mk XIX
(no control)	(1 CRBFD)

NOTES: (1) Not investigated and may not be possible. (2) The present equipment has virtually no AA value.

Torpedo and A/S:

(1) Fit A/T countermeasures equipment.

(2) Equip with A/S homing torpedoes.

(3) Install tubes for discharge of A/S torpedoes, provide stowage for reloads.

(4) Install A/S torpedo control system.

(5) Fit Nightshirt.

(6) Fit with the most up to date equipment for self-protection against mines.

(7) Modernize existing Asdic sets (to Type 165 and 147F).

(9) Fit Cockschafer (Type 162).

Radar:

Fit radar.

(1) Maneuvering and pilotage sets.

(2) 293Q

(3) IFF.

(4) Radar beacons.

To modernize AIO.

Communications:

To accommodate the communications staff requirements, separated offices (receiving forward, transmitting aft) will be required. Fitting of modern radio warfare equipment, particularly D/F sets will require an additional 95ft^2. A 100 per cent (approx) increase in V-UHF sets is required.

River Class A/S frigates

Present gunnery	*Proposed*
2 single 4in Mk XXIII	1 twin 4in Mk XIX
(no control)	(1 CRBFD)

NOTES: (1) Not investigated and may not be possible. (2) The present equipment has virtually no AA value.

Torpedo and A/S:

(1) Fit A/T countermeasures equipment.

(2) Equip with A/S homing torpedoes.

(3) Install tubes for discharge of A/S torpedoes, provide stowage for reloads.

(4) Install A/S torpedo control system.

(5) Fit Nightshirt.

(6) Fit with the most up to date equipment for self-protection against mines.

(7) Modernize existing Asdic sets (to Type 165 and 147F).

(9) Fit double Squid in place of Hedgehog.

Radar:

Fit radar.

(1) Maneuvering and pilotage sets.

(2) 293Q.

(3) IFF.

(4) Radar beacons.

To modernize AIO.

Communications:

To accommodate the communications staff requirements, separated offices (receiving forward, transmitting aft) will be required. Fitting of modern radio warfare equipment, particularly D/F sets will require an additional 95ft^2. A 100 per cent (approx) increase in V-UHF sets is required.

MINE WARFARE VESSELS

Algerines

Present gunnery	*Proposed*
1 single 4in Mk III	1 twin 4in Mk XIX
(no control)	(1 CRBFD)

NOTE: Not investigated and may not be possible.

Torpedo and A/S:

(1) Fit new loop magnetic sweep.

(2) Equip with outfits of improved dan buoys.

(3) Fit Ingolin (HTP) acoustic sweep.

(4) Equip with sweep for pressure mines or with mine location and destruction gear (it is not yet clear what form this equipment will take).

Radar and Communications:

Modernized radar and communications.

Fit maneuvering and pilotage radar.

Dan layers

Torpedo and A/S:

(1) Equip with outfits of improved dan buoys.

(2) Fit self protection equipment against influence mines.

Radar and Communications:

Modernize.

Coastal mine sweepers (MMS Types)

(1) Fit light type of new loop magnetic sweep.

(2) Fit Ingolin (HTP) acoustic sweep.

(3) Equip with outfits of improved dan buoys.

(4) Equip with sweep for pressure mines or with mine location and destruction gear.

Radar and Communications:

Modernize.

Coastal mine sweepers (ML Type)

(1) Fit Mk VII wire sweep with power winches where applicable.

(2) Fit Ingolin (HTP) acoustic sweep.

(3) Equip with outfit of improved dan buoys.

(4) Equip with sweep for pressure mines or with mine location and destruction gear.

Radar and Communications:

Modernize.

SUBMARINES – T-Class

(1) Conversion to fast battery type (intermediate B type).

(2) Modernization of torpedo discharge system (to cater for all classes of mines and firing from all depths).

(Above require major structural alterations.)

(3) Fitting modern torpedo control system.

(4) Modernization of periscopes to include radar and navigational aids.

(5) Outfitting with A/S torpedoes, improved anti-ship torpedoes, and mines suitable for all classes of submarines.

(6) Modernization of acoustic equipment (to include depth measuring equipment).

Type 167.

(7) Provision of higher capacity batteries.

(8) Modernization of all W/T aerials to allow communication when submerged.

(9) Provision of radio navigational aid when submerged.

(11) Provision of satisfactory cryptographic machines.

(12) Fit with Snort (practically complete) [snorkel].

(13) Fit external angling gear.

S-Class

Fit Snort and Seaguard radar, otherwise as for T-Class.

DEPOT SHIPS

Present gunnery	*Proposed*
4 twin 4.5 Mk III	2 Flyplane to control 4.5
(2 HACS or FKC)	

Torpedo and A/S:

(1) Fit A/T countermeasures equipment.

(2) Supply stocks of A/S homing torpedoes (for submarines or surface ships) and new anti-ship torpedo.

(3) Fit with most modern equipment for self protection against mines.

Communications:

To be fitted as wireless transmitting ships. Space is available as at present allocated [long-range].

Radar:

Maneuvering and pilotage radar.

Type 992 or 293Q.

Modernize AIO.

APPENDIX II: GLOSSARY

NOTE: In the text, British radars are often referred to by their Type numbers without the word 'Type,' as in '983'; they are listed here under their Type numbers.

AAW Anti-Air Warfare.

ACNS Assistant Chief of Naval Staff (British).

AD Aircraft Direction (British term).

AGC Amphibious command ship (US).

AIO Action Information Organization (British), equivalent to the US CIC, the center into which all information was fed to be evaluated and acted upon. CDS (see below) was an attempt to automate AIO so as to be able to react to larger numbers of faster-moving aircraft.

AKL Small cargo ship (US).

AMS The postwar US wooden coastal minesweeper, later redesignated MSC.

AOE Underway ('one stop') replenishment ship, similar in concept to an AOR (see below) but emphasizing ammunition for strike carriers; faster than an AOR (26 *vs* 20 knots in existing types).

AOR Underway ('one stop') replenishment ship, which could replace a variety of more specialized replenishment ships with a single hull.

AORN Proposed nuclear-powered AOR.

APD Fast personnel transport, a converted DE (US).

ASR Admiralty Standard Range (diesel engine).

ASSP Personnel-carrying submarine for amphibious assault (US); see also SSP.

ASW Anti-Submarine Warfare.

A/T Anti-Torpedo (measures), (British).

Auto-Follow As applied to gun mountings (British), arrangement by which the mounting automatically tracks targets under director control. Such mountings were designated RPC (Remote Power Control).

AV Seaplane tender (US).

AVA Attack seaplane tender, armed to operate independently in forward areas; projected type.

AVL Small seaplane tender (postwar US). The first were to have been modified small wartime-built seaplane tenders (AVP).

AVO Seaplane tender/refueller, a converted light cargo ship.

BB Battleship (US).

BBG Missile-armed battleship (US); projected class.

Barrage Director A wartime British anti-aircraft expedient: a simple director which allowed a cruiser's guns to be fired in barrage, at a fixed range, against an incoming target. The associated radar was Type 283.

CA Heavy cruiser (US), ie, with 8in guns.

CAG Missile conversion of heavy cruiser (US); later CG.

CAP Combat Air Patrol; carrier fighters on patrol awaiting air attack.

CDS Comprehensive Display System; a British automated plotting device similar in concept to the later US Naval Tactical Data System (NTDS).

CEP Circular Error Probable. Half of all shots fall within a circle of this radius.

CG Missile cruiser (US).

CL Light cruiser (US), ie, with 5 or 6in guns.

CLC Command cruiser (US); a designator applied only to the prototype *Northampton*. Later command ships were specially modified missile cruisers, which retained their missile batteries.

CLG Missile conversion of light cruiser, later CG.

CLK Anti-submarine cruiser (US); the *Norfolk* was the only example. She was completed under the designation DL.

CORSAIR A British fixed underwater surveillance system, first proposed about 1953. It was described as a shallow-water system, unlike SOSUS, with limited range.

CRBFD Close Range Blind Fire Detector.

CV Fleet aircraft carrier (US).

CVA Fleet aircraft carrier or attack carrier (US).

CVE Escort carrier.

CVHG Light fleet aircraft carrier converted to carry helicopters and defensive missiles; a US concept.

CVL Light fleet aircraft carrier. In US parlance, this was a converted or redesigned cruiser hull; in the Royal Navy, it was a specially-built austere carrier, smaller than a fleet carrier.

CVS ASW support aircraft carrier, a converted fleet carrier.

DACR Direct Acting Close Range (British), referring to a gun using contact rather than time fuzes. Generally, applied postwar to the abortive sextuple L70 (Mark 12) Bofors gun, but it was a generic phrase.

DAW Director of (Naval) Air Warfare in the Admiralty (British).

DD Destroyer (US).

DDG Missile destroyer.

DDE Destroyer converted for ASW; initially applied to US fleet destroyers converted to fast escorts.

DDK Destroyer converted for ASW, and contrasted with DDE. They were conceived as units of HUK task groups. However, they were soon redesignated DDE.

DE Destroyer escort (US); the US equivalent of the British frigate. Redesignated 'ocean escort' postwar, and later redesignated frigate, FF.

Deep and dirty Standard postwar British design standard for speed and endurance: fully loaded (deep), six months out of drydock in the tropics (dirty); prewar standards had not included fouling (the dirt).

DER Radar picket conversion of the wartime destroyer escort (US), comparable to the British AD frigates.

D/F (Radio) direction finder; the abbreviation is also sometimes used as a verb, as in 'the ship was DF'ed', meaning, the ship was located by radio direction finder(s).

DGD Director of Gunnery in the Admiralty (British).

DL Large Destroyer (US), officially a frigate, and not to be confused with the small escort called frigate by other navies.

DLG Missile-armed large destroyer (US). The DLGs were later redesignated DDG or CG.

DNC Director of Naval Construction (British); the letters stand both for DNC himself and for his department, which designed virtually all British warships.

DND Director of Navigation and (Fighter) Direction in the Admiralty (British), responsible for fighter control.

DPT Digital Pilot Transmission, by means of which ships could exchange CDS information.

DTASW Director of Torpedo, mine, and Anti-Submarine Warfare (British).

DTSD Director of Tactical and Staff Duties Division (of the Admiralty), responsible for framing staff requirements; they were circulated with the prefix TSD and a number.

FADE Fleet Aircraft Direction Escort (British); roughly comparable to the US DDR (radar picket destroyer) concept.

FD Fighter Direction (British).

Flyplane British fire control predictor, considered the first effective Royal Navy heavy anti-aircraft type, postwar. It was developed as an interim predictor for the Mark VI director, replacing the earlier FKC. It calculated the great circle containing the present and predicted position of the target, and used a gyro-stabilized line of sight. Sea trials were conducted in 1947.

FKC Fuze-Keeping Clock, the basis of prewar and wartime British destroyer main battery anti-aircraft fire control systems.

FPB Fast Patrol Boat (British); a term replacing earlier MTB and MGB.

FPS Flyplane (Fire Control) System (British).

GDS Gun Direction System (British).

GNP Gross National Product.

GWS Guided Weapon System (British); GWS1 was Seaslug.

HACS Prewar-designed British high-angle (AA), medium-calibre fire control system, considered obsolescent during World War II.

HDA Harbor Defence Asdic (British), a sonar on or near the harbor bottom to detect submarines attempting to penetrate.

HDWS High Definition Warning Surface, or high-precision surface search radar (British); high definition was valuable for both navigation and for periscope or snorkel detection.

HE High Explosive (as in a shell or bomb).

HEP High Explosive Piercing, a shell type projected for the abortive British 5in gun.

HFDF High Frequency (Radio) Direction Finding or Finder, used to locate the originator of an HF radio message. Often referred to as 'huff-duff'.

HTP High-Test Peroxide; British term for Hydrogen Peroxide, H202.

HUK Hunter-Killer; a form of ASW in which submarines are located and attacked in the open ocean; contrasted with convoy or barrier ASW.

Legend In British practice, the summary set of preliminary design ship characteristics prepared for submission to the Board of Admiralty for approval before proceeding with the design of the ship.

K Tower Standard wartime British destroyer main battery director, superseded by versions of the Mark VI.

LOFAR Long-range, low-frequency passive sonar, a signal processing concept applied to many systems, including sonobuoys.

LORAD Very long-range (multiple convergence zone) active sonar (US project).

LRS Long-Range (Fire Control) System (British), an abortive heavy gun control system begun during World War II; it led directly to the Seaslug missile control system, GWS 1.

LPH Helicopter-carrying carrier for amphibious assault (US).

LRO The US Navy Long Range Objectives group, formed in 1955 to study the shape of the future Navy.

LSD Landing Ship, Dock (US), a large ship carrying smaller landing or other craft in a floodable well deck.

LST Landing Ship, Tank (US), a long-range (trans-oceanic) beaching ship carrying large numbers of vehicles.

MAC Merchant (Ship) Aircraft Carrier, a merchant ship converted into a minimum aircraft platform, still retaining cargo capacity. MACs were devised during World War II, and were proposed postwar as an emergency means of augmenting the small British carrier force.

MC Medium Capacity (in a bomb) (British), comparable to the US general purpose, as opposed to armor piercing.

MCDP Medium Calibre Dual Purpose (British) gun, the postwar replacement for the 6in gun: the 5in gun project.

MDAP Mutual Defense Assistance Program (US); a postwar (cold war) program by which the United States transferred military equipment to her allies. See also OSP.

MRS Medium Range (Fire Control) System (British).

MMS The British World War II Motor Mine Sweeper, roughly equivalent to the US YMS.

MSML Mine Sweeping Motor Launch.

MSF US World War II-built steel fleet minesweeper, as redesignated in the 'fifties.

MTB Motor Torpedo Boat.

N113 Supermarine Scimitar jet carrier fighter (British); all-weather fighter and attack versions were also proposed.

NA 39 Blackburn Buccaneer jet carrier attack bomber (British).

NC Non-Cemented (plating), the British equivalent of the US STS light armor or anti-splinter armor.

nm Nautical miles of about 2000 yards each.

OSP Off-Shore Purchase; equipment such as ships, built abroad but paid for by the United States under MDAP.

PBC Proposed coastal ocean radar picket (US).

PBG Proposed missile-armed ocean radar picket (US).

PC Coastal escort (US); the wartime 173-foot steel escort and her proposed much larger postwar successor, which became a DE.

Pounds (lb) Referring to plating, this is a thickness expressed in weight per square foot, with 40 pounds to the inch.

PPI Plan and Position Indicator; the type of radar or sonar display which shows a map of targets in the surrounding area.

PUFFS A US passive underwater fire control system, designated (in its ultimate form) BQG-4, which found range by triangulation, using three transducers spaced out along the submarine's hull.

RFW Reserve Feed Water (for steam powerplants).

SACLANT Supreme Allied Commander Atlantic; a NATO commander.

SAM Surface to Air (anti-aircraft) Missile.

SAP Semi Armor Piercing (bomb).

SBU Small Battle Unit, midway between pygmies (such as manned torpedoes, also known as Chariots) and midget submarines.

SCB Ship Characteristics Board (US); SCB projects (which became ships) were designated in a series of SCB numbers, eg, SCB 27A was the modernized *Essex* class fleet carrier. Sometimes the same numbers were prefixed by SBP, Shipbuilding Project.

SDPC Ship Design Policy Committee (British).

SHFDF Super High Frequency Direction Finder, to locate sources of radar emissions.

SIOP The US Single Integrated Operations Plan, the overall plan for strategic attack by the US Air Force and Navy, first formally formulated in 1960.

Sniffer A device for automatically detecting snorkel exhaust gas, code-named Autocylcus in British service.

Snort British term for snorkel; later superseded by the US term.

SOSUS The system of fixed long-range deep water surveillance devices, begun by the United States and later extended through NATO.

SR 177 Projected British Saunders-Roe rocket/jet deck-launched carrier interceptor; cancelled under the 1957 Defence Review.

SSA Cargo-carrying submarine (US).

SSG Cruise-missile submarine.

SSK Anti-submarine submarine.

SSO Submarine oiler (US).

SSP Personnel-carrying submarine (US).

SSR Submarine Radar Picket (US).

SSN Nuclear Submarine.

STAAG Stabilized Tachymetric Anti-Aircraft Gun, a twin 40mm Bofors with an on-mount control system, including a radar; it was a maintenance nightmare (British).

STD Simple Tachymetric Director (British), similar in concept to the US Mark 51.

Threat Axis Direction from which an attack is expected.

TIU Target Indication Unit (British), by means of which a gunnery officer could designate targets to particular guns.

TOM Tachymetric One Man director (British).

TS Transmitting Station (British); the below-decks gunnery calculation position.

Type 277 Standard British postwar height-finding and surface search radar; it was an effective surface search set by virtue of its narrow beam.

Type 901 Missile control radar for Seaslug missile system (British); an improved version, Type 902, was projected.

Type 960 Standard British postwar long-range air search radar. Its beam was too wide for direct use in target designation, so in most cases it fed into a narrow-beam two-dimensional radar, such as Type 992. Type 960 was successor to the wartime Types 279 and 281.

Type 982 Standard postwar British high-resolution two-dimensional air search radar, giving target range and bearing only. Used in combination with Type 983.

Type 983 Standard postwar British height-finding radar, superseding the wartime-developed Type 277. The combination of Type 982 and Type 983 gave three-dimensional data required for fighter control.

Type 984 British three-dimensional radar, supplanting the previous combination of Type 982 and Type 983.

Type 992 Standard British postwar target designation radar, replacing the wartime Type 293.

VA Carrier attack bomber (US); this symbol is also used to designate attack bomber *squadrons*.

VAH Heavy (ie, strategic) attack bombers (US).

VF Carrier fighters (US).

VP Patrol aircraft, land- or sea-based (US).

VSTOL Vertical/Short Take-Off and Landing.

V-UHF Where this appears in Appendix I, it means the combination of VHF (Very High Frequency) and UHF (Ultra High Frequency) radio sets.

VW Early-warning aircraft (US).

VTOL Vertical Take-Off and landing.

XMAP Cylindrical pressure mine countermeasure (US).

YAGR Ocean radar picket for US continental air defense; a converted Liberty ship.

YEAD Yarrow/English Electric Advanced Development; a postwar British ship propulsion plant.

YMS The World War II wooden 136-foot motor minesweeper (US), superseded postwar by the AMS, later designated MSC (coastal sweeper).

APPENDIX III: EXERCISE TRIDENT: WARTIME LESSONS LEARNED AND FUTURE IDEAS, 1948

This appendix summarizes notes prepared by the DNC department in December 1948 for a classified Royal Navy exhibition on modern naval warfare, Exercise Trident, conducted in 1949. Trident was intended as a showcase of the Royal Navy's 'new (postwar) look'. Material for this appendix was taken from the DNC papers held by the National Maritime Museum, Greenwich. The lecture was actually presented by Admiral Sir Philip Vian, but it is not clear to what extent he followed the prepared text.

No comparable US Navy summary appears to exist; the closest approach is a series of relatively lengthy reports prepared by the Pacific Fleet in the fall of 1945. Notes (by the author of this book) in square brackets indicate, in some cases, parallel US Navy experience.

The order of these notes is not precisely that in Trident, because some of the notes duplicated other material.

The very brief notes at the end of this Appendix describe the DNC department models shown at Trident (which in turn indicate the state of British warship design in 1948-49) and the operational lectures, which describe a typical British naval war scenario of the time.

1. *It is futile to agree to the limitations of displacement and other warship characteristics by international treaty without absolute safeguards and inspection.*

The Washington (1921), London (1930), London (1936), Anglo-German (1937) and Anglo-Soviet (1937) Naval Treaties all proved to be a rigorous handicap to the British warship designers. Other foreign powers disregarded the treaties and Japan failed to sign the 1936 London Naval Treaty. *Bismarck* exceeded the treaty limit of 35,000 tons by 7-8000 tons. The Italian cruisers were about 2000 tons above the 10,000-ton standard displacement limit. The German *Prinz Eugen*, nominally 10,000 tons standard displacement, was about 15,700 tons.

2. *The necessity for extended sea trials or special cruises in peace time under war conditions in heavy weather, arctic and tropical conditions.*

Prewar cruises were too stereotyped; economy undoubtedly prevented the Navy and Admiralty departments from becoming, and remaining, trial-minded. Exercises at sea and tests and other trials were not pushed beyond the point of minor damage. They generally failed to reveal unsatisfactory living and working conditions for war service. Thorough closing down of our ships for weeks on end would inevitably have revealed how much (and why) operational efficiency would be lost under heavy weather, arctic and tropical conditions. The onus for such trials must rest largely with Naval authorities at sea, strongly supported by Admiralty Departments.

On one spring cruise, Home Fleet destroyers were forced at speed in bad weather causing damage to boats, light structures, etc. As far as is known this type of cruise was seldom, if ever, repeated.

In wartime, paravane gear was found unsatisfactory in heavy weather. In peacetime, the procedure was to bring paravanes in when there was a risk of loss or damage. [That would have been impossible in wartime.]

The [torpedo] warheads were kept in warhead magazines. The war found crews unused to having them permanently attached to the torpedoes, and this presented several problems.

Realistic testing is essential to ensure that ships and equipment shall be built as efficient as possible for war service. Alterations are extremely difficult to carry out under war conditions when ships should be fully fit and ready for operational service.

[The prewar US Navy could easily be charged with similar shortcomings. The failure of the magnetic exploder for the Mark 14 torpedo can also be traced to a lack of prewar testing, although in its case a desire to preserve the secret of a special weapon may have been more to blame.]

3. *Maintenance quality under war conditions becomes more important as apparatus aboard ship becomes more delicate.*

It can only be tested by quite extended (peacetime) operations on a war basis, as otherwise we may find much of this equipment will prove of little value when it comes to the test. Short tests will not show up the difficulties.

Between the wars, financial difficulties and fear of expensive damage brought about a policy that exercises and tests were not pushed beyond the point where damage was no more than minor. The fact that this limit was far short of war requirements appears not to have been appreciated. This applies not only to damage to materials from weather, long continuous operation and other causes, but also to damage to personnel due to unsatisfactory living and working conditions.

[This point would seem to apply particularly to the complex postwar guided missile systems, which did not really reach reasonable reliability until the mid 'sixties.]

4. *Watertight integrity and damage control tended to be neglected or overridden before the war.*

Starting from the Welfare Committee of the 1920s, a period in which no naval war could be foreseen and various disarmament conferences were

held, it rapidly became accepted in fact, if not in declared policy, that ease of peacetime operation and the contentment of officers and crew were primary requirements of HM ships and took precedence over ability to stand damage, fire resistance and similarly purely wartime requirements. To a certain extent the same thing is happening today [ie, 1948]. There is considerable pressure to devote weight and space to amenities, to ease up on wartime restrictions and accept some risk from overweight and inadequate stability.

[The postwar US Navy has also been accused of emphasizing habitability over survivability.]

5. *Ventilation generally was not up to standard for war in tropical waters.*

The Royal Navy often did operate in the tropics before the war. Daylight and fresh air on mess decks, etc. were considered so important to maintain the health of ships' companies that many scuttles were fitted. However, they were so positioned that it would have been necessary to rely on their watertightness in the event of serious damage; in wartime, then, they had to be sealed off. Because they could be opened in peacetime, however, artificial ventilation seemed less important; their constant use masked the shortcomings of the ventilation provided. It was peacetime practice to close scuttles on going to action stations but in such conditions very few men were on the mess decks. As soon as the exercise was over and the men returned to the mess decks the scuttles were opened. In addition, in peacetime, awnings were kept spread whenever possible. They in turn reduced the sun's heating effect on the ships. There is always a considerable risk of including in a ship's fittings and equipment items which cannot be used in war.

Other important reasons for the deficiencies were:

(a) many ships were old, eg, the *Royal Sovereign* class, and ventilation was designed for service in the North Sea in winter.

(b) All ships were crowded on account of additions of equipment and increased complements.

(c) Fleets or squadrons did not, in peacetime, exercise for long periods in the tropics under war conditions; as a result we did not discover faults until the war began. Serving month after month in tropical conditions closed up for war is very different from spending an occasional week under these conditions, and prolonged cruises under realistic conditions are essential.

(d) Wild heat, due to super-heated steam etc, had not been properly confined by lagging.

[Accounts of life aboard US warships in the South Pacific show that this wa also a serious problem for the US Navy, which was, in theory, designed largely for Pacific operations. However, the US Navy did introduce air conditioning of key spaces during World War II, and its fleet submarines were air-conditioned.]

6. *Worldwide docking facilities.*

Adequate drydocking and repair facilities are needed at strategic points on a worldwide basis. The size of dry docks imposed limitations on ship design. [For example, the design of the abortive *Gibraltar* class fleet carrier was limited by the size of British Empire drydocks. The US Navy encountered no such limits.]

The lack of such facilities was very costly to Pacific and Eastern Fleet operations. [Note, however, that British war planners did not envisage the fall of Singapore, which had one of the largest graving docks in the British Empire. More generally, a survey of British Empire drydocking facilities shows that the British Isles themselves were most deficient, apart from a few private docks designed for transatlantic liners.] World War I did not bring the deficiencies to light because operations were largely confined to the North Sea and North Atlantic. It was necessary to limit the design dimensions, particularly the beam, of capital ships to suit dry docks. This limitation on beam also implied a limitation on metacentric height and stability. *Bismarck* had much greater stability than *King George V*. The Post World War I Questions Committee reported that attention should be given to the question of drydocking. Nothing, however, was done between the wars.

7. *Fire-fighting in H.M. ships was neglected before the war.*

During the period 1918–39, progress in the design and supply of fire-fighting equipment was restricted by the policy of economy and weight restriction, although Admiralty departments gave sympathetic interest to each new feature, particularly in the case of foam apparatus and water sprinklers. The appearance of aircraft carriers and catapult ships emphasized the problem. Existing carriers (*Glorious, Courageous, Furious* etc.) were fitted with special equipment to cope with hangar and petrol fires.

Generally, however, during those years the scale of supply was subordinated to the overriding question of cost and the items allowed each vessel kept to the absolute minimum. Coupled with this was the absence of any co-ordinating authority to assume responsibility for fire-fighting in HM ships, so that progress was inevitably slow.

The urgency of the problem became apparent early in the present war, and the loss of several ships through fire indicated that existing fire-fighting appliances were far from satisfactory. The whole position was reviewed and steps taken to organize it on a more realistic basis. New equipment was ordered, contemplated allowances being on a much more lavish scale and arrangements made for the adequate training of personnel.

Early losses attributable to fire included the cruisers *Southampton, Sussex* and *Trinidad*, the fast minelayer *Latona*, the destroyers *Dainty* and *Imogen*, and the armed merchant cruiser *Comorin*. When equipment became available and personnel were sufficiently trained, the results were far-reaching, and many instances occurred of vessels seriously damaged by fire being safely brought to port.

In ships possessing a particularly high degree of fire vulnerability, such as aircraft carriers, the allowance of fire fighting equipment was correspondingly generous. The precautionary aspect of reducing fire risk was also given special attention in all classes of ships, and the amount of inflammable material used for fittings reduced to a minimum. In this respect, it was most noticeable in the later stages of the war how much more thoroughly the Americans had stripped their ships in order to reduce the fire hazard because of the earlier war experience.

8. *Necessity for a larger Royal Corps of Naval Constructors and for more constructor officers to serve at sea with the fleets.*

The shortage of fully-trained constructor officers was seriously felt in all branches of ship production, repair and design work before and throughout the war. The RCNC is at present under strength and is diluted by about 40 per cent non-RN College, Greenwich-trained officers. Numbers of additional fully-trained naval constructors available in emergency would be extremely small. Unremitting requests from Cs-in-C during the war for constructor officers for service at sea had to be refused on account of shortage of numbers. The future conditions of service, recruitment, complement, etc. of the Royal Corps of naval constructors still remain undecided.

9. *Increases in ships' complements.*

Major increases in ships' complements during the war were responsible for greatly reduced habitability standards and for reductions in endurance for such things as fresh water, provisions, cold storage, etc.

Typical increases in ship's complements were: battleship *Ramiles*, 950 to 1550; minesweeper *Ipswich*, built for 66, accommodated 101. The carrier *Implacable* is another example: original staff requirements gave a complement of 1390, DNC provided accommodations for 1700 and the actual number aboard was 2220.

[The US Navy suffered similarly, due in part to vast increases in light anti-aircraft weapons.]

10. *Standardization.*

To facilitate production and ship repairs and to reduce the size of stockpiles, greater efforts must be made to standardize designs, equipment and fittings.

11. *Reserves of strategic materials.*

The shipbuilding industry in the UK is dependent on imports of a number of valuable materials and if a break in supply is to be avoided adequate stocks must be built up and maintained, particularly in the early stages of a war. For example, to produce adequate numbers of Coastal Forces craft, wooden minesweepers, harbor servicing craft, etc, it is considered necessary to carry heavy stocks of boatbuilding timber stores in the UK, eg, about 1000 tons of first-grade timber were used per month during the last war. In Germany, prewar planning resulted in the accumulation of first class mahogany for boat planking, which covered all the production of E-boats and R-boats [MTBs and motor minesweepers] during the war period.

[Strategic stockpiling was an important US postwar program. Its cost was borne by the general defense budget, and the initial strategic

materials purchases contributed to the tightening of defense resources in FY49-50.]

12. *Overseas building in the Commonwealth.*

It is essential that steel production overseas in the Commonwealth should be encouraged and that shipbuilding, particularly in the smaller classes of warships, should also be fostered.

[Note the partial wartime reliance on Australia and Canada for frigates, corvettes, minesweepers, small craft and, in the case of Canada, steam-powered LSTs. The British conducted special studies of mobilization requirements, such as requirements for warship construction in Australia, in the late 'forties.]

13. *Mass-production research yard.*

The importance of rapid production in a future emergency and the skilled labor shortage is certain to call for an extension of line-production for all craft up to the size of escort vessels.

The absence of a mass-production research yard to develop ships and craft on such lines, prepare drawings, jigs, and moulds, is bound to be felt in a future war.

[Note that the postwar frigates, Types 12, 41 and 61, were all designed for mass-production, They would have been built in modular form, away from the shipyards, and assembled on the slips in minimum time, to minimize their exposure to air attacks on these vulnerable assembly centers. The proposed research shipyard, however, was never established.]

14. *Reserve shipbuilding equipment.*

If ship repairs are to be carried expeditiously, provision must be made for several stores of shipbuilding equipment and material to be maintained in a 'ready for issue' state.

15. *Complexity and numbers of warships.*

The greater the complexity of modern ships and the increase in amentities, etc, the larger the ships become and the less the number which can be built.

Ships should be as simple as possible for their job and even greater emphasis given to their fighting qualities, and consideration given to more reliance being placed on base ships for accommodation, rest and repairs.

[This reflects early DNC thinking on future destroyers, as described in Chapter 6. Several DNC papers of this period show a determination to cut back the size and cost of ships, so as to achieve sufficient numbers. The British considered such contemporary US designs as the *Norfolk* and the *Mitscher* impossibly extravagant.]

16. *Production bottlenecks during war.*

Typical production bottlenecks during the last war:

— Steel plates (in the thinner gauges) and sheets (we were largely dependent on supplies of steel plates from USA for our frigate and landing craft programmes and also for the building of many auxiliary vessels).

Steel castings (this bottleneck was relieved so far as possible by alternative use of fabricated steel and steel forgings).

Chain cables and shackles; Admiralty pattern blocks; and hull auxiliary machinery. It was necessary to increase the field of production by enlarging plants, introducing other manufacturers, and where practicable, simplifying designs and technique.

Although difficulties were experienced in production of these and other hull items, they were successfully overcome without causing delay in the completion of vessels.

In general, the availability of main and auxiliary machinery (particularly electrical and gunnery items) became the determining factors in the completion of ships as the war progressed. During the early stages of the frigate building programme, completion dates were largely determined by availability of machinery. In the case of C class destroyers, completions were dependent upon delivery of directors. Some destroyers with hull and machinery completed waited 12 months for their fire controls.

[The major US Navy bottleneck was machinery, as exemplified by the destroyer escort program. Postwar, the US Navy made special efforts in escort design to reduce future bottlenecks, one result being the choice of single-screw machinery for the *Dealey* class – and thus, as it happened, for all but one of the subsequent ocean escort classes. The sole exception, the *Claude Jones*, sacrificed performance for what was thought to be ease of production, in the form of diesel propulsion. Ironically, it required gears too large for easy production.

17. *Long-term planning for warship building.*

The increased complexity of modern warships involves increased call on factories and time for their construction and longer time for equipping and converting merchant ships.

18. *Spare parts supply.*

The necessity for a good organization for the supply of spare part stores and such items as ventilating fans, etc. This was particularly felt in the Mediterranean and Far Eastern operations.

19. *Staff requirements and planning.*

It is necessary to plan on long-term basis for future war rather than for the last.

Staff requirements for endurance, etc, of ships designed during the 1930s appear to cater for operations in the North Sea rather than for operations over long distances when at sea for long periods. Replenishment at sea was neglected.

[This note is particularly ironic in view of the fact that a Japanese, rather than a European, war formed the basis of much British naval planning after 1919. The explanation is presumably that the British expected to operate from a series of bases, such as Singapore, which were relatively close together. Thus they would not have equated a Pacific War with long endurance.]

[The US experience was quite different. Even before 1914, the US Navy had to contemplate both Atlantic and Pacific war scenarios, the latter being associated with long-range. From 1907 on, US Pacific war plans contemplated steaming a battle fleet across that wide ocean to relieve the Philippines. Thus World War II became, for the US Navy, a continuation of pre-World War I concerns. For the Royal Navy, however, the shift to an Eastern war scenario was a shift to a very different kind of war. The fall of Singapore radically changed the basic British scenario, whereas the US Navy's prewar ideas remained more or less valid throughout.]

20. *Destroyers.*

Development of destroyer design before the war would repay study in the light of future destroyer requirements. The prewar view of what a destroyer should be like can be ascertained from the design papers. In the L class papers (1937), remarks generally ignore the anti-aircraft and anti-submarine angle. Interest is centred on the low angle armament and silhouette, which were 1914-18 war requirements. In the preparation of this design, the Admiralty requested the views of the Cs-in-C of the Home Fleet and Mediterranean Fleet. All of these papers approach the problem on the basis of fleet action of the Jutland type. Cost was the material factor in the discussion. These are not isolated observations. A review of these papers will make it clear that everyone was consulted and the problem very fully considered before decision was reached on the type of destroyer we required. 1938 papers on escort destroyers discuss the relative requirements for anti-aircraft and low-angle guns; these papers still, however, talk of Jutland. Even in 1939, in discussions of a possible intermediate type destroyer, there is little interest in anti-submarine issues.

Almost all of the wartime changes in destroyers were aimed at improving offensive powers against aircraft and submarines at the expense of anti-surface ship armament, even including torpedoes. The only other notable change was a considerable increase in fuel endurance. Further modifications thought desirable in the same ships in 1947 all concern habitability; the problem is how far it can be improved without an unacceptable reduction of military characteristics.

The staff requirements for destroyers, which are based on what the staff want them to have and to do always lead to ships which are unacceptably large and expensive. A process of pruning the requirements then takes place. During building, and after, there is a constant effort to work in the things which were approved in the first place plus many later developments. During this process, and especially in peacetime, there is a marked tendency to ignore that loss of qualities such as strength, ability to withstand damage, or performance under extreme conditions, in favor of the more obvious advantage of the additional gun, the new radar set, or the larger cabin. As an example, at first sight it may seem simple and easy to increase the oil fuel capacity by turning a watertight compartment into an oil fuel tank, but we are inclined to forget that this will overload the ship with all its risks and disadvantages. It is the equivalent of habitually loading a merchant ship below the load line, a practice which no one would recommend. Generally, insufficient margin is allowed in

the design for probable changes. Perhaps this is right, but the margin is invariably one of the first things to be cut when war starts. In fact, during the tenure of the treaties it was declared [Admiralty] Board policy to have no margin at all or a negative one. To allow a margin of one ton in ship whilst maintaining the same standards involves an increase in displacement of about four tons.

[The US Navy also eliminated margins from its design practice in the 'thirties, so as to squeeze as much as possible from available treaty tonnage. As a result, at the beginning of the war, most US warships were somewhat overweight. Destroyers built in the late 'thirties were a particularly unfortunate case.]

21. *Warships for Arctic service.*

In planning Operation Catherine [a proposed British operation in the Baltic planned for early 1940] considerable work was done on the study of 'arcticization'.

Minutes of the General Investigations Committee – GIC (Staff of Operation Catherine) should give information on:
— arcticization, ie, lagging, heating, electrical heating of gun barrels – steam jets, etc;
— gun crew shelter;
— splinter protection around guns;
— cold weather clothing;
— dehydrated vegetables, etc, to increase stowage in existing store rooms;
— fast tankers and store ships, eg, *Glen* class.

22. *Aircraft carrier design.*

It is considered essential that armor protection to roof and sides of hangars should continue to be fitted in future fleet carriers. War experience proved its value. The US Navy is following British practice in armoring the hangar of its large 1000ft carrier.

[This referred to the *United States*, CVA 58. However, in that ship flight deck armor was used, at least partly, for sheer hull strength. Certainly the deck thickness in later US carriers was determined more by strength than by protection considerations. Note that the British decision largely to abandon hangar protection in the last wartime carrier design, the *Malta*, had apparently been forgotten.]

The three boiler room and three engine room abreast machinery arrangement as fitted in *Illustrious* is considered unsound on account of the difficulty of obtaining good sub-division. Alternative arrangements of boiler rooms and engine rooms should be provided.

The single hangar design of aircraft carrier is preferable to the two hangar design on account of the difficulty of obtaining good sub-division in the two hangar arrangement.

[Note, however, that the last British fleet carrier to be built, the *Ark Royal*, had a double hangar. The next design, the abortive *Malta*, had a single – and relatively unarmored – hangar.]

Naval aircraft must be designed for operating from aircraft carriers, eg, undercarriages should be specially designed (not too much bounce). Naval aircraft should not, however, be much inferior in performance to land aircraft.

[This was not a problem for the US Navy; the remark presumably reflected unhappiness with the poor deck-landing characteristics of the Supermarine Seafire, a major wartime British naval fighter.]

Petrol in aircraft carriers is a great danger. Steps are being taken to eliminate it, although time will elapse before that occurs.

It is considered necessary that aircraft carriers should be standardized in design to the extent that British aircraft carriers should be able to operate British or US aircraft or vice versa. This matter is being further investigated.

[Many British official papers of this period reflect an assumption that, as in World War II, Fleet Air Arm strength would be built up in wartime out of US production. The much smaller British aircraft production base would be required to support the RAF.]

23. *Endurance.*

Tabulated prewar endurances of a number of ships were not realistic, Endurances were limited not necessarily by oil fuel but by fresh water, etc. Endurances under trial conditions are given by DNC and based on fuel consumption trials carried out in new ships. They are considered a sound guide for comparison between ships and of possibilities under the best conditions. Endurance under so-called 'operational conditions' are worked out by E-in-C [Engineer in Chief], who consults DNC as required. In practice, he never asks us for more than estimated speeds under certain conditions. We have pressed him for years to make these tables consistent and the 1945 edition of CB 1815 [the official British tabulation of warship characteristics] was reasonable. Since that time E-in-C has modified them on the basis of information received from ships and they are again almost as inconsistent as they were before the war.

The trouble is that what happens in the ship during the trial is affected by many variables besides speed and time out of dock, ie, weather, auxiliary machinery in use, amount of helm used, fouling – which itself can show wide variation for the same time out of dock. E-in-C has never got down to analyzing the ship results to eliminate the effect of these variables. The lower the speed, the greater the effect is. From the point of view of endurance it would be difficult to define exactly what is meant by 'operational conditions' in any cases; whatever the definition it would seldom apply to any actual operation.

In our view the available information on endurance is still quite unsatisfactory from the operational point of view. I believe in aircraft they work on trial conditions less a percentage and say 'that is all we can rely on doing although we can often do much more'. To me this is more reliable.

Endurance other than fuel was much reduced in many ships due to the great increase in wartime complement above that for which the ship was designed. This seriously affected such things as provision, cold storage, water, etc. It also had a marked adverse effect on living conditions. For example, the war complement of the early emergency destroyers as designed was 163 in the destroyer and 196 in the leader. The actual number on board in war was not less than 210 in the destroyer and 240 in the leader. This represents a reduction of about 25 per cent in the number of days for which provisions, etc, could be carried. The complement of the *Battle* class, as designed, was 236 in the destroyer and 262 in the leader. The present approved complement is 270 in the destroyer and 296 in the leader. The same thing is happening in the *Daring* class where, by various devices, the complement on paper has been cut to fit the number who can be properly accommodated. There is no doubt that if the bodies are available in war a considerably increased number will be on board.

The endurance given in the staff requirements for ships with clean bottoms is that to be expected under trial conditions as regards weather, sea, etc, and is the only means of forming a comparison between British ships of the same type. It also allows a direct and reliable comparison between ships of all nations. In estimating the figures, account is taken of the reduction in horsepower required to drive the ship as the oil is consumed. They are checked from the consumption figures obtained on the contractor's trials on completion of the vessels when steam is used under the most economical conditions (the minimum auxiliary machinery running, armament, radar, etc, not in use, and steam for all other purposes kept to a minimum). Special arrangements are made to accurately measure the oil consumed. These figures are the maximum that can be achieved.

For the *Battle* class with 691 tons of oil fuel and 40 tons diesel oil, and the *Weapon* class with 597 tons of oil fuel and 34 tons diesel oil, the figures so obtained were the same for each Class, viz, about 4500nm at 20 knots, 5 per cent being allowed for residue oil in the tanks. Very little information is given as to the conditions on which the figures reported … are based. At 20 knots, at which only a small fraction of the available steam is being used for propulsion, wide variations are clearly possible.

Little reliable data is available to the Admiralty regarding the increased resistance of ships due to time out of dock, particularly in tropical waters, as the amount of fouling varies considerably from place to place with the ships' service and with time steaming at sea. Since the staff requirements for the *Battles* were prepared, staff requirements for new construction of British warships now stipulate maximum speed and endurances under operational conditions when six months out of dock in tropical waters [deep and dirty, a condition introduced into British staff requirements about 1944]. To obtain further information advantage was taken in 1945, of the concentration of HM ships in Far Eastern waters, to carry out special speed and fuel consumption trials on a selected ship of each type of British warship. Very detailed reports have been received from C-in-C BPF for four vessels, viz *Venerable, Euryalus, Barfleur* and *Totem* (submarine). The analyses of the reports are proceeding and the information available so far indicates that the usual allowance made in

this department as to fouling in tropical waters is on the high side, especially for those vessels coated with new type compositions.

[The US Navy encountered similar sharp decreases in effective endurance. By 1945, it was calculating on the basis of a 25 per cent increase in required SHP due to fouling and weather. US wartime and postwar endurance requirements also specified operation in 'split plant' mode, ie, with two independent machinery plants, so that a ship would not be immobilized by a single underwater hit. That required that auxiliaries otherwise not needed, be operated, and so further reduced steaming endurance.]

24.   *Submarines.*

The submarine fleet in the beginning of the war consisted largely of out of date types, a result of small naval programmes and the wasting away of design, building and repair staffs during the slump.

The few new ships that had been completed appear to have been satisfactory in essentials. There were, of course, many alterations and additions due to new equipment coming forward, and to developments in submarine warfare. Notable among these was the need for silencing auxiliary machinery and systems, a need which grew as enemy listening apparatus improved.

It was not until our submarines had to operate in the Far East that any drastic changes had to be made in their endurance. All S and T Class submarines then had certain main ballast tanks converted to carry oil fuel.

Early experience in the Far East indicated that the dehumidifiers in the S and T classes were inadequate, and urgent measures had to be taken to replace them by efficient Freon air conditioning plants.

The advantages of deep diving qualities were also demonstrated by war experience.

There were far-reaching effects on enemy submarine design, now reflected in our own designs [ie, in the installation of snorkels], on account of the efficiency of our radar, which forced the enemy submarines to keep continuously submerged.

Most of the above were in the nature of development inspired by war experience. The insufficient endurance for Far Eastern warfare may be explained partly by the unexpected fall of Singapore.

[At this time the Royal Navy had only one submarine capable of high underwater speed, the specially streamlined *Scotsman*. She, however, lacked commensurate battery-charging power and hence was unsuited to operational use. She required many hours to recharge after each half-hour dash. The US Navy enjoyed the services of about 20 fully operational Guppies. The British T class conversion program, comparable in concept to the Guppy, was only beginning.]

25.   *Coastal Forces craft.*

Due to lack of Naval interest and lack of planning in the decade before the war, British naval coastal forces were almost completely neglected until a year after the outbreak of war.

Throughout the war we were completely dependent, first on Italy and then on USA, for engines suitable for Coastal Forces craft.

26.   *Coastal Forces bases and maintenance.*

There was no prewar organization of bases for, or maintenance of, Coastal Forces, and throughout the war operational activity was hindered in consequence.

An MTB, being a short-range weapon, entails a maintenance problem similar to that of a bomber aircraft. Organization for spare parts, repairs, slipping, etc, should be arranged when an operation is in the early planning stage.

On account of the short ranges of MTBs, mobile base maintenance, either ship-borne or lorry-borne, is an essential camp follower on MTB operations. A very forward base within 100nm or so of the striking point is required, and a rear base, including slips, pontoon docks and a maintenance ship as near forward as is acceptable from the point of view of air attack.

[The US Navy in the South Pacific made extensive use of MTB (PT) tenders.]

27.   *Wooden Minesweeper.*

Before 1939, there were no wooden minesweepers and the advent of the German magnetic mining campaign found Britain with no boats of low magnetism available for use as sweepers.

It appears that little thought had been given to anti-mine warfare against possible use by the enemy of a magnetic mine.

[The Royal Navy had actually employed magnetic mines, laid by fast coastal motor boats in 1918.]

28. *Harbour servicing boats.*

In the years before 1939 very few harbour service boats were available under the control of the Admiralty. The evacuation of Dunkirk involved a crisis for naval servicing craft.

The main lessons to be learned from our experience over naval servicing craft is that there is a substantial reservoir of craft available in an emergency for naval servicing craft to be requisitioned from the fleet of motor boats, passenger launches, etc, in UK. It is necessary to organize a shadow programme in peacetime for building naval servicing craft to meet an emergency.

29. *Staff requirements and patrol craft.*

When the 72ft motor launches (HDMLs) were designed, it was stated by the Staff that they would be transported abroad as a deck cargo.

When the time came for transport abroad, no ships were available for transport and the MLs were required to make the passage on their own keels. Fortunately, they were designed to have maximum seaworthiness for their size and were able to make those passages. It is useless to rely on a basis of transport by ship as intensive submarine mining campaigns may well produce such a shortage that transport will not be available.

30. *Engine Room ventilating fans.*

Some engine room ventilating fans in ships must be steam-driven.

In *Prince of Wales*, loss of electrical power deprived the engine room of ventilation, making the compartments untenable although the machinery was intact and steam was therefore available.

[The US Navy tended instead to emphasize emergency diesel generators with shock-resistant switchboards. Royal Navy practice generally emphasized steam as opposed to electrical systems.]

31. *Hood was sunk by a small number of shell hits from* Bismarck.

It was known before the war that the horizontal protection of *Hood* would not keep out large calibre shell at long ranges. Non-cemented deck armor had not yet been invented when *Hood* was built, and she was to have been taken in hand for modernization following *Queen Elizabeth*. The war intervened and work was not started.

The shortage of money in the 1920s and early 1930s limited the possibilities of doing all the desirable alterations in the older capital ships.

[What was not said was that worldwide British peacetime and crisis commitments made it impossible to withdraw so important a ship for reconstruction, given the limited overall size of the British battle fleet – a size limited by treaty much more than by finances. The United States benefited greatly by its much more limited concentration on one ocean, the Pacific.]

32. Ark Royal *was sunk by one torpedo.*

Ark Royal was hit by one torpedo, which ran very deep and detonated under the starboard boiler room. It is not known whether the torpedo was fitted with a contact or a non-contact pistol – the former is more probable. The position of detonation was the worst in the ship as regards the list it would cause, ie, it was about amidships, where list caused would be greatest, and its position relative to the transverse bulkheads was such that the starboard compartments in four main transverse sub-divisions eventually flooded, together with 106ft of the starboard bilge compartments. This flooding produced an immediate list of ten degrees which increased to 17 degrees in 20 minutes. Within 20 minutes two of the three boiler rooms had been put out of action by flooding.

In spite of these circumstances the ship was in no immediate danger of being lost and could, it is considered, have been saved had the proper damage control measures been taken.

Ark Royal possessed a large reserve of buoyancy. The ship sank after 14½ hours afloat because this reserve of buoyancy was allowed to dwindle away instead of being utilized to keep the ship afloat.

All personnel were withdrawn from the machinery spaces to sort out those who were to leave the ship immediately and those who were to remain. Among the personnel who left the ship were the whole of the shipwright staff, who should have been among the important members of the damage control parties. It was some hours before the shipwrights returned. Important numbers of the electrical staff also left and were hours away, and much delay in getting electric light occurred.

A long period elapsed before the machinery personnel returned to the machinery spaces and any attempt at counter flooding was made. When this was ordered, only half the compartments on the undamaged side provided with flooding arrangements were flooded because the people concerned were ignorant of the flooding arrangements fitted. Having flooded certain compartments, the flooding valves of these compartments were not closed, and in consequence the counter flooding water was gradually expelled and its effectiveness reduced as additional water seeped into the ship on the damaged side. Had immediate and full counter flooding been undertaken the story would have been a very different one.

Owing to withdrawal of the engine room staff, feed water was lost, and it was not possible to commence to raise steam in the undamaged boiler room for a long period. The ship's staff worked heroically and under great difficulties at the task of trying to raise steam, whereas they should have concentrated on putting the ship into an upright position in order to make use of the reserve of buoyancy and remain afloat.

The sea was calm and it is not clear why towage to Gibraltar, which was only 25nm away, was not possible.

It may be doubted whether in 1933, the year of the inception of the *Ark Royal* design, sufficient data existed to enable a satisfactory anti-torpedo structure to be designed for a ship of 22,000 tons displacement. Had an establishment like NCRE [Naval Construction Research Establishment], Rosyth, been developed after the 1914-18 war we should have been in a much better position to tackle such problems.

[NCRE was responsible for post-World War II ship target trials, which investigated various forms of damage in great detail.

Note that *Ark Royal* was comtemporary with the US *Yorktown* (CV 5) class, which showed considerable resistance to torpedo damage in wartime. US constructors tended to emphasize resistance to extreme lists such as *Ark Royal* experienced. For example, the carrier *Yorktown* sank on an even keel, her buoyancy totally exhausted. It could not, then, be argued that she could have been saved by counter flooding.

Some US wartime and postwar documents noted that the Royal Navy tended to use longitudinal bulkheads, which made listing more likely. US practice was to avoid such bulkheads, allowing water to flood all the way across the beam of a ship.]

33. Naiad *was sunk by one torpedo.*

The cruiser *Naiad* was lost as the result of one torpedo because:

(i) She was hit at the very worst point, *viz*, at the bulkhead separating the machinery units, causing immediate flooding of forward engine room and after boiler room.

[This was a problem with contemporary US cruisers as well. It could be avoided only by widely separating the forward and after machinery spaces, which would result in a long hull; or by adopting 'unit' machinery, in which any one of four boiler-engine spaces could drive a ship.]

(ii) The wing compartments abreast the after boiler room caused appreciable unsymmetrical flooding, and a large heel.

(iii) It is probably that the final loss was due to the flooding of after engine room and lower deck … engine room.

(iv) The rapidity with which the ship listed, and the failure of power and light prevented steps being taken to establish a damage boundary and counter flood.

34. *Shock in ships.*

Extensive shock damage to cast iron fittings, etc, occurred from enemy action during the war.

Before the war the threat of shock damage to machinery and fittings had not been considered very important. After all, machinery had withstood vibration at high speeds as well as shock due to the firing of guns and the dropping of depth charges. Previous war experience had not revealed any weakness in this respect when ships were hit by shells or torpedoes, In spite of Job 74 [prewar target] trials and other experience, Admiralty departments were not fully alive, before the war, to the possible devasting consequences of shock damage. Late in 1939, however, *Belfast* was mined by a magnetic mine on the sea bed, and the very extensive damage to machinery and hull structure caused by this mine exploding some 80-90 feet away from the hull focussed attention on the new type of attack.

This incident was followed by many more of a similar nature when the various types of non-contact mine employed by the enemy, as well as the underwater explosion of near-miss bombs, caused a considerable number of ships to be laid up for long periods of repair. In all, over 100 ships suffered shock damage during the war – much of it of a serious nature.

35. *Conversions of merchant ships, trawlers, etc. for naval service in war and*

defensive equipment of merchant ships.

Preparations for conversions of merchant ships, trawlers, etc, for naval service in war and for defensive equipment of merchant ships must be made in peacetime and materials should be available in quantity on the outbreak of war if major delays are to be avoided.

Before the last war, Supply Committee III (a sub-committee of the Principal Supply Officers Committee of the Imperial Defense Committee) fulfilled an essential function in allocating shipyard capacity for this work vis-à-vis naval and merchant shipbuilding repairs. Attempts to revive this Supply Committee since the war have been unsuccessful. During the recent period of international tension [Czech crisis, 1948] a lack of this or a similar Committee was felt.

36. *Replenishment at sea.*

One of the largest single replenishment at sea items is fuel. Commercial tankers are slow and their speed is further reduced if steam is used for pumping fuel.

The Navy needs high-speed tankers capable of rapid pumping. It is therefore necessary to build special naval replenishment tankers.

[This was not a problem for the US Navy, which had developed underway replenishment before 1941 as a prerequisite for success in a transpacific campaign. Underway replenishment was seen, postwar, as vital to sustained carrier operations, in which aircraft (if not ship) fuel would be consumed very rapidly.]

37. *Ships for fleet train.*

Several valuable seagoing merchant ships were taken up unnecessarily for naval service during the last war.

Many of the fleet train functions of supply, repair, and accommodation could have been fulfilled by standard prefabricated vessels of low mobility which would normally reside at advanced bases.

38. *Fleet train – repair or replacement parts.*

Some vessels, eg, aircraft engine repair ships, were found in the last war to be redundant. Fleet manpower may well be wasted in repair of fittings and equipment when replacement of items would be a sounder policy. These remarks are also applicable to repair versus replacement in fighting ships and the possible reduction of workshop space in such ships.

Workshop space in USN ships is considerably less than in British ships.

*   *   *

Trident Exhibits

Unfortunately, photographs of the exhibits do not appear to have survived. A frequently-published photograph of a model of *Formidable* with an angled deck, often dated 1949, was probably not part of Trident, and has almost certainly been misdated.

Models of a task force at sea and of atomic bomb damage by an underwater bomb. They used small models of ships to represent the task force, with a model of a bomb explosion (as at Bikini). Damage to structure, personnel, etc was shown for each type of ship.

The coastal forces section included models of prototype A/S boat (medium speed, which became the Ford class); conversion of Fairmile D as prototype for emergency conversion; prototype convertible Coastal Forces craft (latest attempt to meet staff requirements, the *Bold* class). The model was to show the hard chine alternative.

Aircraft Carrier section: *Ark Royal* (the latest carrier) and aircraft model; model of *Ark Royal* island; diagram or staple deck model of design study (B); deck model or staple model of *Formidable* as rebuilt; model of *Hermes* brought up to date; *Implacable* model. Design study (B) was a fleet carrier modified to launch a large bomber carrying a 10,000-pound (ie, atomic) bomb. *Formidable* was replaced by *Victorious* in the carrier reconstruction program. *Implacable* was a typical wartime carrier.

Surface Combatants sections: model of fleet aircraft direction escort; *Daring* model; *Daring* bridge model; diagram to show trend of destroyers after *Daring*; model of *Tiger* as rearmed; wall diagrams of A/A and A/D; celluloid models of A/A and A/D frigate bridges; diagrams showing typical arrangements in a ship to deal with cold weather and/or Arctic operations. Note the absence of any model of the type 15 destroyer conversion or of a future anti-submarine frigate.

Submarines: Model of experimental HTP driven non-operational submarine with very high underwater speed for A/S exercises (*Explorer*);

model of T class submarine converted for fast battery drive with high underwater speed. Note the absence of any model of a future *operational* HTP or fast battery drive submarine.

NCRE: 1/50 scale models of merchant ships and submarines as damaged by 1/50 scale atomic bombs. These were to be simple structural models representing average surface ships and submarines all having been subjected to explosion tests with depth charges (to same scale as atomic bomb). Two damaged models of each type were to be supplied together with an undamaged sample for comparison. A notice board would describe exhibits and display photographs of the surface phenomena. Blast trials model showing launching gear, a Seaslug, blast gauge, etc. This exhibit was to include photgraphs, pressure time curve and description.

*   *   *

The Scenario

A Trident conference program shows lectures on the expected state of affairs in 1957, a date already selected as the years of maximum danger. It appears that a war scenario, beginning with mobilization, was developed. The scenario included a joint planning staff conference shortly before the war on the case for establishing an allied maritime zone of control in the Arctic. The Chiefs of Staff directed action in the Arctic. A conference at Area Combined HQ at the Clyde was simulated. A lecturer described enemy targets suitable for attack from the maritime zone of control in the Arctic. The scenario showed both offensive operations in the Arctic and the defence of a convoy against air attack. There was a raid on the west coast of Spitzbergen. Submarines operated in enemy controlled waters and off enemy bases. Enemy shipping was attacked.

Other lecturers described probable future trends in ship design, and the expected effect of weapons of mass destruction on maritime warfare.

APPENDIX IV: NAVAL STRENGTHS OF THE MAJOR POWERS, 1939-57

This appendix provides an approximate measure of the naval strengths of the major powers discussed in this book, as they were affected by the changes in naval strategy and technology which have been described. The listing for 1939 is included for comparison. US 1945 figures are for VJ-Day (as far as possible), and thus do not include ships completed late in the year. British figures are for 8 May 1945 (VE-Day), and thus do not reflect the run-down of ASW forces after that date. They also do not include ships in reserve, which represented a considerable force, mainly of older types.

The lists for each power include, so far as possible, only active ships. Thus ships undergoing major refits and reconstructions have been excluded, wherever possible. Ships commmissioned for training are included in parentheses. They are to be counted *in addition* to those in full commission. Note that it is sometimes difficult to obtain such data (as opposed to total numbers on the Navy lists), and therefore that all figures are somewhat approximate. The US Navy figures *do not* include coast guard ships, craft, and aircraft, nor do aircraft figures include marine aviation.

Standard US Navy nomenclature is used, except that US destroyer escorts are listed as frigates (FF) for comparability with foreign navies. The *Hunt* class small destroyers, which were later re-rated as frigates, are listed here as frigates throughout. The symbol BB has been used for all heavy-gun capital ships, both battleships and battlecruisers. Although some carriers operational in 1939 might be considered CVL in later terms, they are not so described here. The symbol DDE is used for destroyers converted to escort configuration, whether for air defense or for ASW. MCM* indicates coastal minecraft. The 1945 US and British figures for escort carriers (CVE) are deceptive in that many ships were being used as aircraft transports, not combatants.

Aircraft are included as full squadrons: VF for fighter, VA for attack, VAH for heavy or strategic attack, VP for patrol, VP* for seaplane, VS for ASW, VW for land-based early warning, ZP for blimp patrol. Dive and torpedo bomber units are combined as VA; the composite (escort carrier) squadrons of 1945 are included as VS, to show continuity with later practice. Note that later the VC designator was used for heavy attack squadrons; they are included in the VA numbers. VP* indicates seaplane patrol squadrons. In some cases, the US Navy listed its carrier aircraft by *carrier air groups*: CVBG for the *Midways*, CVG for the *Essexes*, CVLGs for light carriers, and CVEGs for the larger escort carriers (VCs for the smaller CVE 55 class). This listing has been preserved in the tables.

Patrol aircraft included in the Royal Navy list were operated by RAF Coastal Command; they are included for comparative purposes. Note that figures for Royal Navy and RAF operational squadrons at any given date include those working up and about to disband, and thus considerably exceed those fully operational units mentioned in the text. Moreover, some fighter-bomber squadrons have been listed as strike squadrons, based on their squadron designations.

US Navy

	1939	1945	1948	1950+++	1952###	1957
CVLG=	—	9	1(ASW)	—	—	—
CVEG=	—	12	6(ASW)	—	—	—
VC/VS	—	21	3	7(25)	15(15)	10
HS	—	—	—	—	4(4)	10
AEW units	—	5	—	—	—	—
VW	—	—	3++	2@	2	12SSS
VF	7	—	—	@@@(128)	64	52
VA	15	—	—	7@@(41)	23&	67S
VP	—	40##	18	14(29)	34(22)	27
VP*	21	22	13	6	(11)	—
ZP	—	39	—	2(5)	4(4)	3SS

US Navy

	1939	1945	1948	1950+++	1952###	1957
CV/CVA	6	18	11	7	14	15
CVL	—	8	2	3	5	—
CVE	—	72	7	4	17	11+
BB	15	23	2	(1)	4	—
CA/CB	18	25	7	9	15	13
CL	19	48	18	4	4	3
DD	127	372	135(10)	109(10)	211(10)	212(9)
DDE	—	—	—	33	33	33
FF	—	482==	13(24)	11(15)	89(17)	71(30)
SS	61	237	76(12)	73	100	129
CM/DM	5	13	70^	4	—	—
MCM	37	209	—	22	53	61
MCM*	—	384	—	27(17)	56	25
SC/PC	14(8)	631	99	39	13	15(11)
MTB	—	491	4	4	4	—
APA/AKA	—	345	146|||	91|||	80	36
LST	—	738	—	28	96	51
LSD	—	15	—	—	21	25
LSM	—	483	—	—	22	—
CVBG&&	—	2	6	3	—	—
CVG&&&	—	37#	10	6	(14)	—

Royal Navy

	1939	1945	1951	1954	1957
CV/CVA	5(1)	6	1(1)	1(3)	2
CVL	—	4	3(1)	2(1)	2(2)
CVE	—	32	—	—	—
BB	12	7	(1)	1	—
CA/CB	12	43	—	—	—
CL	44	—	13(2)	10(1)	8(1)
DD	100	108	28(18)	26(3)	19(3)
DDE	58	55*	—	—	—
FF	43	598	36(13)	33(21)	26(23)
SS	38	123*	32	37	39
MCM	42	244	13(3)	23(3)	6(3)
MCM*	—	443**	—	15(8)	21(21)
SC/PC	5	27	—	—	15
MTB/MGB	18	326	—	—	9(2)
LST	—	115	—	—	2(2)
LSD	—	4	—	—	—
LSM	—	—	—	—	3(1)
VF	4	44	12	17	16
VA	12	23	4	4	3
VP	9	23	7	9	11
VP*	8	16	4	3	2
VS	—	—	5	6	9
VW	—	—	—	1	1

French Navy

	1939	1945	1951	1957
CV/CVA	1	(1)	—	—
CVL	—	—	2	3
CVE	—	1	1	—(1)
BB	6(1)	2	2	2
CA/CB	7	3	—	—
CL	10(2)	5(1)	5(1)	3(1)
DD	57	15	11	19
FF	46***	35	44	61
SS	81	29	19	21
MCM	1	9	11	15
MCM*	—	54	26	112
SC/PC	13	129	114	58
MTB	4	19	2	—
VF	—	—	2	6
VS	—	—	2	3
VP	—	—	6	6
VP*	—	—	—	1

Royal Netherlands Navy

	1939	1945	1951	1958
CVL	—	—	1	1
CVE	—	1	—	—
CL	4	2	2	2
DD	8	5	5(1)	12(1)
DDE	—	—	—	3
FF	5	6	16	18(4)
SS	21	11	7	6
MCM	—	—	4	6
MCM*	—	—	33	64
SC/PC	—	1	13	6
MTB	2	—	—	—
LSM	—	—	8	5
VF	—	—	1	2
VS	—	—	1	2
VP	—	—	3	1
VP*	—	—	1	—

Soviet Navy

	1941	1945	1955
BB	3	3	1(2)===
CA/CB	5	7	7
CL	4	3	20
DD	42%	45	140
FF%%	22	48	60
SS	213	173	425⎮
MCM	68	81	100⎮
MCM*	70	250%%%	
PC/SC	2	350%%%	230‖
MTB	269	393	310‖

Notes to Tables

* Many used for trials and training.
** Plus 350 trawlers of every type.
*** Includes 12 small destroyers/torpedo boats.
+ CVS (ASW support carrier) conversions of fleet carriers.
++ Two for carrier operation, one land-plane (VPW) squadron.
+++ Figures in parentheses for this year indicate Reserve squadrons.
# 32 day, 5 night.
20 four-engine, 20 two-engine.
Aircraft data as of 1 July 1953, with 17 August 1951 figures in parentheses for comparison.
S Two of these squadrons are all-weather attack. The rapid growth in attack squadrons was due to the redesignation of fighter-bomber units. Eight squadrons are heavy (ie, strategic) attack units. Seven were minelaying squadrons. There were also two fleet countermeasures (VQ) squadrons and two photographic squadrons (attack) not included in this total.
SS One of these was a blimp airborne early warning (ZW) squadron.
SSS Of this total, two were carrier-based, four were land-based fleet early warning aircraft, and six supported the Continental Air Defense barrier system.
@ Carrier early warning composite squadron; there were also land-based early warning squadrons.
@@ These comprise two composite night attack squadrons, and five composite heavy attack squadrons, beyond those in the carrier air groups.
@@@ These figures do not include marine fighter squadrons, which were (and are) carrier-capable. For example, in 1950, the number of marine fighter squadrons was cut from 23 to 16.
& Including two composite night attack and five heavy attack squadrons.
&& Consisting, in 1945, of two double (32-airplane) fighter and two double (32-airplane) attack squadrons, plus special purpose aircraft. A third fighter squadron was added in 1948. In 1950, the CVBG consisted of five 20-airplane squadrons. In 1954, a sixth squadron (either fighter or heavy attack) was added.
&&& Consisting, in 1950, of five 16-airplane squadrons: four VF, one VA: two jet interceptor/strike escort squadrons, two propeller-driven fighter-bomber squadrons, and a medium attack bomber squadron. Ships would also operate detachments (DET) of composite squadrons providing photo reconnaissance, all-weather attack, heavy attack, and carrier airborne early warning services. The propeller-driven fighter-bomber units were replaced by light jet attack squadrons, the former attack squadron becoming a medium attack squadron. By the mid 'fifties the former pair of jet interceptor squadrons had been replaced by one day and an all-weather fighter squadron.

= CVEG and CVLG each consisted of one fighter and one attack squadron.

== Includes frigates (PF) and corvettes (PG) and one surviving *Erie* class gunboat.

=== Reflects reclassification of two old battleships as training ships in 1954. The figures in this column are extremely approximate, and *do not reflect the fact that at least some, and perhaps many, units were in reserve.*

% Plus 17 old destroyers useful only for secondary purposes. The figure given includes seven flotilla leaders.

%% Torpedo boats and guard ships in Soviet parlance; the later equivalents were the *Kola* and *Riga* classes.

%%% Very approximate figure.

| This includes about 236 existing submarines of prewar design, including 106 very small coastal units (M-V class). Many had probably been laid up.

|| This figure reflects postwar construction only; it is not clear how many (or whether) the obsolete craft still existing in 1945 remained ten years later.

||| Total number of active amphibious ships at the end of the fiscal year, 30 June of that calendar year. By way of comparison, the figure in 1945 was 1256, and in 1952, 231. Detailed breakdowns are not available for these years.

^ Total number of active minecraft. By way of comparison, 611 were active in 1945 (five coastal minelayers were not included in the figures given) and 75 in 1950.

Sources for Tables

US Navy: ship figures (except 1945) are based primarily on summaries in *Ships and Aircraft* for 1939, 1945 (1948 appendix), 1950 (**data for 1** January 1950 and, with appendix, August 1952), and 1958 (1957 data). The 1945 figures are based largely on the volumes of *Ships Data US Naval Vessels 1945*, and all figures have benefited from aggregated force level tables prepared by the US Navy Operational Archives in 1973. Aircraft figures are primarily official data supplied by Roy Grossnick of the US Naval Aviation Historical Office. The data marked 1952 are actually for 1 July 1953, with 1951 data in parentheses for comparison. Note the shift from carrier air groups to individual squadrons in the official returns of this period.

Royal Navy, 1939: S Roskill, *The War at Sea*, Vol. 1 (HMSO, 1954); Strength, 1945: S Roskill, *The War at Sea*, Vol. 3 Part 2 (HMSO, 1961). Later listings are based on those in the annual official White Papers. British naval air strengths have been estimated by using squadron histories in R. Sturtivant, *The Squadrons of the Fleet Air Arm* (Air-Britain, 1984). Coastal Command figures have been taken from squadron histories in JDR Rawlings, *Coastal, Support, and Special Squadrons of the RAF and Their Aircraft* (Jane's, 1982).

French Navy: strengths for 1939 and 1945 have been taken from contemporary *Jane's Fighting Ships*, with minor corrections; they are approximate at best.

Royal Netherlands Navy: strengths are based on contemporary editions of *Jane's Fighting Ships*, and are therefore approximate.

Soviet Navy: figures for 1941 and 1945 have been taken from J. Meister, *Soviet Warships of the Second World War* (Macdonald & Jane's, 1977).

APPENDIX V: POSTWAR BUILDING PROGRAMS

Programs are listed by program or financial year. Note that the British fiscal year begins on 1 April, so that the 1944 fiscal year corresponds (in later parlance) to the later 1944-45 year, or (roughly) to the US FY (fiscal year) 45. The US fiscal year begins on 1 July of the *previous* calendar year. Thus the British 1944 program and the US FY45 program are the final war programs. The US program was limited by the very large programs already underway. A larger proposed program was vetoed by President Roosevelt on 22 March 1945. For both navies, the notation 'FF(2nd)' indicates a second-rate frigate; the US version was the *Claude Jones*; the British, the Type 14.

In the case of British conversion programs, note that dates are usually approximations based on dates ships were ordered.

NOTES:

1. *Neptune* or *Minotaur* class large cruisers, not laid down. A sixth ship was added out of the 1941 program.
2. Fourteen 1944 *Battle* class (ie, *Daring*) and eight 1944 *Weapon* class (ie, *Gallant*). Of all these ships, only eight *Darings* were ever completed.
3. Modified *Black Swan* class sloops, cancelled at the end of the war.
4. A class submarines, not built; the number corresponded to the *annual* rate of loss.
5. Small-type MTBs, to take account of wastage. This series included the two earliest postwar MTB prototypes, *MTB538* and *MTB539*. In addition, this program included nine conventional British Power Boat and ten conventional Vosper MTBs. Two of the Vosper boats and one BPC boat were completed as controlled targets (CT)
6. Steam-powered LST(3)s, ordered in Canada, to take account of wastage. Early proposals for the 1944 program included another 42 LSTs, to add a fourth division of amphibious lift. However, such an undertaking was beyond the capacity of the British shipbuilding industry.

These ships supplemented 45 units ordered in Britain, and another 35 ordered in Canada in December, 1943. None of the 1944 LST(3) were delivered, but a total of 35 British and 26 Canadian units of the 1943 program was completed.

7. Prototypes of Types 41 and 61; the program initially included four frigates.
8. HTP prototype (non-combatant) *Explorer*. Earlier versions of the 1945 program also included three improved A-class submarines.
9. *Bold* type experimental convertible MTB/MGBs.
10. LSD, cancelled 1949. This program also included a 'build-up amphibian' vehicle, also ultimately cancelled.
11. *Whitby*, Type 12 frigate prototype.
12. Cruisers *Birmingham* and *Newcastle*.
13. Prototype Type 15 conversions, *Rocket* and *Relentless*. There was no formal building program; these were paid for out of R&D funds.
14. Prototype T-class submarine conversions to FBD, *Taciturn* and *Trump*. Paid for out of R&D funds, as above.
15. *Rothesay* (improved Type 12) class.
16. One Type 12, one Type 41, one Type 61.
17. *Porpoise* class, postwar new-construction FBD prototype class.
18. Ton class; includes three coastal minehunters.
19. Ham class, including three inshore minehunters (Ley class) in 1950/51, and five in 1951/52.
20. Including two seaward defense boats in 1950/51, and 15 in 1951/52. The nineteenth (last) *Dark* class FPB was not completed.
21. Type 16 prototype *Tenacious* and Type 15 conversions *Volage, Verulam, Venus, Virago*.
22. FBD reconstruction of *Thermopylae* and *Totem*.
23. It was announced in 1953 that further units of this (*Porpoise*) class would not be built pending the construction of nuclear submarines. Note, however, the choice to build the *Oberons*, which were the only class of major combatants not to be cut during and after the Radical Review.
24. Four Type 12, four Type 41, three Type 61.
25. Seven Type 15 (*Quadrant, Rapid, Roebuck, Vigilant, Wakeful,*

Royal Navy

YEAR	1944/45	1945/46	1946/47	1947/48	1948/49	1949/50	1950/51	1951/52	1952/53	1953/54
NEW CONSTRUCTION:										
CL	5(1)	—	—	—	—	—	—	—	—	—
DLG	—	—	—	—	—	—	—	—	—	—
DD	22(2)	—	—	—	—	—	—	—	—	—
FF	5(3)	2(7)	—	—	—	1(11)	3(16)	11(24)	—	—
FF(2nd)	—	—	—	—	—	—	—	12	—	—
SS	20(4)	1(8)	—	1	—	—	6(17)	2(23)	—	—
CMS	—	—	—	—	—	2	16(18)	43	37	7
IMS	—	—	—	—	—	—	21(19)	32	27(26)	11
FPB	32(5)	—	—	2(9)	—	—	5(20)	44	—	—
LPD	36(6)	—	—	1(10)	—	—	—	—	—	—
CONVERSION:										
CVA	—	—	—	—	—	1	—	—	—	—
CL	—	—	—	—	—	2(12)	—	—	—	—
DDE	—	—	—	—	2(13)	—	5(21)	11(25)	8(34)	7(35)
SS	—	—	—	—	2(14)	—	2(22)	2(27)	2(28)	—
MCM	—	—	—	—	—	—	—	—	—	—

Whirlwind, and *Wrangler*) and four Type 16 (*Orwell, Termagant, Tyrian,* and *Tuscan*); this year included *Quadrant* for the Royal Australian Navy.

26. Fifteen transferred to France under MDAP (ten this year, five the following year). Two were transferred to India in 1955. Three inshore survey versions of this class were built under the 1952/53 estimates.

27. T-class FBD conversions *Truncheon* and *Tiptoe* (second group)

28. T-class FBD conversions *Tabard* and *Trump* (second group)

29. *Royalist*.

30. *Belfast*.

31. *Swiftsure*, not completed.

32. Cancelled under the 1957 Defence Review.

33. *Brave Borderer*.

34. Five Type 15 (*Grenville, Undaunted, Undine, Urchin,* and *Wizard*) and three Type 16 (*Paladin, Terpsichore, Tumult*)

35. Five Type 15 (*Queenborough* and *Quiberon* for Australia, plus *Ulysses, Urania,* and *Ursa* for Royal Navy) and two Type 16 (*Petard* and *Teazer*)

36. One Type 15, *Zest*.

37. Three Type 15, *Quiberon* for Australia and *Troubridge* and *Ulster* for the Royal Navy.

38. A class streamline conversion prototype *Artful*. Note that program dates have not been found for three of this class (*Alcide, Aeneas,* and *Astute*). They were probably converted after 1961.

39. Three A class (*Auriga, Andrew, Anchorite*) and two T class streamline (*Talent, Token*)

40. One A class (*Ambush*) and one T class (*Teredo*) streamline.

41. Two A class (*Artemis, Alderney*) and two T class (*Tapir, Tireless*) streamline.

42. One A class streamline (*Amphion*)

43. Two A class streamline (*Alliance, Acheron*)

44. One A class streamline (*Alaric*)

45. Three are Type 81 (*Tribal* class)

46. Type 81 (*Tribal* class)

47. Nuclear prototype *Dreadnought* and first four *Oberons*.

48. Weapon class radar picket conversions (estimated date)

49. Battle class radar picket conversions (estimated date)

50. Nuclear submarine *Valiant* and final *Oberons*.

51. Nuclear submarine *Warspite*.

52. Ballistic missile submarines (SSBN)

53. Prototype conversion of Ton class coastal sweeper to minehunter. This program also included the conversion of two Tons and two Hams to survey ships.

54. LST *Sir Lancelot*.

55. *Sheffield*. The ship had already undergone a long refit in 1949-51 to fit her as a flagship for foreign stations, with added communications equipment.

56. Commando carrier conversion of *Bulwark*.

57. Commando carrier conversion of *Albion*.

58. Conversion of *Triumph* to heavy repair ship.

1954/55	1955/56	1956/57	1957/58	1958/59	1959/60	1960/61	1961/62	1962/63	1963/64	1964/65
3	—	—	—	—	—	—	—	—	—	—
—	2	2	—	—	—	—	—	—	—	2
—	—	—	—	—	—	—	—	—	—	—
5(15)	8(45)	4(46)	—	—	—	3	—	3	3	3
—	—	—	—	—	—	—	—	—	—	—
—	—	5(47)	2	2	2	4(50)	1(51)	—	4(52)	1
12	10(32)	—	—	—	—	—	—	—	—	—
—	2	—	—	—	—	—	—	—	—	—
1(33)	1	—	—	—	—	—	—	—	—	—
—	—	—	—	—	—	1(54)	1	1	—	—
—	—	1(58)	—	1(56)	1(57)	—	—	—	—	—
1(29)	1(30)	1(31)	1(55)	—	—	—	—	—	—	—
1(36)	3(37)	4(48)	—	—	4(49)	—	—	—	—	—
1(38)	5(39)	2(40)	4(41)	1(42)	2(43)	1(44)	—	—	—	—
—	—	—	—	—	—	—	—	—	1(53)	2

NOTES:

1. Cancelled; the ship authorized the previous year was completed as the DL *Norfolk*.
2. Completed as the DLs of the *Mitscher* class.
3. Cancelled: super-carrier *United States*.
4. Two attack submarines, one ASW submarine (SSK).
5. Two attack submarines, two ASW submarines (SSK).
6. Plus two DDE, two DDK modified from unfinished wartime hulls.
7. Eight DDE, six DDK.
8. Two CVL converted for ASW; two fleet carriers (CV) converted for jet operation.
9. And two XMAP mine countermeasures, one of which was later cancelled.
10. One later cancelled to help pay for experimental submarine *Albacore*.
11. One to SSA (cargo submarine), two to SSP (personnel transport submarine), three to SSR (radar picket), two to SSG (missile submarine).
12. One to SSO (submarine oiler), one to submarine radar picket (SSR).
13. To SSK.
14. Plus 18 MSB (minesweeping boats)

15. 102 destroyers fitted with Hedgehog; 24 DDR rearmed, and 10 fleet destroyers rearmed with 3in/50.
16. Radar pickets; also ten Guppy IA and 16 fleet snorkel.
17. Prototype nuclear submarine and two radar pickets (SSR).
18. Plus 30 MSB (minesweeping boats).
19. One missile submarine, six SSK, four radar pickets. Also 16 Guppy IIA.
20. Missile submarine (SSG)
21. Minehunter (MHC)
22. Six DE to radar pickets (DER)
23. Two nuclear attack submarines, one missile submarine (SSG)
24. Includes one CVE converted to helicopter assault carrier.
25. Missile submarine (SSG)
26. Three diesel-electric and three nuclear attack submarines, one missile submarine, one nuclear radar picket submarine.
27. Twelve DE converted to radar pickets (DER)
28. Four attack submarines, three ballistic missile submarines (SSBN)
29. Including six ballistic missile submarines (SSBN)
30. Hydrofoil ASW craft.
31. FRAM I reconstructions; the less ambitious FRAM II reconstruction

US Navy

NOTE that missile destroyers are *not* distinguished from conventional destroyers; similarly, missile frigates (DEG) are not distinguished from gun-armed frigates (DE) in the lists of new construction ships. Some reconstructions were not financed under regular budgets, and hence are not listed here.

YEAR	FY45	FY46	FY47	FY48	FY49	FY50	FY51	FY52	FY53	FY54
NEW CONSTRUCTION:										
CVA	12(34)	—	—	—	1(3)	—	—	1	1	1
CG	—	—	—	—	—	—	—	—	—	—
CLK	—	—	—	1	1(1)	—	—	—	—	—
DLG	—	—	—	—	—	—	—	—	—	—
DD	—	—	—	4(2)	—	—	—	—	3	3
FF	—	—	—	—	—	—	—	1	2	2
FF(2nd)	—	—	—	—	—	—	—	—	—	—
SS	—	—	—	3(4)	4(5)	—	—	3(17)	1(20)	1
MSO	—	—	—	—	—	1(9)	32	17(18)	9	4
MSC	—	—	—	—	—	—	2(14)	31(37)	20	1(21)
FPB	4	—	—	—	—	—	—	—	—	—
LST	—	—	—	—	—	—	—	15	—	1
LSD	—	—	—	—	—	—	—	4	—	2
LPH	—	—	—	—	—	—	—	—	—	—
LPD	—	—	—	—	—	—	—	—	—	—
CONVERSION:										
CVA	—	—	—	—	4(8)	2	4	4	2	1
CG	—	—	—	—	—	—	—	2	—	—
DDE	—	—	—	9(6)	14(7)	7(10)	(15)	—	—	6(22)
DER	—	—	—	—	2	—	—	—	—	—
SS	—	2(35)	12(36)	8(11)	2(12)	1(12)	2(16)	5(19)	—	—

was carried officially as a major refit.

32. Including ten ballistic missile submarines (SSBN)
33. Fast gunboats (PGM)
34. Missile conversions of destroyers and large destroyers (DL)
35. Guppy conversion (Guppy I) prototypes *Odax* and *Pomodon*
36. Guppy II
37. Coastal minehunter conversions (AMCU)

FY55	FY56	FY57	FY58	FY59	FY60	FY61	FY62	FY63	FY64
1	1	1	1	—	—	1	—	1	—
—	—	1	—	—	—	—	—	—	—
—	—	—	—	—	—	—	—	—	—
—	6	4	3	7	—	3	7	—	—
5	7	8	5	5	3	2	—	—	—
8	—	—	—	—	2	2	6	8	10
—	2	2	—	—	—	—	—	—	—
3(23)	8(26)	6	7(28)	11(29)	4	11(32)	13(32)	14(29)	12(29)
3	—	—	—	—	—	—	—	—	—
—	2	—	2	—	—	—	—	—	—
—	—	—	—	—	1(30)	—	—	2(33)	2(33)
6	—	—	—	—	—	—	—	—	—
2	—	—	—	—	—	—	—	—	—
—	—	—	1	1	1	—	1	1	—
—	—	—	—	1	1	1	3	4	—
4(24)	6	4	—	—	—	—	—	—	—
—	2	5	1	2	—	—	—	—	—
(22)	12(27)	(22)	—	—	8(31)	14(31)	14(31)	24(31)	7(34)
—	—	—	—	—	—	—	—	—	—
1(25)	—	—	—	—	—	—	8(31)	—	—

INDEX